TÁIN BÓ CÚAILNGE

TÁIN BÓ CÚAILNGE

Recension I

EDITED BY

CECILE O'RAHILLY

⸙

SCHOOL OF CELTIC STUDIES
DUBLIN INSTITUTE FOR ADVANCED STUDIES 2006

Reprinted by Dundalgan Press, Dundalk, Co. Louth

CONTENTS

INTRODUCTION

Táin Bó Cúailnge, the longest and most important tale of the Ulster cycle, has been preserved in three recensions. Recension I, the oldest manuscript version, is the text here edited.

The growth and development of TBC and the interrelations of the three recensions have been exhaustively dealt with by Thurneysen in Die irische Helden- und Königsage (pp. 96–244)[1]. Here it will be sufficient to discuss and compare the four manuscripts which contain a version of Recension I[2]. These manuscripts are:

(1) Lebor na hUidre (U), the oldest surviving manuscript of Irish prose tales, dated ca. 1100[3];

(2) the Yellow Book of Lecan (Y), a late 14th-century manuscript[4];

(3) Egerton 1782 (W), dated early 16th century[5];

(4) O'Curry MS. 1 (C), a late 16th-century paper manuscript (recently rediscovered)[6].

(1) U

As Best has shown[7] Lebor na hUidre is the work of two main scribes whom he called A and M. M has been identified as Mael Muire mac Céilechair †1106[8]. Later a third scribe, denoted as H, added many interpolations throughout the manuscript[9].

---

[1] Cf. also Thurneysen in ZCP ix 418–43, and C. O'Rahilly in Táin Bó Cúailnge from the Book of Leinster xiv–xvi.

[2] The whole of Recension I TBC is sometimes loosely called LU-TBC, the oldest MS. version having been preserved in Lebor na hUidre (LU). TBC[2] is the abbreviated reference to the edition published in 1912, TBC having been appropriated for Windisch's edition of LL-TBC (1905)

[3] Lebor na Huidre, ed. Bergin and Best (Dublin 1929) ll. 4479–6722.

[4] Táin Bó Cúailnge, ed. Strachan and O'Keeffe (Dublin 1912).

[5] Táin Bó Cúailnge nach der hs. Egerton 1782, ed. Windisch, ZCP ix 121–58 (1913).

[6] Táin Bó Cuailnge, ed. Pádraig Ó Fiannachta (Dublin 1966).

[7] Ériu vi 161 ff.

[8] H. P. A. Oskamp suggests that there may be some doubt about this identification (Voyage of Máel Dúin, Groningen 1970 p. 3). In a recent article (The Reviser of Leabhar na hUidhre, Éigse xv 277–88) Tomás Ó Concheanainn gives convincing arguments for identifying Maelmuire with the H- interpolator. In the present work I have found it convenient to retain Best's denotation of the three scribes as A, M and H.

[9] U[H] denotes the interpolated version in LU.

In all four manuscripts the text is incomplete. The following diagram represents roughly the extent of the text preserved in each of the manuscripts. The numbering of lines is that of the present edition.

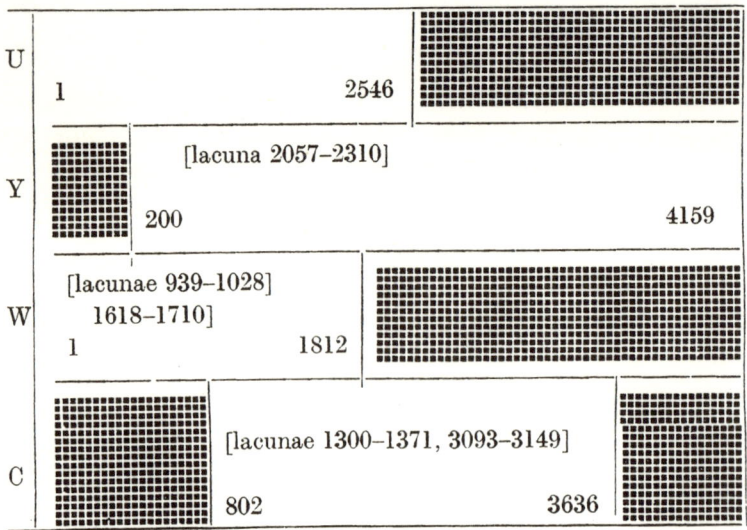

The text of TBC in LU was begun by A but he wrote only $53a^1$–b^{33}, the remainder of the tale up to 82b where it breaks off being written by M. The interpolator H inserted interlinear words or marginal glosses throughout, and in addition added four passages of some length, one on the space gained by erasure of M's text, two on intercalated vellum sheets and the fourth on the space left blank on p. 82b. These H- interpolations are found incorporated into the text in what survives of W; none of them occur in Y.

Even without the H-interpolations it is obvious that U is a compilation. The compiler quotes throughout 'from another version' or 'according to other books' i.e. manuscripts. His reference to 'books' shows that his sources were written ones, not oral.

The earliest study of TBC was that of Zimmer in 1887[1] when the only matter of Recension I available was the incomplete text of U^H. In his analysis[2] Zimmer compared the LU text in detail with

---

1 Über den compilatorischen charakter der irischen sagentexte im sogenannten Lebor na hUuidre, KZ xxviii 426–554.

2 'Eine der doubletten in LU stimmt immer genau mit der version der Táin, die uns in LL vorliegt', loc. cit. p. 476. It is not strictly accurate to imply that the LL-version has no 'doublets'. Repetition of motifs is not uncommon in Recension II. Cf. Táin xvii–xix.

the equivalent passages of Recension II in LL. He noted the many repetitions, inconsistencies and contradictions of U^H and pointed out that where variant versions ('doublets') of an incident were given in U^H, LL invariably gave only one version. This led him to conclude that Recension I of LU was itself a compilation worked together from two sources, and that one of these sources was the Mid.-Ir. LL-version, the other an older unknown version (or versions) which he called x^1.

Many years later when the full text of Recension I was available together with Best's notes on the scribes of LU, Thurneysen published his analysis of TBC. He rejected Zimmer's conclusion that the Mid.-Ir. LL-version was one of the sources of Recension I. His theory was that Recension I TBC was a conflation of two parallel 9th-century versions of the whole tale, now lost.[2]. He enumerated certain criteria by which one could decide from which of these two sources, which he named A and B, a particular passage or episode had been taken. Thus, according to Thurneysen's theory:

(1) Conall Cernach is with the enemy in A, with the Ulstermen in B;

(2) in both sources Cú Chulainn has a friend in the enemy camp. In A it is Fiacha mac Fir Febe from Ulster; in B it is Lugaid mac Nóis from Munster;

(3) in A the Connacht forces have as allies seven Munster under-kings and the Gailióin; in B their supporters are called *ceithre cóicid Érend* or *Fir Érend*;

(4) in B alone the title of a section (usually at the end) has the words *ar Tána* or *ar Tána Bó Cúailnge* added.

These criteria for the attribution of some passages to Source A and others to Source B seem quite arbitrary. One could suggest other criteria just as cogent and assume further sources C, D etc. For instance, one might distinguish between the fights in which Cú Chulainn kills his opponent with a sling-shot (usually aimed at the head) and those in which he uses spear or sword. Thus Órlám, Lethan, Lócha and many others are killed by the sling, but Etarcomal and Nad Crantail by the sword. Or again one might

---

[1] His argument might equally well have been that LL was drawn from a version of U as it would appear if stripped of some variants and all interpolations. This is the conclusion I reached in my study of the LL-TBC.

[2] Thurneysen noted that in addition the compiler had some more modern pieces. These were the H-interpolations of U and W, the passages In Carpat Serda ⁊ Brislech Mór Maige Murthemne, Comruc Fir Diad, Toichim na mBuiden and Tochustal Ulad.

note that in the final sentences of certain episodes a *dindṡenchus* based on it is given but not in other episodes. No *dindṡenchus* is given in the Macgnímrada. In Aided Fraích we get both *Áth Fraích* where Fráech was drowned and *Síd Fraích* to which his body was taken. Similarly for *Lia Úaland*, *Áth nBuide* etc. But despite the detailed account of Cú Chulainn's encounter with Nad Crantail or with Etarcomal, no place-name is mentioned as resulting from the fight. Again, if there is inconsistency about Conall Cernach, there is also some discrepancy in the rôle of Bricriu[1]. At first sight Lugaid mac Nóis would seem to play a much more prominent part than Fiacha in dealing with Cú Chulainn on behalf of Medb and Ailill. The explanation of this seeming prominence lies in the fact that most of his visits to Cú Chulainn to ask for a truce, to offer terms etc. occur in the long passage called *córugud aile* or in the H- interpolations. If we discount these references Lugaid plays no more important a rôle than Fiacha, certainly a lesser one than Fergus, another of his friends from Ulster.

Despite his rejection of Zimmer's suggestion of a two-fold origin of TBC, it seems quite possible that Thurneysen was himself influenced, albeit subconsciously, when he formulated his theory that TBC was a conflation of two sources A and B.

Perhaps the most interesting point about U is the contribution made by H to the original text. Thurneysen has dealt at length with these H- interpolations, in particular with those on intercalated vellum leaves pp. 71–72, 75–76[2]. Since these interpolations are found incorporated into the text in what survives of the W-version, Thurneysen concluded that they were not first inserted into U by the H- interpolator but were drawn by him from a manuscript of the W type which he called w[3].

The first interpolation, written on an erasure, is the prophetic poem chanted by Fedelm Banḟáith. As Thurneysen noted, what we should expect the prophetess to chant here would be a *rosc*, not syllabic verses. If a *rosc* has been erased here, it must have been shorter, for the final lines of the verses have had to be squeezed into

---

[1] This type of inconsistency is very common in a work of some length, not necessarily because two different sources have been used but merely through the carelessness of the compiler or his inability to keep the whole work in mind at the same time.

[2] See Thurneysen, Heldensage 236–41, ZCP ix 430–32. Cf. also Táin xxvi–xxvii.

[3] The fragmentary W does not contain the whole of p. 72 and it breaks off before pp. 75–76.

the space afforded by the erasure. This is the only H- interpolation which is found also in Recension II.[1] There seems no reason to doubt that in this instance it was taken by the H-interpolator from a version later than U and like Recension II.

The second interpolation, a long passage on an intercalated vellum leaf (71–72)[2], is of great interest. In part it contains matter which shows some affinity with the long section called by the scribe *córugud aile*, the opening and connecting passages of which may have been composed at a later date to introduce and join together what Myles Dillon has called the 'canonical text', that is, the older stratum of verse dialogue or *roscada*. In part too, this second H-interpolation offers a re-telling with slight variation of episodes which occur in the later part of the full TBC as it is found in Y and C (and also in Recension II). The linking passages of these episodes may be compared with those of the *roscada* in the earlier section. Thus in the *córugud aile* Cú Chulainn asks Lugais mac Nóis: *A popa Lugaid, inim áigetar-sa in tslúaig?* (1179); in the interpolation he asks Lugaid: *Cinnus atú-sa innosi ocon tslóg?* (1548). In the *córugud aile* Cú Chulainn demands that the physicians shall supply him with food every night (1189–90); reference to Cú Chulainn's being supplied with food by the enemy is made in the interpolation (1551). In the earlier *córugud aile* Lugaid asks for a truce for his men: *Conom raib cairte lat frim budin* (1186). There is no suggestion of asking for a truce elsewhere in the main body of the text, but here in this H- interpolation the Connachtmen send to ask Cú Chulainn for a cessation of hostilities, *carti chlaidib* or for permission to move camp *claemchlód magni* (1545, 1555, 1564). Terms have already been offered to Cú Chulainn by Fergus, but here in the H- interpolation other terms are offered to Cú Chulainn and he accepts them (1564–8).[3] In both the *córugud aile* and the interpolated passage there is a suggestion that the *cess noinden* is intermittent; in both it is referred to as *a tinnorcan* (1219, 1630).

---

[1] A brief interlinear note in hand H in U but not in W names Flidais among the Connacht notables. Flidais is named also in Recension II. See Táin xxvii n.1.

[2] The last 15 lines of 70ᵇ (1545–61) are written on an erasure. The passage erased was undoubtedly the opening of Aided Cúir which H re-tells on 72ᵇ in a form slightly expanded to coalesce with Tuirem na Cles on 73ᵃ. (The expansion can be measured by comparison with the equivalent passage in Y).

[3] Immediately after the account of Etarcomol's death, H inserted a note between columns in which he refers briefly to the reparations offered to Cú Chulainn and to his being supplied with food, a repetition of his account here on pp. 71–2, Cf. infra 1387ᵃ.

In the language of both passages one small quirk of style strikes one immediately. That is the use of *ecmaic*, 3 s. pret. protot. of *ad-cumaic* (*ad-cumaing*), petrified into a kind of adverb in Mid-Irish and used at the beginning of a sentence. Literally it means 'it happened', but it corresponds to some such adverbial phrase as 'in fact' or 'actually' in English. In TBC *ecmaic* occurs in this usage only in the section *córugud aile* (1044, 1061, 1191, 1211) and in this particular H- interpolation (1599, 1617, 1660).

As noted above, Thurneysen's view was that H took this whole passage from a manuscript which contained a variant text independent of U. Against this one might suggest that H or his predecessor, with or without the aid of written sources, compiled this long interpolation, re-fashioning some episodes which properly occur later in the full text and introducing them with short passages influenced by the earlier *córugud aile* or composed by H himself to conform with that *córugud*. For we should not completely reject the possibility that H sometimes offered his own original composition[1]. Most of the incidents, Bánchath Rochada, Comlann Munremair etc. can be explained as later episodes here out of context, but the passage headed Comrac Con Culaind fri Findabair strikes a discordant note. It may have been an invention of H. It opens with a two-fold repetition of an earlier passage (1246 ff.) when Mac Roth goes to offer terms to Cú Chulainn. Here the messengers are first Maine and then Lugaid, and the girl Finnabair is offered as a bribe to Cú Chulainn. Elsewhere in the text in all three Recensions this offering of the girl is made only to Cú Chulainn's enemies as an inducement to fight him. The treatment of both jester and girl by Cú Chulainn presents some strange features. As I have suggested (infra n. 1600) it seems as if Finnabair's death should have occurred here but that the squeamish scribe shirked describing it or that he knew of the later Imslige Glendamnach passage in the full version where an account of her death is given. The final sentence (*Ní baí trá carti dóib la Coin Culaind iar tain* 1608) is contradicted in a later passage, of the same interpolation ('*Guitter dano cairdi chlaidib dún for Coin Culaind*', for Ailill ⁊ Medb 1686–7).

Alternatively the whole passage pp. 71–72 may represent merely another *córugud aile*, here inserted without regard to congruity or to the continuity of the tale. There can be no doubt that U itself, as distinct from U[H], while perhaps incorporating some floating oral

---

[1] I shall deal with this point again in discussing the interpolation on pp. 75–76.

traditions, was based on an assembly of written themes and story-components relating to TBC. Hence the contradictions and inconsistencies which mar the narrative. In the first *córugud aile* in hand M Cú Chulainn takes a warning to Conchobar (1214). In the late part of TBC in Y the same warning in almost identical words (3425) is taken on behalf of Cú Chulainn to the Ulstermen by his father Súaltaim. This led Thurneysen to suggest that the passage Sírrabad Súaltaim in Y was a later elaboration based on the earlier incident. Actually Sírrabad Súaltaim occurs where we should logically expect it; the earlier warning seems definitely premature. Thus in the first *córugud aile* we get an incident which, I suggest, properly comes later in the tale, just as we get Bánchath Rochada, Comlann Munremair misplaced in the H- interpolation. If in fact this H-interpolation is a *córugud aile* it must have been borrowed piecemeal by the interpolator. The episodes mentioned are out of context. Aided na Rígamus is a distorted reminiscence of the passage which follows Bángleó Rochada in the Y-continuation; Aided na Macraide is another version of an incident which occurs in the section Breslech Maige Muirthemne in all three recensions, while the description of Cú Chulainn's *riastrad* is a commonplace in TBC and other Ulidian tales. Out of context too are the passages linking these episodes. When the Ulstermen have risen from their *cess* and begun to fight individually on Cú Chulainn's behalf, the time is long since past when Medb and Ailill would offer terms or ask for a cessation of hostilities.

Furthermore the long H- interpolation pp. 71–72 has a certain importance in that it may supply a clue to the dating of the loss of the ending of TBC in LU. Best calculated that ten or more pages of TBC are missing after Comrac Maind. If in fact these missing pages had contained the final part of TBC as we now have it in Y (and C) in the twelfth century when H was at work, it would be hard to explain why, with the later episodes before him, he should insert a vellum leaf in which he gives another version of Bángleó Rochada or another account of Munremar's stone-throwing. So we might conclude that the missing pages of LU must have been already lost before the twelfth century[1]. Zimmer, writing at a time when the different hands in LU had not yet been identified and before the

---

[1] Dr. Oskamp would agree that it is possible that the first foliation was made after the loss of the pages following Comrac Maind. See his Table III PRIA 65 C no. 6. But, as I suggest later, it is just possible that the LU manuscript did not contain the final part of TBC but broke off p. 82[b], leaving the text unfinished.

full text of Y had been published, pointed out with great perspicacity that the long passages LU 5834–952 were quite out of place at this point in the narrative[1].

The third long interpolation, pp. 75–76[2], is also on an intercalated vellum leaf of smaller dimensions than the preceding or following leaves[3]. The point at which this leaf has been inserted is note-worthy. It is preceded by a passage (1884–1903) which at this point seems quite out of place and which as I have suggested else-where is an obvious interpolation[4]. Significantly the passage does not occur in Y. It is a doublet or a mere misplacement of a later passage which tells how on the day after Sesrech Breslige Cú Chulainn dons his festive garb and the women climb on men's shoulders to catch a glimpse of him (2354–70). Before this doublet comes Immaccallam na Mórrígna fri Coin Culainn[5], at the end of which in U, but not in Y, is a brief reference to a variant version: *Combad sechtmain dó-som for Áth Grencha ⁊ dotuitted fer cach laí i nÁth Grencha laiss .i. i nÁth Darteisc* (1872–3), 'It may be that (according to another version)[6] he spent a week at Áth nGrencha and that every day a man fell at his hands in Áth nGrencha, that is, in Áth Tarteisc.'[7] If this be the Áth nGrencha which changed its name to Áth nGabla in an earlier passage[8], then the variant quoted

---

[1] 'Das stück LU 70ᵇ, 30–72ᵇ, 24 rapräsentiere ein blatt der recension *x*, welches der redaktor von LU bloss an falscher stelle eingefügt habe' KZ xxviii 520.

[2] The last nine lines of 74ᵇ (1904–11) which contain the beginning of the interpolation are written on an erasure. The erased passage is given at the end of 76ᵇ and is expanded in order to fill the whole side of the page. Cf. the Y-version of that passage which is shorter and less verbose.

[3] See H. P. A. Oskamp, Notes on the History of Lebor na Huidre PRIA 65 C No. 6; Roger Powell, Further Notes on Lebor na Huidre, Ériu xxi 99–102.

[4] Táin xxxv.

[5] Windisch, as early as 1887, suggested that the Immaccallam was an interpolation in the main text (IT II² p. 240). It does not occur in Recension II.

[6] The words *iar n-araile slicht* are to be understood in this type of sentence where the 'conjectural subjunctive' is used. See Strachan, Subj. Mood §25.

[7] Scribe M would seem to have added the identification to link up the reference to the passage where the poet Gabrán gives the name *Áth Tarteisc* to the ford where Lóch and Cú Chulainn fought.

[8] There Cú Chulainn had beheaded at Áth nGrencha four men sent forward as scouts by Medb and had impaled their heads on a forked pole (*gabal*), whence the name *Áth nGabla* for what had previously been *Áth nGrencha* (infra 335).

here is completely out of place. The compiler of Recension I TBC makes occasionally such asides, as it were, giving a misplaced quotation of a variant[1]. Here it would seem as if this sentence in U suggested to the H- interpolator the opening passage of the interpolation. It begins with a clumsy repetition of the making of Cú Chulainn's false beard, a stock description in the scribe's repertoire or an echo of another tale in which a similar situation occurred[2]. Then, despite being urged by the women to fight with a now seemingly bearded Cú Chulainn, Lóch postpones the meeting for a whole week. This part of the interpolation may be, I suggest, the original contribution of H himself and not drawn from another version. In a text which must have been frequently handled and which had such a large stock of stereotyped expressions and commonplaces one might well suspect that some of the additions of H (or of his predecessor) were not borrowings from a variant version but rather his own original work[3]. The compiler of Recension I TBC (U) has tried to follow the geographical indications of Medb's advance in the sequence of events. How far he has succeeded we cannot always tell as many of the places mentioned, some of which indeed may be mere inventions to provide a *dindšenchus*, are not now identifiable. But in the two long interpolations pp. 71–72, 75–76 the H-interpolator shows little regard for the proper sequence of events or their geographical location. Thus here, after the account of the week's exploits at Áth nGrencha we move at once to 'Ard Aignech, now called Focherd' where a meeting has been arranged between Medb and Cú Chulainn. (This is a doublet of their earlier meeting at Glenn Fochaíne in Recension II and Recension III).[4]

---

[1] Another instance of such a misplaced reference to a variant occurs after the account of the fight with Cúr. It must refer to a very different account of his death. Imšlige Glendamrach, one of the three bloodiest battles on the Táin (2313–4), was fought between Medb's forces and her Munster allies and it occurs at a much later stage in the Y- continuation of TBC after the episode Bángleó Rochada. (3358–63).

[2] The same sentence occurs, word for word, in Immaccallam in Dá Thúarad LL 24238–40. See infra n. 1904–5.

[3] That some of the H- interpolations in, for example, TBDD were inventions of H himself or of his predecessor seems probable. On a leaf of smaller dimensions 93–94 intercalated by H there are added fourteen descriptions of members of Conaire's household. They are brief, rather abrupt in style and the introductory words of the descriptions as written by M are here omitted. Among the fourteen only one known warrior, Cuscraid Mend, is named. See Nettlau's percipient note on these descriptions RC xiii 201. See also H. P. A. Oskamp loc. cit. p. 126.

[4] The killing of *fir Chrónige* and the *dindšenchus* of *Focherd* is also a doublet of an earlier passage. See Táin n. 1767–71.

In the H- passage Medb is represented as behaving treacherously to
Cú Chulainn, pretending to make peace and setting fourteen men
to lie in ambush and kill him. We might compare Ailill's perfidious
conduct in the other long H- interpolation when he pretends to go
in person to offer Finnabair as a peace-offering to Cú Chulainn.
Elsewhere in the main text there is no suggestion of such treachery
on the part of Ailill and Medb.

An interesting point abut this H- interpolation on pp. 75–76
is that it occurs verbatim at the same point in the tale in Recension
III. Thurneysen concluded that it was taken from U^H into
Recension III. But nowhere else in Recension III do we find such
wholesale borrowing from Recension I^1. It is more than probable
that here the compiler of Recension III drew on the same source
as the H- interpolator or on a copy or part of a copy of U^{H2}.

The fourth and last long interpolation in hand H is written on
the space left blank (twenty-one lines) on p. $82b^3$. Above this M
had written twenty-three lines, a heading for the next piece between
columns and the opening words *Foidis Medb*[4]. The title of the piece
was erased and H wrote on the erasure *Comrac Maind*. Then he
used the opening words in hand M to begin his account of Mann's
fight. Many of the texts in LU break off unfinished because of the
loss of the following leaves. But they break off in the middle of a
sentence only when it is the end of a leaf. Here M stopped short
in the middle of a page after writing a title and the two opening
words of the next piece.

One cannot say with certainty, however, although some points
may suggest it that this piece Comrac Maind was H's own invention.
The only other instance when Cú Chulainn fights with an unarmed
opponent is in Aided Fraích, itself an early interpolation in TBC as
Professor Carney has shown[5]. The H- interpolator may, if this

---

[1] The verbal forms and general grammatical correctness and the spelling
in this passage of Recension III contrast strongly with the garbled verb
forms and spelling of much of the rest of the text which had obviously
drawn on many sources of varying age.

[2] Five lines of Éle Loga in hand H in LU are also given in Recension III
(RC xv 74 §123). The same lines are also in C.

[3] The only other blank half page in the manuscript is that on 37^b. It
has been filled in with two precatory entries by later scribes.

[4] The piece which follows here in Y is Cú Chulainn's fight against
Gaile Dána and twenty-eight followers. It opens with the words *Foidis
Medb* . . .

[5] Like Aided Fraích, Comrac Maind does not form part of Recension II
or Recension III.

passage be his own contribution, have based some features of Mann's fight on that earlier episode. Fráech and Cú Chulainn wrestle in the water; Mann and Cú Chulainn wrestle on land[1]. The comparison of Mann's qualities with those of Ulster heroes who are named is a distinctive touch not found elsewhere in TBC. A scribe who was familiar with the Lives of Saints would have such comparisons ready to his pen[2]. The name of Mann, a mighty warrior, does not seem to occur elsewhere[3], not even in the long list of great Connacht warriors which is given in Táin Bó Flidais II[4].

It has never up to now been suggested that the manuscript LU may not have contained any more of TBC than has survived[5]. But the abrupt dropping of his pen by M is curious, and in fact we have no certain proof that the saga was continued in the manuscript on to the end as it now is in Y. There is however a high degree of probability that the Y- continuation existed in some form when the scribe wrote U. Twice there is reference to the battle called Imślige Glendamnach which in Y is a sequel to Bángleó Rochada[6].

In conclusion one might suggest that these H- additions on pp. 71–72, 75–76 represent some of the many disjointed and disconnected themes of TBC which were available to the H- interpolator (or his predecessor). But we should not rule out the possibility that he sometimes added connecting passages of his own invention. And of course we must admit that he (or his predecessor) inserted the interpolations pretty much at random on pp. 71–72, 75–76.

Thurneysen held that the redaction of Recension I TBC was an attempt to collect together all that was available of the tale[7]. Hence the many variants introduced. In comparison with the unified,

---

[1] See Táin xxxi.

[2] See infra n. 2527–9.

[3] A brief reference to the fight of Mann and Cú Chulainn is given in a prose *dindsenchus* of Mag Mandachta, obviously taken from this H- interpolation MD iv 278.

[4] Celtic Review ii 124ff. Both Fráech mac Fidaid and Fer Diad mac Damáin feature prominently in TBFlid II.

[5] By a curious coincidence, but probably no more than a coincidence, Recension III also breaks off after the fight with Ferchú Loingsech. The scribe of Recension III, however, knew of certain episodes which were to follow, namely, Comrac Cailitin (= Comrac Gaile Dána Recension I) and Comrac Fir Diad (RC xv 208 §§ 230, 231).

[6] There is also a passing reference to Comrac Fir Diad in the second H- interpolation (1624–5) but perhaps not to the version now extant.

[7] 'Sein Ziel ist nicht ein künstlerisches Ganzes zu schaffen sondern womöglich keinen der Einzelzüge, die er vorfindet, zu übergehen' Heldensage 101.

coherent and simplified narrative of Recension II, as found in LL, the LU text might be called nothing more than a mass of workshop fragments, not yet assimilated or amalgamated.

(2) Y

The scribe of that part of YBL which contains TBC was Gilla Ísa mac Firbisig[1]. Y is acephalous, beginning l. 200; it also has a lacuna which includes the opening part of Breslech Mór Maige Murthemne, but it is the earliest attainable copy of Recension I TBC which carries the tale to its end. Because the version of TBC in Y agrees with U, that is, the uninterpolated LU-version, up to the point where U breaks off, it has been generally assumed that the remainder of the tale in Y is the same version as we should have had if scribe M had finished it. But YBL is of much later transcription than LU and it is possible that the part of Recension I contained only in Y has suffered some change. Here we have as control Recension II, the LL- version. Recension II follows the main narrative of LU as it would appear stripped of variants and of interpolations[2]. For the continuation of the tale LL agrees more closely with Y. So the question arises: if the M scribe had continued and concluded the saga in the LU manuscript, would his version be what we now have in Y or would he have introduced into that part also references to variant versions and sundry interpolations? Only one variant is quoted in the Y- continuation: a second account of the death of Súaltaim[3]. Again, in the early part of the saga in both U and Y there are long passages of the obscurely worded rhythmical dialogue known as *roscada*. In the Y- continuation the *roscada* which occur are not dialogue, and only one is introduced with the archaic formula *co cloth x*. In Y the *roscada* are prophecies or exhortations spoken in a trance by various warriors from Ulster or from Connacht. (In the attribution of these prophecies to their speakers the compiler of Y expresses uncertainty; there is no such uncertainty in the LL-version). In the long passage describing the wounds inflicted on Cethern mac Fintain, additional attackers named in Y suggest expansion by some scribe at some time, or possibly an abbreviation by the scribe of LL. Again additional warriors are described in

---

[1] A second scribe takes up where Gilla Ísa breaks off p. 39[b]6, and gives an inadequate summary of the ending of Comrac Fir Diad. See infra n. 2567.

[2] I use 'interpolations' to include not only the H- additions but also some other passages. See Táin xxix–xxxv.

[3] See infra n. 3446.

Toichim na mBuiden. Of course such descriptive lists lend themselves easily to expansion or contraction at all times[1]. On the other hand the compiler of Y or of his archetype would appear to have at times condensed the narrative and rendered its meaning obscure. For instance, the short passage describing how Conchobar and Celtchair sally forth to attack the enemy in advance of the main army, must be elucidated by reference to Recension II[2]. In the short episodes which describe how some of the Ulster warriors come to Cú Chulainn's aid, the titles Fiacalgleó Fintain, Bángleó Rochada are given in Y without any explanation. Contrast the LL- version where they are fully explained.

There is one point in particular which suggests that the Y- scribe may have taken the continuation from a different compilation. Immediately after the long drawn out Fer Diad episode, obviously a late interpolation, the Y- continuation opens with a list of the chief episodes which follow, *Dinda na Tána*[3]. I cannot recall any saga-tale in which a list of this kind breaks into the middle of the narrative. A scribe drawing part of his material from a different compilation might well preface that section with such a list, if only as an economic device[4].

Thurneysen believed that, besides the two old parallel versions of the whole Táin (A and B) which he postulated, the redactor had access also to many more modern pieces[5]. Among these he enumerates in U the H- interpolations, and the long passage entitled In Carpat Serda ⁊ Breslech Mór Maige Muthemne which, he suggests, may have been an independent narrative, elaborated and embellished in great detail at a later period. For the Y- continuation, besides the Fer Diad episode, he would place among the more modern pieces

---

[1] Descriptions of twenty bands in Toichim na mBuiden are given in Y and LL, but they do not tally. Against these twenty the II[b] Recension (Stowe) describes no less than twenty-nine! See Stowe TBC xi-xiii and n. 4199ff.

[2] This whole passage Thurneysen would assign to a different and later version.

[3] In Y there is a scribal addition or invention, Tochustal Fer nÉrend. This is shortened in LL and given as a list of Medb's *ferchuitredaig*. That this catalogue was a scribal addition seems to be proved by the fact that despite its heading it is not enumerated in the list *Dinda na Tána*.

[4] In Y the whole of the preceding page (40) has been left blank, presumably for the final part of Comrac Fir Diad, not then available for the scribe. See infra n. 2567. This may possibly explain the insertion here of *Dinda na Tána*; it would serve to ensure a continuation of the narrative in due order.

[5] See Heldensage 102–7.

the long catalogue of warriors, Tochustal Ulad. He would also include Sírrabad Súaltaim on the ground that it is a doublet of an earlier passage[1]. Further he suggests that Toichim na mBuiden, the long detailed description of the Ulster warriors advancing into battle with their men, may have been an independent passage, expanded and elaborated before its introduction into the tale by the redactor[2]. One can hardly agree, however, with this last attribution. Such descriptive passages were a recognized convention in many of the older tales: Togail Bruidne Da Derga, Fled Bricrend, Siaburcharpat Con Culaind, Tochmarc Emere, to name only those contained in the oldest manuscript, LU.

(3) W

W contains only fragments of Recension I. It runs from the beginning up to l. 938; then there is a lacuna extending to l. 1028 owing to loss of a leaf, another lacuna from l. 1618 to l. 1710, again with loss of a leaf. From l. 1812, the end of the Fer Báeth episode, the remainder of the test is illegible[3]. The long H- interpolations of U are found in W where it coincides with U^H, that is, it contains the poem *Atchiu fer find* and part of the second long interpolation breaking off half way through Comlann Munremair ꝛ Con Roí. Thurneysen postulated a version *w* as the original from which U^H and W ultimately derived. He assumed that H copied his interpolations from an earlier interpolated version. Against this assumption, we might surmise that H's additions in U were first introduced by H, that successive scribes copied U^H and that many of these copies must have intervened between the 12th century when H worked and the 16th.

(4) C

C is incomplete. The beginning is wanting; it opens with the description of the boy Cú Chulainn returning to Emain at the end of the Macgnímrada section. It breaks off with the description of

---

[1] The argument that a doublet denotes a different or a later source will not hold. Cf. Táin xvii–xx. Note that the first 'warning' occurs in what is denoted as a variant.

[2] Heldensage 106–7.

[3] W was written by two scribes. The first hand is from p. 88ᵃ to 89ᵇ, then the second p. 90ᵃ to 97ᵇ, while the first hand resumes from p. 98ᵃ to the illegible end.

Eógan mac Durthacht in Toichim na mBuiden. There are also gaps owing to loss of leaves[1].

Essentially C offers the text of U^H + the Y continuation. It has sometimes preserved more faithfully the original readings, and is thus of value for a comparison with the text of U^H and Y. The compiler of C had also access to other versions of TBC. He has inserted into the text whole passages from Recension II and from a modernized version of Recension II (of the Stowe type)[2]. These interpolations have been so clumsily introduced that even without the control of Recension II they would easily have been recognized as foreign elements. In addition to these interpolations from some version of Recension II, C has some extra lines of verse, some of them so imperfectly recorded in comparison with the surrounding text as to give rise to doubts of their origin. These lines may well be attributed to C or to the compiler of his exemplar, and need not necessarily be taken as an essential part of the text[3]. In the Breslech Maige Murthemne passage, which is practically identical in all three recensions, C alone places the Éle Loga, an incantation to arouse Cú Chulainn, in its proper place.

The late interpolation, Comrac Fir Diad, is incomplete in C. Though the compiler has drawn some material for the early part of the episode from Recension II, he does not appear to have had the full Recension II version at his disposal. As the editor of C suggests, C's exemplar may here have been defective. So too was that of Y, and the final summary account of the death of Fer Diad, which in Y has been written in a different hand in part of the space left empty for it in the manuscript, is, astonishingly enough, found also in C with just a slight variation in wording. This would seem to point definitely to the use of a copy of Y.

A detailed comparison of C and W where they coincide would suggest that they both derive from the same source. Any small points in which they differ are merely scribal errors or omissions. Where C gives the better reading, it may be that W erred, and

---

[1] A clear and detailed analysis of C and its component parts has been given by the editor, Pádraig Ó Fiannachta pp. xi–xiii.

[2] This use of two versions of TBC is further confirmed by the fluctuation in the form of proper names: *Glenn Fochaine* (401–2) = Recension II, *Glend Ochaine* (425) = *Ochaine* of Recension I, *Findbéc*, wife of Cethern (2411) = Recension I, *Inda ingen Échaid Sálbuide* (2427, 2461) = Recension IIb. Another very clear instance of the confusion of two versions is found ll. 2658–69.

[3] Two extra lines are added in Éle Loga (1231–2); many extra lines in the FD poems.

similarly that C erred when the W- reading is preferable. For we must recognize the fact that small variations in wording, the addition or omission of a phrase, may be attributed to a practised scribe who almost unwittingly changed or corrected his exemplar even as he copied it.

These remarks could, of course, be applied to all four manuscripts, U, Y, W, C. Because of such small differences and variations between U and W, and because the H- interpolations occur in exactly the same place in U^H and W, Thurneysen felt bound to postulate a version w. Both U^H and W go back according to Thurneysen to this common source, expanded and changed from the version which Y represents and which U originally contained before the intervention of H. This theory would hold only if we assume that H himself was not the composer or compiler of the interpolations. If these additions to U were first made by H, as I am inclined to believe, then we may assume that W was based on a later copy of U^H plus a copy of the uninterpolated text as we find it in Y. W agrees with U^H in the H- additions, but in the main text it sometimes gives the U- reading, sometimes the Y- reading. The same may be said of C. It was of course a common practice at the date of W and C for scribes to work from more than one manuscript. We might instance the Stowe version of TBC based on Recension II but drawing also on Recensions I and III. For the late (15th century?) version of Comrac Fir Diad as an independent tale Thurneysen maintained that the redactor drew on no less than four manuscript sources! The compiler of C made U^H + Y his main text, but also had before him both the older and the more modern version of Recension II.

Edition

The text of the present edition is a transcript of that part of TBC contained in LU, and for the part missing in LU a transcript of the continuation of TBC in YBL. Readings from other manuscripts are given throughout in footnotes. Punctuation and capitals have been inserted and marks of length have been supplied where omitted by the scribe.

The older manuscript, LU, presents some special characteristics. In the opening passages written by the scribe A, the 'middle quantity' of syllables is frequently marked, e.g. *cénd, Médb, fordérg, Feidélm*[1]. Occasional instances are found also in the rest of the

---

[1] For this use of the length-mark see D. Greene, Middle Quantity in Irish, Ériu xvi 212–8.

text written by scribe M. In all cases I have omitted the length mark. The diphthongs *éo, íu* are sometimes written *eo, iu* without accent, but the instances of *eó, iú* far outnumber the others. I have generalized all instances to *eó, iú*[1]. Where the scribe uses the mark of length merely to distinguish the letter *i*, e.g. *tochim, ingen*, it has been written *i*. The mark of length occurs frequently in the plural verb-endings *-mar, -tar*[2]; I have followed the scribe in these cases. In Mid.-Ir. the O.Ir. verb-ending *-th(a)e* or *-t(a)e* (as in 2 s. past subj., past subj. passive, imperfect passive plural and preterite passive plural) is usually reduced to *-t(h)a*. In LU- TBC, as in many other Mid.-Ir. texts, the final vowel of these forms is sometimes marked long[3]. There are instances of this length-mark in passages written by all three hands in LU. I have followed the usage of the scribe. The future and preterite of the copula are sometimes marked long in LU (as they are in the Glosses): *nipá mesc, in tan bá gilla* etc.

The scribe of Y, on the other hand, hardly ever marks length in vowels. For my transcript I have given the pagination of the fac-simile. As one would expect when dealing with a later manuscript, there has been occasion to emend here and there. The scribe is given to misplacing words. He often corrects his original spelling with subscript letters or letters inserted over the line. Words omitted and recognized by him as such are inserted marginally or above or below the line. Secondary lenition of the mediae is often by a later hand. For this part of the text I have frequently drawn on Recension II for variant readings. In a very few instances I have disagreed with the reading of the editors of TBC[2], but in these cases I have given their reading in footnotes.

Dublin Institute for Advanced Studies.   CECILE O'RAHILLY

---

[1] See J. Carney's note on the rhyme *eú:béulu* Poems of Blathmac 227–8. Meyer, Misc. Hib. 44, quotes Mid.-Ir. instances of the rhyme *mōir:deōid* and *ceólda:cróda*.

[2] 'In the first 800 lines of the LU Táin, there are 42 examples of *-tár* against 17 of *-tar*' D. Greene. Ériu xxiv 125.

[3] For a full discussion of lengthening in verbal endings see D. Greene, Ériu xxiv 124 ff. Cf. also V. Hull, ZCP xxv 263 who quotes an instance of lengthening of 3 s. pres. subj. ending in the present text: *arnacha n-aithgné* (LU 5870).

Acknowledgements

I acknowledge gratefully permission to edit the text from manuscripts in their possession given to me by the Council of the Royal Irish Academy and by the Board of Trinity College, Dublin.

I owe thanks to Dr. D. A. Binchy without whose encouragement and generous advice I should not have undertaken this edition of TBC; to Professor Brian Ó Cuív whom I have consulted with profit at every stage of the work; to Professor E. G. Quin who read the notes to the LU-text in typescript and to whom I am indebted for valuable suggestions; to Professor David Greene who read the Introduction and suggested some clarifying additions; finally to Máire, Bean Uí Chinnseala who with cheerfulness, speed and accuracy undertook the typing of the whole work.

Táin Bó Cúailnge inso sís

TArcomlad[1] slóiged mór la Connachtu .i. la hAilill ⁊ la Meidb, ⁊ hetha húaidib cossna trí chóiced aili. Ocus foíte techta ó Ailill co secht macu Mágach .i. co hAilill, co Ánlúan, co Moccorb[2], co Cet, co Én ⁊ Bascall ⁊ Dóche, trícha cét la cach n-áe, [5] ⁊ co Cormac Cond Longas mac Conchobair cona [3]thríb cétaib[3] boí for condmiud la[a] Connachta. Tecait uile íarum co mbátar hi Crúachnaib Aí.

Trí luirg didiu do Chormac oc tochim do C[h]rúachnaib.

In cétna lorg broitt brecca i forcipul co filliud impu. Fortíi [10] berrtha[4] foraib. [5]Leíni fo thairinniuth[5] cota nglún, ⁊ fotalscéith foraib ⁊ manaís lethanglas for crund midśing i lláim cech fir.

In lorg tánaisi broit dubglasa impu-side ⁊ lénti co ndercintliud co horcnib sís, ⁊ monga tara cenna síar, ⁊ lubne gela foraib ⁊ slega cóicrinne[6] inna lámaib.   [15]

'Ní hé Cormac beus,' or Medb.

Tic an tres lorc dano. Broitt chorcra impu ⁊ lénte culpatacha fo derggintślaid co traigthe, ⁊ ber[r]thai slechtai co guaille, ⁊ cromscéith co fáebraib condúala impu ⁊ turre rígthige i lláim cach fir.

'Is é Cormac inso hifechtsa,' or Medb.   [20]

Doecmalta dano íarum ceithre cóiced Hérend co mbátar hi Crúachnaib Aíi. Ocus nís teilcset a fáthi ⁊ a ndruíd ass sein co cend cóicthigis oc irnaidi śeóin.

Asbert Medb íarum fria haraid a lláa documlásat:

'Cach óen scaras sund trá indiu', ol sí, 'fria chóem ⁊ a charait, [25] dobérat maldachtain form-sa úair is mé dorinól in slúagad sa.'

'An-su didiu,' ol in t-ara, '[7]co n-imparrá[7] in carpat deisel ⁊ co tí nert in tśeúin ara tísam ar frithisi.'

---

[a] nó fó [M]: *not in* W

[1] Tarcomlád U, Tarchomlad W   [2] Modh Corb W   [3-3] trib cetaib W; *read* thríchait cét?   [4] bértha U, bertha W   [5-5] leni fotairindin W   [6] cóicrinné U   [7-7] co n-impar W

1

In tan didiu dosoí in t-ara forsin carpat ⁊ lotair do thecht ass co
[30] n-accatár in n-ingin macdacht remib. Folt buidi furri. Bratt
brecc impe, delg n-óir and. Léine c[h]ulpatach co nderggintślaid
impe. Dá assa co foraib óir impu. Agad ḟochóel ḟorlethan[1]. Dí
55ᵇ broí duba dorchaidi. | Abrait duib dáin[2] co mbentaís foscod i
mmedón a dá grúaide. Indar latt ropo di partaing imdéntai a
[35] beóil. Indar lat ba fross do némannaib boí inna bélaib .i. a fíaclai.
Teóra trillsi fuirri .i. dí thriliss immo ccnd súas[3], trilis tara haiss
síar co mbenad a dá colptha inna díaid. Claideb corthaire do
ḟindruine inna láim, esnaid[4] óir and. Trí meic imlisse cechtar a
dá súla. Gaisced lasin n-ingin ⁊ dá ech duba foa carput.
[40] 'Cia do chomainm-siu?' ol Medb[5] frisin n-ingin.
'Fedelm banḟili do Chonnachtaib mo ainm-sea,' or ind ingen.
'Can dothéig?' or Medb.
'A hAlbain iar foglaim filidechta,' or ind ingen.[5]
'In fil imbass forosna lat?' or Medb.
[45] 'Fil écin,' or ind ingen.
'Décai dam-sa didiu co bbia mo ḟechtas.'
Dosnécce ind ingen íarum. Is and asbert Medb:
'A Ḟeidelm banḟáith, co acci[a] in slúag?'
Frisgart Fedelm co n-epert:
[50] 'Atchíu forderg, atchíu rúad.'
'Ní fír són ém,' ol Medb, 'ar atá Conchobor ina chess i nEmain ⁊
hUlaid imbi co neoch as dech a n-ócc, ⁊ ráncatár mo thec[h]ta-sa co
tucsat fis scél dam-sa ass.'
'Fedelm banḟáith, co acca ar slúag?' ol Medb.
[55] 'Atchíu forderg, atchíu rúad,' ol ind ingen.
'Ní fír són,' ol Medb, 'ar atá [6]Celtchar mac Guthidir[6] co tríun
hUlad imbi i nDún Lethglaisse, ⁊ atá Fergus mac Roeich meic
Echdach lenni sund for longais co tríchait chét imbi. Fedelm
banḟáith, co acca [7]ar slúag[7]?' ol Medb.
[60] 'Atchíu forderg, atchíu rúad,' ol ind ingen.
'Ní báa aní sin trá,' ol Medb, 'ar bít imserga ⁊ círgala ⁊ fuili for-
dergga i cach slúag ⁊ i cach thaurchomrac dúnaid móir. Déca
atheruch dúnd dano ⁊ abbair a ḟír frind Feidelm banḟáith, co
acca [7]ar slúag[7]?'
[65] 'Atchíu[8] forderg, atchíu rúad,' ol Fedelm[9].
[10]Conid and asbert[10]:

'Atchíu fer find firfes cles
co lín créchta fora chnes[1]
lúan láith i n-airthiur a chind
óenach mbúada a thulchind.   70

'Fail secht ngemma láith ṅgaile
for lár a dá imlisse
fil fuidrech fora glinni[2]
fil leind ndeirg ndrolaig immi.

[3]'Dofil gnúis as gráto dó[4]   75
dobeir mod don banc[h]ureo
duni óc is álaind dath
dofeith deilb ṅdracuin don chath.

'Cosmail innas a gaile
fri Coin Culaind Murtheimne   80
nocon fetar cúich in Cú
C[h]ulaind asa caini clú
acht rofetur-sa amne
is[5] forderg in slúag sa de.[6]

'Atchíu fer mór forsin maig   85
dobeir tres dona slógaib
cet[h]ri claidbíni cles n-án
fil i cechtar a dá lám. |

56ᵃ | 'Dá gáe bolga immosbeir
cenmothá colg dét i[s] sleg   90
ardaric imbert don tslúag
sain gním fris téit cach n-arm uád.

'Fer i cathḟochrus bruit deirg
dobeir[7] in cosmail cach leirg[7]
ardaslig tar fonnad clé   95
cotagoin in ríastarthe
delb domárfas fair co se
a[t]chíu imrochlád a gné.

---

[1] chness W, chnis U   [2] ghlaini W (rinne LL)   [3] *first line reads*
Ilar nderggmartra dogni W, *this is second line*   [4] atchiu *add.* W
[5] (bid LL)   [6] W *here inserts a repetition of Medb's question and Fedelm's*
answer: Fedilm banfaith co acca *etc.*   [7-7] (a choiss for cach leirg LL, *sicleg.* ?)

'Ro gab toscugud don chath
mani airlestar bid brath
dóich lim iss é dobobsaig[1]
Cú C[h]ulaind mac Súaldaim.

'Slaidfid for slúagu slána
fochiuchra for tiugára
fáicfidi leis míli cend
ní cheil in banfáith Fedelm.

'Snigfid crú a cnesaib curad
do láim laích bid lánpudar
oirgfid ócu imregat fir
do c[h]llannaib Dedad meic Sin
beit cuirp cerbtha caínfit mná
la Coin na Certa atchíu-sa.'

     a.

.r.[2] IN lúan iar samain is and documlaiset. Iss ed dollotar
sairdes a Crúachnaib Aíi .i. for Muicc Cruinb, for Terloch
Teóra Crích, for Túaim Móna, for [3]Cúil Sibrinne[a3], for Fid,
for Bolga,[4] for Coltain, for Glúne Gabair, for Mag Trego, for Tethbai
túascirt[b] for Tethbai descirt, for Tíarthechta, for Ord, for Slaís
fadess, for Indiuind, for Carnd, for Ochtrach, for Midi, for Findglassa Assail, for Deilt, for Delind, for Sailig, for Slaibre, [5]for Slechtai
selgatar[5], for [6]Cúil Sibrinni[6], for Ochuind fadess, for hUatu fathúaid,
for Dub, for Comur fadess, for Tromma, for Othromma[7] sair, for
Sláini, for Gort Sláni, for Druim Licce fadess. for Áth nGabla, for
Ardachad, for Féraind fothúaid, for Findabair, for Assi fadess, for
Drúim Sálfind, for Druim Caín, for Druim mac nDega, for Eódond
Mór, for Eódond mBec, for Méthe Tog, for Méthe nEóin, for Druim
Cáemtechta, for Scúaip, for Imscúaip, for Cend Ferna, for Baile, for
Aile, for Báil Scena, for Dáil Scena, for Fertse, for Ross Lochad, for

---

a .i. Loch Carrcin. ⁊ o Silind ingin Madchair ro ainmniged. [H]; *not in* W
b .i. Carpri [H]; *not in* W.

---

[1] dobursaigh W   [2] *in margin* U, *om.* W; *list of names written in two cols.*
U W   [3-3] Cuil Sibrille no Sillinne W; *read* Cúil Silinne   [4] Bagnai W
[5-5] for Sléchtai selgatar U, for Slechta selgatar W   [6-6] Cuil W
[7] Fothrumma W, *sic leg.*

Sále[1], for Lochmach, for Ánmag, for Deind, for Deilt, for Dubglaiss[2], for Fid Mór[a], for Colbtha, for Crond hi Cúalngi.   130

A Findabair Chúalngi is ass fodáilte in tslóig Hérend fón cóiced do c[h]uingid in tairb.   [3]Ár ropo thairsiu sin dochótar céin co ráncatar Findabair[3].

Finit a titulrad.   [3]Incipit in scél iar n-urd[3].

56[b] | In scél iar n-urd inso sís   135

Ó dodeochatár a cétna n-ude a Crúachnaib co mbátár hi Cúil Sibrinne[4b], asbert Medb fria haraid ara n-indled a noí carpti[c] dí coro lád cor isin dúnad co n-accad dús cía lasmboth scíth[5d] ⁊ lasmboth laind techt in tslógaid.

Focress a phupall colléic for Ailill ⁊ sudighthe a thincur eter 140 choilcthe ⁊ brothracha.   Fergus mac Róich didiu for láim Ailello isin phupull.   Cormac Cond Longas mac Conchobair fora láim-sidi. Conall Cernach fora láim-side.   Fiacha mac Fir Febe fora láim-side, mac ingine Conchobair.   Medb ingen Echach Fedlig fora láim aili do Ailill.   Findabair ingen Ailella ⁊ Medbi[c] fora láim-sidi.   Cen- 145 mothá fossu ⁊ timthirthidi insin.

Tic Medb iar ndéscin in tslóig ⁊ asbert ba n-espa do chách dul in tslógaid dían téset in trícha cét Galión[6].

'Ced ara tánsi na firu?' or Ailill.

'Ní dá tánsem dam,' ol Medb.   'It ána ind óic.   In tan ro mboí 150 cách oc gním a sosta, ro scáig dóib-seom tuga a sosta ⁊ fune a mbíd. In tan ro mboí cách oc praind, ro scáig praind dóib-seom hi suidiu, ⁊ [7]ro bátár[7] a cruti ocaó n-airfitiud.   Is espa[f] didiu,' ol Medb, 'a techt.   Is foraib bíaid búaid in tslóig.'

'Is airiund arbáget dano,' or Ailill.   155

'Ní regat lend,' ol Medb.

'Anat didiu,' ol Ailill.

'Nach ainfet dano,' ol Medb.   'Ficfit[8] fornd iar tiachtain dúin[9],' ol sí, '⁊ gébtait ar tír frind,'

'Ceist, cid dogéntar friu,' or Ailill, 'innách maith a n-anad nách 160 a techt?'

---

[a] .i. Trúailli [M]; *not in* W   [b] .i. áit hi fil Loch Carrcín indiu [H]; *gloss not in* W   [c] .i. nónbor cairpthech [*leg.* noí carpait?] no bídsi for leith arná salc[h]ad dendgur in mórslúaig hisi [M]; *not in* W   [d] .i. lasmad dolig [M] [e] fora láim-sidi Flidais [H]; *not in* W   [f] .i. is feles [H]; *not in* W

[1] Aile W   [2] Dubruais W   [3–3] *om.* W   [4] Sibrille W; *read* Silinne   [5] lescc W   [6] na nGálion W   [7–7] rob | bátár U [8] fichfit W   [9] duin W, *om.* U

'A nguin!' ol Medb.

'Ní chélam as banchomairle,' or Ailill.

Ní maith a n-asbir ¹la sanais ón¹,' ol Fregus. 'Ní 'maricfe, úair
165 is áes comhchotaig dúinni 'nar nUltaib, acht má non gontar uli.'

'Cid ed ón dorigénmaís-ni*,' ol Medb, 'ár atú-sa sund mo šain-
teglach díb tríchtaib cét,' ol sí, '⁊ atát na secht Mane .i. mo šecht
meic secht tríchait cét. Cotaroí a toccad,' ol sí, '.i. Mane Máthramail
⁊ Mane Athramail ⁊ Mane Mórgor ⁊ Mane Mingor ⁊ Mane Móepirt—
170 .i. iss éside Mani Milscothach—Mane Andóe ⁊ Mane Cotageib Ule—
is éside tuc cruth a máthar ⁊ a athar ⁊ a n-ordan díb línaib.'

'Nípá fír són,' ol Fergus. 'Atát secht ríg sund din Mumu ⁊
trícha cét la cech n-áe comchotach dúinni 'nar nUltaib. Dobér-sa
cath duit,' ol Fergus, 'for lár in dúnaid hi tám cosna secht tríchtaib
175 cét sin ⁊ com thríchait chét fadéin ⁊ co tríchait chét na nGalión. Acht
ní thacér-sa aní sin,' ol Fergus. 'Airlifim-ni² na hócu chena conná
57ᵃ gébat forsin³ tslóg. Secht tríchait | chét déac lenni ⁴hi sund⁴, ol
Fergus, 'iss é lín ar ndúnaid cenmothá ar ndáescorslúag ⁊ ar mná—
ar itá a rígan la cach ríg sund hi comaitecht Medba—⁊ cenmothá
180 ar maccáemu. Iss é in t-ochtmad trícha cét déac inso .i. trícha
cét na nGalión. Fodáilter fón slóg ule.'

'Cumma lem,' ol Medb, 'acht ná robat isin chaír chomraic i táat.'

Is ed dogníth and íarum. Fodáilte in Galióin fón slóg.

Dollotár ass arna bárach do ⁵Móin Choíltrae⁵. Dosnáirthet ocht
185 fichit oss n-allaid and i n-óenalaim. Cúartait impu. Nos gonat
íarom. Nách airm thrá i mbuí fer donaib Galiónaib is hé ard-
daánaic, acht cóic oss⁶ arránic in slóg ule díib. Dotháegat iar
sudiu i mMag Trego ⁊ scurit and ⁊ arfognat dóib.

Asberat-som is and sin ro gab Dubthach in laíd seo:
190 r.⁷   'Atmaid nád chúalaid co sse
                costecht fri tress⁸ nDubthaige
                slúagad n-imdub arubthá
                fri Findbend mná Ailellá.

ᵃ ro fétfaimmis a dénom [M]; *not in* W

¹⁻¹ laissin ni son W; *read* .i. la sanais ón? *or place phrase after* Fergus?
² Airlichfimne W   ³ frissin W   ⁴⁻⁴ *sic* W, *om.* U   ⁵ Móin
Choltni W, *sic leg.*   ⁶ nammá *add.* W   ⁷ *in marg.* U, *om.* W
⁸ reis W, *sic leg.*

'Doficfe in slúagadach
gébas ar[1] cend éte Murthemne   195
ibait fíaich lugbairt [1a] lacht
di gnáis inna muccaide.

'Gébaid Crann fóitech[2] fríithu[3]
nís léicfe i Murthemniu
[4]con roisc opair fer Féne   200
isin tsléib túad[5] Ochaíni.[6]

'Crib ol Ailill fri Cormac
taít co comsaigid[7] far mac
ní tháet di magaib in búair
nach robda[8] fúam in tslúaig.   205

'Bid cath inso iarsind úair
la Meidb co tríun in tslúaig
bíait colnai [9]de iné[9] de
dianub thí in ríatarthe.[10]

Dosfóbair thrá ind Némain[a] la sodain ⁊ níp sí sin adaig ba sámam   210
dóib la buadris[12] ind athig[b] triana chotlud. Foscerdat [13]inna
buidne[13] fo chétóir ⁊ focherd dírna mór din tslóg co luid Medb día
chosc[14].

Dothíagat íarom co feótár i nGránairud Tethba túascirt[c], [15]iar
tabairt imthúsa fordallaig forsin slúag dar grellacha ⁊ dar sruthra.[15] 215

Dobreth robud ó Fergus i suidiu co hUltu ar chondalbi. Bátir-
side[16] hi cess calléic acht Cú Chulaind ⁊ a athair .i. Súaltaim. Dolluid
Cú Chulaind ⁊ a athair iar ríachtain ind robaid ó Fergus co mbátár i
nIraird Cuillend[d] oc frecomét in tslúaig and.

'Attá menma in tslóig ocom[17] innocht,' ol Cú Chulainn fri[a]   220
athair.

<a> .i. in Badb [M]; .i. in badb *overhead* Y   <b> .i. Dubthaig [M]
<c> .i. Gránard indiu [M]; Irardd indiu W   <d> .i. Crossa Caíl [M]; *not in* W

[1a] lúgbairt U   [1] dar W   [2] fóethech W   [3] *sic* U, fri hithu W
[4] Y begins   [5] thuaid Y   [6] Ochéniu W   [7] cumscaigid W
[8] rouba Y, rubda W   [9-9] de ine Y, dine W. *Read* doíne   [10]ríastarthé U   [12] *sic* YW, budris U   [13-13] inambuidne *with* b *over* e Y,
ina mbudne W   [14] cosc YW, *sic leg.*   [15-15] *om.* Y   [16] bátirsidé
U, batirside Y, batarside W   [17] and Y W

'Ortha[a][1] úan co rrobud do Ultaib. Isim écen-sa techt i ndáil
Fedelmae Noíchride—.i. i ndáil a hinailte boí i comair Con Culaind
i ndormainecht[b]—dim glinniu fadéin dochóid friae.'

225   Dogní id n-erchomail íarom ría techt ⁊ scríbais ogum inna menoc,
⁊ focheird im úachtar in c[h]orthe.

57[b]   Dobreth didiu túus na conaire[2] do Fergus ríasin slúag. | Luid
Fergus didiu fordul mór fadess[3] co fórsed[4] do Ultaib terchomrac
slóig. Ar chondailbi doróni-seom sin.

230   Airigthi Ailill ⁊ Medb[5]. Ba and asbert Medb:

        'A Ferguis, is[6] andam amne
        cinnas conaire cingme[7]
        fordul fadess nó fothúaid
        tíagmai tar cach n-ailetúaith.

235   Atotágathar dia m(ͻb)rath
        Ailill Aíe lía slúagad.
        Ní tharat menmain co se
        do thús inna conaire.

        'Máso chondalbi dogní
240   ná tuíd inna echraidi.
        Bés adchotar nech aile
        do thosach na conaire.'

    Ro recair Fergus:

        'A Medb, cid not medraisiu
245   ní cosmail fri mrath inse.
        Is la hUltu, a ben, trá
        a tír tarṅdotuidisa.

        'Ní ar amlessaib in tslúaig
        tíagu cech fordul a húair.
250   [8]Do imgabáil[8] in mórgeine
        immandig[9] Mag Murthemne.

        'Ní arná corad mo chiall
        arna fordulu no tíag.
        Dús [10]i[n] rimgaib[10] ced iar tain[11]
255   Coin Culaind mac Súaltaim.'

---

[a] .i. eirg [M]; .i. ercc W   [b] .i. fó chlith [H]; .i. hi clith W

[1] orthá U   [2] dirma Y   [3] ⁊ budh thuaid *add. over the line* Y, bud túaidh
⁊ bu dess W   [4] foirsed Y, fóirsed W   [5] anni sin *add.* Y W   [6] *om* W.
[7] inse Y; chingme W   [8-8] d'imgabail W   [9] immadich Y W
[10-10] *erasure after* dús *and then* dingaib (d *not unlike* a) Y; irrimgaib W
[11] táin U

Tecait trá co mbátár i nIraird Chuillend.ᵃ   Eirr ⁊ Inell, Foich ⁊
Fochlam a nda ara, ¹cethri meic Iraird meic Ánchinne¹ᵇ, it éside² no
bítis remáin rési[n] slóg do i[m]didnad a [m]bretnas ⁊ a fortcha ⁊ a
mbrat ar nácha salchadh dendgor in dírma   Fogabat-side in n-id
focheird Cú Chulaind ⁊ arigsitárᶜ in geilt³ geltatár ind eich.   Ar ²⁶⁰
geltatar dá ech Súaltaim a fér cona bun a talam.   Lelgatárᵈ immorro dá ech Con Culaind in n-úir co rrici na clocha i ndegaid ind
feúir.   Sudit íarom co tánic in slóg ⊣ aruspetteteᵉ a n-áes ciúil.
Dosberat i lláim Fergusa meic Róich in n-id.   Arléga-side in n-ogum
ʼboí isind id.   ²⁶⁵
    Asbert Medb iar tiachtian:
'Cid frisin n-anaid and⁴?'
'Anmai,' or Fergus, 'frisin n-id n-ucut.   Atá ogam inna menuc,
⊣ iss ed fil and: "Ná tíagar secha co n-étar fer ro láa id samlaid cona
óenláim, ⊣ óenŝlat día tá, ⊣ friscuriur mo phopa Fergus."   Fír,' ol ²⁷⁰
Fergus, 'Cú Chulaind rod lá, ⊣ it é a eich geltatar in mag so.'
    Ocus dambeir i lláim in druad, ⊣ cachain Fergus in laíd so sís:

'Id inso, ced sloindnes dún⁵?
Ind id ⁶cia fo tá a rún⁶?
Cía lín ro lá insé,   ²⁷⁵
inn úat[h]ed nó in sochaide?

'In déne erchóit don [t]ŝlúag
má docóiset ude n-úad?
Finnaid, a druíde, ní ar sin
cid frisi farcbad in t-id.'   ²⁸⁰

⁷In druí dixit⁷:

'Crephnas churad caur rod lá
lánaingces for erreda,
astúd rurech ⁸ferg i ndá⁸
⁹óenfer co n-óenláim ro lá⁹ᶠ.   ²⁸⁵

ᵃ .i. is fris atberar Crossa Caíl indiu [M]; id. W   ᵇ [in marg.] nó cethri
meic Nera meic Núado meic Taccain ut in alis libris inuenitur [M]; not in W
    ᶜ .i. atconcotár [M]; not in W   ᵈ .i. lomraiset [M]; .i. lomraigsitar W
ᵉ .i. sennit [M]; not in W   ᶠ nó feirg i ndáil ro lá óenfer co n-óenláim [M]

¹⁻¹ om. Y W   ² esidé U   ³ gleith Y   ⁴ sunn Y W   ⁵ duind
Y duin W   ⁶⁻⁶ cid fotha a ruin Y, cia fotha a rúin W   ⁷⁻⁷ between
cols. U, om. Y   ⁸⁻⁸ ferg i ndáil Y (fer co ndáil LL)   ⁹⁻⁹ rolaa enfer co
n-enlaim Y

'In nách diá réir slúag ind ríg
inge má ¹ro choilled¹ fír
conid ro lá úaib nammá
óenfer amal fer ro lá.
290 Nocon fetur acht insin
ní frisi corthe in t-id.'

Id inso .c. s.

Asbert Fergus íarom friu:
'Má sáraigthe in n-id se,' ol sé, 'nó má thíastá² secha, cia beith i
295 lláim duni nó i taig fó glas, ricfe i ndead ind fir ro scríb in n-ogum
n-ind, ⁊ génaid-side guin dune díb ría mmatain mani láa nech úaib
id samlaid.'

'Ní háil dúinni ém guin dune dín fó chétóir'. ol Ailill. 'Regmai
for muncind ind feda³ móir ucut frind andes⁴, ⁊ ní ragam tairiseom
eter.' |

58ᵃ Ra selgatár na budni íarom in fid résna carptib. Iss ed ainm in
puirt sin Slechta. Is and atá Partraige.

⁵Mad iar n-arailib immorro dorala and so imacallaim eter Medb
⁊ Fedelm banfáith, amal ro innisimar remoind, ⁊ dano is iarsind
305 frecra do rat-si for Medb ro slechtad in fid⁵ .i. 'Déca dam,' or Medb,
'co bia mo fechtas.' 'Is anso dam,' or ind ingen. 'Níro láim súil
toraib isind fid.' 'Is ar⁶ bías ón⁷, or Medb. 'Silsimini⁸ in fid⁹.
¹⁰Dogníther dano aní sin¹⁰. ¹¹Conid sed¹¹ ainm in puirt sin Slechta.

Feótár íarom i Cúil Sibrilleᵃ. Ferais snechta mór forru co fernnu
310 fer ⁊ co drochu carpat. Bá moch a mmatan arna bárach do érgiu.
Nírbo hí sin adaig ropa sám¹² dóib lasin snechta, ⁊ ní airgénsat
bíada dóib ind adaig sin.

Nípo moch didiu dolluid Cú Chulaind asa bandáil. Anais co
foilc ⁊ co fothraic. Dotháet íarom for lorg in tslóig.
315 '¹³Ní má lodmar¹³ dó,' ol Cú Chulaind, 'ná mertamar Ultu. Ro
léicsem slóg forru cen airfius. Cure airdmius dún tarsin¹⁴ slóg,' ol
Cu Culaind fri Lóeg, 'co fessamar lín in tslóig.'

ᵃ .i. Cennannas [M]; *inserted in text* W

¹⁻¹ ro choillset Y W   ² tistai Y, thiastai W   ³ .i. Fid Duin *add.* Y
(*misplaced*)   ⁴ .i. Fid Duin *add.* W (*correct place*)   ⁵⁻⁵ Sed [*read*
secundum] alios libros so sís. Iar tiachtain dóib Feda Duin co n-accadar in
carpat ⁊ ingen alaind and .i. amal ro indisimar remaind tuas scél Feidelme
Banfátha, combad sund in scél sin ⁊ combad iarsin frecra doberad-si for Meidb
ro slechta in fid Y   ⁶ *sic* U Y, ari W   ⁷ *sic* MSS.; *read* and ?
⁸ silsimni Y W   ⁹ didiu amal sin *add.* Y   ¹⁰⁻¹⁰ *om.* Y   ¹¹⁻¹¹ is
ed Y W   ¹² samam Y W   ¹³⁻¹³ ni madlodmar Y   ¹⁴ forsin W

Dogní Lóeg aní sin ⁊ asbeir fri Coin Culaind:
'Is mesc lim-sa,' ol sé, 'aní siu. ¹Ni ermaisim¹.'
'Nípá mesc atchíu acht co rísa,' ol Cú Culaind.   320
'Tair isin² carpat didiu,' or Láeg.
Tic Cú Culaind isin² carpat ⁊ focheird airdmius forsin lorg iar
céin móir.
'Cid tussu,' or Láeg, 'ní réid fort.'
'Is assu ém dam-sa,' ol Cú Chulaind, 'oldás dait-siu, air itát trí ³²⁵
búada form-sa .i. búaid roisc ⁊ intliuchta ⁊ airdmessa. Ro láosa didiu
trá,' ol sé, 'fomus forsaní sin.ᵃ   Ocht [t]ríc[h]ait chét déac inso,'
ol sé, '³ara rím³. acht forodlad in t-ochtmad trícha chét fón slóg
n-ule conid mesc ⁴fria rím⁴ .i. trícha chét na nGalión.'
Dolluid Cú Chulaind íarom timchell in tslóig co mboí oc ⁵Áth ³³⁰
Grencha⁵ Benaid gabail i sudiu óenbéim cona c[h]laidiub, ⁊ sáidsius
for medón na glassi cona díchtheth carpat friae di síu nách anall.
Dofuircet oco Eirr ⁊ Inell, Fóich ⁊ Fóchlam a ndá ara.   Benaid-som
a cethri cinnu díb ⁊ focheird for cethóra benna ⁶na gabla⁶.   Is de
atá Áth nGabla.ᵇ   ³³⁵
Tíagait íarom eich in c[h]ethrair i n-agid in tslóig, ⁊ a fortchai
forderga foraib.   Indar leó bá cath boí ara cind isind áth.   Dothéit
buden úadib do déscin ind átha.   Ní acatár ní and acht slicht ind
óencharpait ⁊ in gabul cosna cethri cinnu, ⁊ ainm ogaim íarna
scríbend ina tóeb.   Ric in slúag uli la sodain.   ³⁴⁰
'In diar muintir-ni na cenna ucut?' ol Medb.
'Is diar munitir-ni ón'⁊ is diar forclidib,' or Ailill.
Ardléga⁷ fer díb in n-ogum ro boí i tóeb na gabla .i. 'Óenfer rod
lá in gabuil cona óenláim ⁊ ní théssid secce conda rala nech úaib⁸ co
n-áenláim cenmothá Fergus.'   ³⁴⁵
'Is machtad,' ol Ailill, 'a thraite ⁹ro bíth⁹ in cethror.'
'Nápad ed bas machdad | lat,' ol Fergus. 'Bad¹⁰ béim na gabla
dia¹¹ bun óenbéim, ⁊ mássu óenleód a bun, is crichidiu de, ⁊ a
intádud¹² in tucht sa, ol ní claide ro clas rempe ⁊ is a íarthur carpait
ro lád co n-óenláim.'   ³⁵⁰

58ᵇ

ᵃ [in marg.] Is sí seo in tres árim is glicu ⁊ is dolgiu dorigned i nHérind
.i. árim Con Culaind for feraib Hérend ár Tána, ⁊ árim Loga for slúag Fomórach,
ar Cath Maigi Tured ⁊ árim Ingciúil for slóg Bruidni Da Dergae [M]; incorporated in text W   ᵇ .i. oc Beloch Caille Móre fri Cnogba atúaid [H]; in
text W

¹⁻¹ nisnermaisim W   ² = asin   ³⁻³ for árim tricha cet W
⁴⁻⁴ fria n-árim W   ⁵⁻⁵ sic W, Áth Grena U, Ath Gabla Y   ⁶⁻⁶ in
craind Y   ⁷ sic for arléga, ardalega Y, with second a below line
⁸ id samlaid added above line Y   ⁹⁻⁹ rombith Y, ronbith W
¹⁰ bád U   ¹¹ sic Y W, di U   ¹² intsathud Y, intsádud W

'Dingaib dind in n-écin seo, a Fergus,' ol Medb.

'Tucaid carpat dam-sa trá,' ol Fergus, 'conda tuc-sa ass co ndercaiss inn óenleód a bun.'

Brissis Fergus íarom cethri carptiu déac día carptib[1] combo assa
355 charput fessin dosbert a talmain [2]co n-aca[2] ba hóenleód a bun.

'Is tabartha do airi,' ol Ailill, 'indass in c[h]eniúil cosa tíagam.
Érgnad cách uaib a bíad. Nírbo sám dúib[3] irraír lasin snechta.
Ocus innister dún ní do imt[h]echtaib ⁊ airscélaib in c[h]eniúil cosa
tíagam.'

360 Is and sin trá adfessa dóib imt[h]echta Con Culaind.

Imcomairc[4] Ailill íarom:

'Inn é Conchobar dorigni seo?'

'Nach hé,' ol Fergus. 'Ní tergad-side co hor críche cen lín catha
immi.'

365 'Ceist, inn é Celtchar mac Uthidir[5]?'

'Nach hé. Ní thargad-side co hor críche cen lín catha imbi.'

'Ceist, inn é Eógan mac Durt[h]acht?'

'Nach hé,' ol Fergus. 'Ní thargad-side tar or críche[6] cen tríchait[7]
carpat n-imrind imme. Is é fer dogénad in gním,' ol Fergus, 'Cú
370 Chulaind. Is é no benfad a crand óenbémim dia[8] bun ⁊ no génad
in cethrur ucut [9]hi prapi[9] [10]ro mbíthá[10] ⁊ doragad dochom críche
⁊ a ara.'

[11]Inna formolta inso sís[11]

' CInnas fir,' or Ailill, 'in Cú rochúalammár la hUltu? Cia
375 háes in gillai sin is irdairc?'

'Ní handsa ém,' ol Fergus. 'Inna chóiced bliadain luid
dia cluchiu[12] cosin macraid do Emain Machi. Issin tsessed[13]
bliadain luid do foglaim gaiscid ⁊ chless la Scáthaig[a14]. Isin
tsechtmad[15] bliadain gabais gaisced. Isin tsechtmad bliadain déc
380 a áes ind inbaid sea.'

'Inn é sin as andsam fil la Ultu?' ol Medb.

---

[a] Obicitur Tochmarc Emire de so [M], *between columns*; Obicitur Tochmarcc
nEmire do so W, *in margin*

[1] charp*tib* U Y, cairptib W   [2-2] co n-acadar Y W   [3] *sic* Y W,
dóib U   [4] Imcomarc U, imchomairc Y, imchomarcair W   [5] Cuithidir
Y, Guthidir W   [6] cococriche U   [7] tricha cet Y   [8] *sic* Y W, di U
[9-9] in praipi Y, a phraipi W; *read* a prapi   [10-10] rombitha Y W
[11-11] *between cols.* U, *om. here* Y *and inserted later; om.* W   [12] chuindchid
gasgid Y, *begun as* clu . . . *and altered,* gasgid *written overhead*   [13] seachtmad Y
[14] ⁊ luid do thochmorc nEmeiri *add.* Y   [15] ochtmad Y

'For cach n-aí ém,' ol Fergus. 'Ní fairgéba-su ar do c[h]ind
láech bas andsu, ná rind bas áigthidiu [1]ná bas altnidi[1] [2]na bas
athlaimi[2], nó láth bas luinniu, ná fíach bas feólchairiu, ná comlond
a áesa ródsá[3] co trían, ná léo bas feoc[h]ru, ná cláriud comlaind [385]
ná hord esorcthe[4] ná comla ergaile ná bráth for buidne ná ergaire
mórslúaig bas inraici. Ní fuircéba-su and fer rosasad a áes ⁊ a ás ⁊
a erriud ⁊ a erúath, a erlabra, a áinius, a irdarcus, a guth, a c[h]ruth,
a chumachta, a c[h]rúas, a chless, a gaisced, a béim, a bruth, a
barand, a búaid, a bráth, a búadrisi, a foraim, a fómsigi, a fían- [390]
choscur, a déni, a t[h]arptigi, a dec[h]rad co cliuss nónbair for
cach rind amal Choin Culaind.'[5]
'Ní dénaim-sea báa de sin,' ol Medb. 'I n-óenchorp atá-side. |
59ª Fodaim guin. Ní móu gabáil, lasanní is áes ingini macdacht insin ⁊
ní thángatár a fergníma beus.' [395]
'[6]Ní ar ni[6] són,' ol Fergus. 'Nibo machdad dagním do dénam
dó-ssom indiu, ar cid in tan ba sóo-som, batir ferdai a gníma.'

[7]Na Macgnímrada inso sís[7]

'ALta-som ém,' ol Fergus, 'la máthair ⁊ la athair ocond
Airgdig[8] i mMaig Murthemne. Adfessa dó airscéla na [400]
macraide i nEmain. Ár bíit trí chóecait mac and,' ol Fergus,
'oc[9] cluchiu[10]. Is amlaid domel Conchobar a flaith: trían ind laí
oc déscin na macraide, a trían n-aill oc imbirt fidchille, a trían n-aill
oc ól chorma conid gaib cotlad de. Cia bem-ni for longais ríam[11],
ní fil i nÉre óclaig bas amru,' ol Fergus. [405]
'Gudid Cú Chulaind día máthair didiu a lécud dochom na
macraide.
' "Ní rega," ol a máthair, "condit roib cáemtecht di ánrodaib
Ulad."
' "Rochían lim-sa anad fri sodain," ol Cú Chulaind. "Incoisc-siu [410]
dam-sa ced leth atá[12] Emain."
' "Fathúaidh amne," ol a máthair, "⁊ is doraid a n-ude," ol sí.
"Atá Slíab Fúait etruib."
' "Dobér indass fair," ol Cú Chulaind, "amin."[13]
'Téit ass íarom ⁊ a scíath slissen laiss ⁊ a bunsach[14] ⁊ a lorg áne ⁊ [415]
a líat[h]ráit. Focherded a bunsaig[15] ríam conda gebed [16]ar loss[16]
resíu dorotsad[17] a bun for lár.

[1-1] *om.* Y   [2-2] na bas bus athluime Y   [3] radsia Y, rosia W
[4] esoircne Y W   [5] Formolta Con Chulaind andsin *add.* Y   [6-6] *sic* MSS.
[7-7] maccerda con culaind so *in marg.* Y, na macgnímrodha inso W
[8-8] *sic* W, ocond dairggdig U Y   [9] oca Y W   [10] do gress *add.* W
[11] *sic* Y W, *om.* U   [12] i tá W   [13] *sic* Y W, amim U   [14] riam *add.*
Y (*misplaced*)   [15] bunsach MSS.   [16-16] *om.* Y   [17] dorótsad U

'Téit cosna maccu íarom cen naidm a fóesama forru ár ní théged
nech cucu ina cluchimag ¹co n-arnastá¹ a fóesam forro². Ní fitir-
420 som aní sin.ᵃ

' "Non sáraigedar in mac," ol Follomon mac Conchobair, "sech
rafetamár is di Ultaib dó. Arguntís³ do. Benaid⁴ fóo."

'Focherdat a trí cóecta bunsach fair ⁊ arsisetar isin scíath slissen
uli les-seom. Focherdat dano a líathróite uli fair-seom ⁊ nos gaib-
425 seom cech óenlíathróit ina ucht. Focherdat dano a⁵ trí cóectu lorg
ána fair. Araclich-som conach ráncatár hé⁶, ⁊ gabais airbir díib
fria aiss.

'Ríastartha immi-seom i sudiu. Indar lat ba tinnarcan⁷ asnort
cach foltne ina chend lasa comérge conérracht. Indar lat bá
430 hoíbell tened boí for cach óenfinnu de⁸. Iadais indara súil dó⁹
conárbo lethiu indás cró snáithaiti. Asoilgg alaile combo móir
beólu midchúaich¹⁰. Doérig dia glaininí co rici a hóu. Asoilg a
beólu coa inairddriuch combo écna a inchróes. Atreacht in lúan
láith assa mulluch.

435 'Benaid fona maccu íarom. Doscara cóecait mac díib síu rístaís
dorus nEmna. Forrumai nónbor díib thorom-sa ⁊ Conchobar.
59ᵇ Bámar oc imbirt fidchille. | Lingid-som dano tarsin fidchill i ndegaid
ind nónbair. Gaibid Conchobar a rig.

' "Ní maith airráilter in macrad", ol Conchobar.

440 ' "Deithbir dam-sa, ¹¹a popa Chonchobair¹¹," ol sé. "Dosroacht
do chluchiu óm thaig, óm máthair ⁊ óm¹² athair, ⁊ ní maith ro
mbátar frim."

'¹³"Cia th'ainm-seo?"¹³ ol Conchobar.

' "Sétanta mac Súaltaim atomchomnaic-se¹⁴ ⁊ mac Dechtere¹⁵ do
445 phethar-su. Níba dóig mo chonpére sund."

' "Ced náro nass do fóessam-su dano forsna maccu?" ol Conchobar.

' "Ní fetar-sa aní sin," ol Cú C[h]ulaind. "Gaib it láim mo
fóesom airtho didiu."

' "Atmu,"¹⁶ ol Conchobar.

450 'La sodain doella-som forsin macraid sethnón in taige.

' "Ced taí dano dóib innossa?" ol Conchobar.

' "Coro nastar a fóesom- [som]¹⁷ form-sa dano," ol Cú Chulaind.

ᵃ .i. in ges boí foraib [H]; *not in* W

¹⁻¹ co narnasta Y W   ² *sic* W, *om.* U, forro *in lower marg.* Y   ³ *sic*
U, arguittis (*or might be read* arguitus) Y, arguintis W   ⁴ Maaigid *with
first* a *partly deleted* Y, maidhit W   ⁵ an U Y, ina W   ⁶ *om.* YW
⁷ indarcan Y W   ⁸ *sic* W, *om.* U, *and added over line* Y   ⁹ *sic* W, *om.*
U Y   ¹⁰ fidchoich Y W   ¹¹⁻¹¹ a phopa a Chonchobar Y   ¹² ómm
U *and second* m *deleted*   ¹³⁻¹³ Cia dia ta .īm. so ol Conchobar ⁊ cia th'ainm-
seo Y, cia hainmsi dano W   ¹⁴ atomcomainmsea Y   ¹⁵ Deichdene Y
¹⁶ .i. foemaim *add.* W   ¹⁷ foesamson Y, fóesamsum W

' "Gaib it láim didiu," ol Conchobar.
' "Atmu," ol Cú Chulaind.
'Lotár uli isa cluchemaig íarom ⁊ atarachtatár in maic hí ro slassa ⁴⁵⁵
and. Fosráthatar a mummi ⁊ a n-aiti.'

'FEcht n-and dano,' or Fergus, 'in tan bá gilla, ní chotlad i
nEmain Macha co matain.'
' "Inndis dam," ol Conchobar fris, "cid ná cotlai."¹
' "²Ní dénaim," or Cú C[h]ulaind,² "cen chomard frim chend ⁊ frim ⁴⁶⁰
chossa."
'Dobreth íarom la Conchobar coirthe fria chend ⁊ araile fria
c[h]ossa, ⁊ dogníth³ imdai fo leith dó etarro.
'Luid in fecht n-aile dano araile fer día dúscud-som co mben-som
dia dur[n]d ina étan co rruc tulchlár ind étain co mboí forsind ⁴⁶⁵
inchind ⁊ cor thrascair ⁴in corthe cá rigid⁴.
' "Rofes," or Ailill, "robó⁵ ⁶dor[n]d níad⁶ ⁊ ropo rig rúanada."
'Ó sin trá,' ol Fergus, ⁷'ní laimthe-som do dúscad⁷ co ndúsced a
óenur.'

⁸Aided na Maccraide inso⁸   ⁴⁷⁰

'BAí in fecht [n-]aile dano oc áni líat[h]ráiti i mmaig in c[h]luche
fri Emain anair. Do leith dano dó a óenur frisna trí cóecto
mac. Conboinged⁹ airthiu íarom ¹⁰cach cluchiu¹⁰ ind indas sin
caidche. ¹¹Gabaid in gilla¹¹ oc sudiu imbirt a dor[n]d foraib conid
apad cóeca mac díib. Téit for teched la sodain co mboí fo adurt ⁴⁷⁵
imdai Conchobair. Conérget¹² Ulaid imbi. Conérgim-se ⁊ Conchobar
lais-seom. Conérig-som fón imdai dano co corastar de in n-imdai
cosin tríchait láth ngaile ro boí indi co mboí for lár in tigi.
'Sedait¹³ Ulaid imbi la sodain isin tig. Córaigmit-ni íarom,' or
Fergus, '⁊ sídaigmít in macraid fris-[s]eom iar sin,'   ⁴⁸⁰

¹⁴Cath Eógain meic Derthacht fri¹⁵ Conchobar inso¹⁴

'BOí imnisse chatha eter Ultu ⁊ Eógan mac nDurt[h]acht.
Tíagait Ulaid don chath. Fácabar-som inna chotlud. Maiti
for Ultu. Fácabar Conchobar ⁊ Cúscraid Mend Macha ⁊

---

¹ ind emain a chu chulaind *add.* Y   ²⁻² *om.* Y *but* ni chodlaim *add.*
overhead   ³ dogni Y   ⁴⁻⁴ co rigid in coirthe Y   ⁵ rob | bó U,
robbad Y, robo W   ⁶⁻⁶ dornn caurad Y W   ⁷⁻⁷ ni laimtiseom
diuscad Y, ni laimthisim duscad W   ⁸⁻⁸ *om.* Y W   ⁹ conbóing U,
conboingath Y, conboingeth W   ¹⁰⁻¹⁰ oca cluchiu W (*after* caidche)
¹¹⁻¹¹ *sic* Y, gabait in gillai U, gaibthi in gillai W   ¹² *sic* U, conerged Y,
coneirget W; *read* Co n-éiget ?   ¹³ saigid Y   ¹⁴⁻¹⁴ *om.* Y   ¹⁵ *sic* W, do U

485 sochaide mór[1] olchena. Dofúsci-seom a ngol. Sínithi íarom co
mmemdatar[2] in dá liic ro bátár immi. Hi fíadnaise Bricriu ucut
dorónad,' ol Fergus. 'Atraig la sodain. Cotricim-se fris i ndorus
ind lis ⁊ mé athgaíte.

' "Fuit! Dia do bethu, [3]a popa Fergus[3]," ol sé. "Cate[4] Conc[h]-
490 obar?"

' "Ní etar-sa", ol mé.

'Téit ass íarom. Ba dorcha ind adaig. Fóbair a n-ármach. Co
60ᵃ n-acca ara chind in fer ⁊ leth a chind fair ⁊ leth fir aile fora | muin.

' "Congna lem, a Chú Chulaind," ol sé. "Rom bíth ⁊ tucus leth mo
495 bráthar ar[5] mo muin. Beir síst lim."

' "Ní bér," or sé.

'La sodain focheirt in n-aire dó. Focheird-som de. Immasíni-
thar dóib. Doscarthar Cú C[h]ulaind. Co cuala ní, in [m]boidb
dinib collaib.

500 ' "Olc damnae laích fil and fo chossaib aurddrag!"

'La sodain fónérig[6] Cú Chulaind ⁊ benaid[7] a c[h]end de cosind
luirg áne ⁊ gabaid immá[i]n líathráite ríam[8] dar in mag.

' "In fail mo phopa Conchobar isind ármaig se?"

'Frisgair-side dó. Téit chuci conid n-acca issin c[h]lud, ⁊ ro boí
505 ind úir imbi do cach leth día díc[h]lith.

' "Cid día tánac[9] [10]isin n-ármag[10]," ol Conchobar, "co ndeochais
úathbás and?"

'Tanócaib asin chlud la sodain. Ní thurcébad sesser linni di
t[h]rénferaib Ulad ní bad chalma.

510 ' "Tair reond don tig ucut," ar Conchobar, [11]co ndernai tenid dam
and.'

'Ataí-seom thenid móir dó.

' "Maith didiu," or Conchobar[11]. "Díanom thísad mucc fonaithe
[12]robadam béo[12]."

515 ' "Rag-sa conda tuc," ar Cú Chulaind.

'Téit ass íarom. Co n-accai in fer ocond fulucht i mmedón ind
feda, indara lám dó cona gaisciud inti, ind lám n-aill oc funi in
tuircc. Ba mór a úathmaire ind fir. Fanópair-som arapa[13] ⁊
dobeir[14] a chend ⁊ a muicc laiss. Loingid Conchobar iar sin in torc.

520 ' "Tíagam díar tig," or Conc[h]obar.

---

[1] ali *add.* W   [2] memdatar *Dipl. Ed.*   [3-3] a phopa a Fergais Y
[4] *sic* Y W, cáte U   [5] for W   [6] faneraig Y W   [7] bennaid U
[8] de *add.* W, *sic leg.*   [9] tudchadso Y W   [10] isinnarmaigh Y W
[11-11] *sic* Y W, *om.* U   [12-12] robadam ślan W   [13] arappaide W
[14] dombeir W

'Condrecat fri Cúsoraid mac Conchobair.   Bátár dano tromgona
fair-side.   Dobeir Cú Chulaind fora muin.   Dollotár íarom a tríur co
hEmain Macha.'

¹Aided na trí nónbor inso ⁊ in fáth arná laimthé² a nguin ina cess.¹

'FEcht aile dano bátár Ulaid inna nóendin.   Ní bí³ nóenden ⁵²⁵
linni íarom⁴,' for Fergus, 'for mnáib ⁊ maccaib nách for neoch
bís fri crích nUlad anechtair nach for Coin Culaind ⁊ fora
athair.   ⁵Ocus ane ní lamar fuligud forro-som, ar conscescing⁶ in
cess for intí nod goin nó a meth nó a garséle⁵.

'Tonnecat trí nónbair⁷ a hInsib Faíche.   Lottar for in n-íarless tan ⁵³⁰
bámár inar nóendin.   Égit in bantrocht isind liss.   Boí in macrad
i mmaig in c[h]luchi.   Doíagat-side⁸ fóna hégme.   Amal atchon-
catár in macrad na firu duba⁹ duabsecha, tíagait ar teched ule acht
Cú C[h]ulaind a óenur.   Imbert-side na lámlecca foraib¹⁰ ⁊ a
luirg áne foraib.   Marbaid nónbor díib ⁊ fácbait cóeca cned fair-seom ⁵³⁵
⁊ documlat ass íarom olchena.

'Fer dorigni inna gníma sin inraptar lán[a]¹¹ a c[h]óic blíadna,
nírbo machthad ¹²cé na thísed co hor cocríchi ⁊¹² cé no éisged¹³ a
cinnu don chet[h]ror ucut.'

¹⁴Aided con na cerda inso la Coin Culaind ⁊ aní día fil Cú Chulaind ⁵⁴⁰
fair-seom¹⁴.

'RAfetammár¹⁵ ém in [n]gilla sin,' ol Conall Cernach, '⁊ ní
messaite fria fís is dalta dún.   Nípu chían íarsin gním
adchúaid Fergus indossa co nderna-som bét n-aile.

'Dia forgéni Cauland cerdd óegidacht do Chonc[h]obur¹⁶, asbert ⁵⁴⁵
Cauland íarom nábad sochaide no bertha chucai áir nípu du thír ná
ferund dó a fuirec dorigni acht do thorud a dá lám ⁊ a tharnaguir.
Luid Conchobar íarom ⁊ cóeca cairptech¹⁷ imbi do neoch | ba
sruthem ⁊ ba ¹⁸haeregdu inna caurad.¹⁸

'Adell Conchobar laiss íarom a cluchemag.   Ba bés dano dó do grés ⁵⁵⁰
a n-adall ⁊ a tadall, oc techt ⁊ oc tuidecht, do chuingid ¹⁹a bennach-
da¹⁹ cosna maccu.   Co n-accai íarom Coin Culaind oc áin líathróti

60ᵇ

¹⁻¹ om. Y   ² lamtha W   ³ sic Y W, boí U   ⁴ om. W   ⁵⁻⁵ om. Y
⁶ sic U, conseiscing W; read conscing   ⁷ nónbor U   ⁸ dothiagadside
Y, Tothíagatside W   ⁹ added alongside H, om. Y W   ¹⁰ om. W, omitt.
¹¹ slana Y, lana W   ¹²⁻¹² om. Y   ¹³ foisced Y   ¹⁴⁻¹⁴ om. Y,
Aidedacht na con do thig Chulaind cerda inso W   ¹⁵ Rofeadarsa Y
¹⁶ sic U, Conchobur Dipl. Ed.   ¹⁷ carp- U, cairp- Y W   ¹⁸⁻¹⁸ sic
U W (for haeregdam na caurad ?), airegdu ina churad Y   ¹⁹⁻¹⁹ a mbendhacta
Y, a mbennachtan W

frisna trí cóectu mac, ⁊ birt a ráena forru. In tan ba háin phuill
dognítis, no línad-som in poll día líathrótib ⁊ ní chumcaitis in
555 meic a ersclaige. In tan batir héseom ule dobidctis[1] in poll, arach-
liched-som a óenur conná téged cid óenlíathróit ind. In tan bá
n-imt[h]rascrad dognítís, dorascrad-som na trí cóectu mac a óenur
⁊ [2]ní chomraiced[2] imbi-seom lín a t[h]rascartha. In tan dano bá
n-imdírech dognítis, dosnérged-som uli co mbítís tornochta, ⁊ nocon
560 ructaís-seom immurro cid a delg asa brot-som nammá.

'Ba hamra la Conchobar aní sin. Asbert-side in etarbíad [3]a
gnimu[3] [4]acht tised dó[4] co áes ferdatad. Asbert cách etardabíad.
Asbeir Conc[h]obar fri Co[in] Culaind:
' "Tair lem," ol sé, "dond fleid día tíagom [5]dáig ot áegi."[5]
565 ' "Nimda[6] sát[h]ech dom c[h]luchi béos, a bobba Conchobair,"[7]
ol in gilla. "Ragat-sa infar ndíaid."

'Ó ráncatár uli íarom don[8][d fleid],[8] asbert Cauland fri Conc[h]-
obar:
' "In frithálid nech infar ṅdíaid?" ol sé.
570 ' "Náthó," ol Conchobar. Nírbo chuman laiss dál a daltai inna
díaid.
' "Atá árchú[a] lem-sa," ol Culand. "[9]Tri slabrada fair ⊢ triar
cacha slabraide.[9] [10]A hEspáin dosfucad[10]. Léicther de dáig ar
n-indili ⊢ ar cet[h]ra, ⊢ dúntar in less."
575 'Tic in gilla fo ṡodain. Fónópair in cú. Nos fethed-som a
cluche colléic. Focherded a líathróit ⊢ focherded a loirg[11] ina díaid
co mbenad in líathróit. Níbo móo in band oldás a chéle. Ocus
focheird[12] a bunsaig[13] inna ndíaid conda gebed[14] re totim. Ocus níro
t[h]airmesc a c[h]luchi immi ce ro boí in cú ocá ascnam. Torbais
580 Conchobar ⊢ a muint*ir* aní sin connárbo étir leó a nglúasacht. Indar
leó ní fairebitís i mbethaid ara cind cid ersloicthe in less. In tan
didiu dolluid in cú chucai-seom, focheird-seom úad a líathróit ⊢ a
loirg, ⊢ frisindle in coin cona díb lámaib .i. dobeir indara láim dó fri
ubull brágat in chon; dobeir araile [15]fria chúl[15]. Bentai frisin
585 corthe[16] inna farrad co sescaind[17] cach ball de a lethe. Mad iar
n-arailiu [slicht] immorro is[18] a líat[h]róit ro lá-som inna beólu
co rruc a inathar thrít.

---

[a] .i. cú doratad dar muir .i. cuilén brotc[h]on [M], *not in* W

[1] dobictis U W, dobicdis Y   [2-2] nicon comraiced Y   [3-3] an gnima
Y W   [4-4] sic W, acht tissed doib U acht tiacht doib Y   [5-5] fobith ad
oegi Y, fobith at óeghi W; *leg.* dáig at áegi   [6] nidom Y, nidam W   [7] a
Chonchobair Y   [8-8] *in rasura* H, don flid Y, dond fleid W   [9-9] ceithri
slabrada fair ⊢ triar i cind cach slabraide W   [10-10] *om.* Y   [11] aine
add. Y W   [12] *sic* U Y, foscerded W, *leg.* focheirded   [13] bunsaid U,
bunsaich Y, bunsaigh W   [14] ar loss *add.* W   [15-15] fri dib culadaib W
[16] buí *add.* W   [17] sceasain (*sic*) Y   [18] issi Y

'Comérgit Ulaid ara ammus, araill díb for[1] less, araill for dorus liss. Damberat i n-ucht Conchobair. Fochertar armgrith mór leó .i. mac sethar ind ríg do folmaisiu a báis. Dothéit Culand issa [590] tech la sodain. |

61[a]   ' "Fo chen duit, a maccáin, fo déig cridi do máthar. Messe immorro, ní mád airgénus fleid. Is bethu immudu [2][mo bethu][2] ⁊ is trebad immaig mo t[h]rebad i ndegaid mo chon[a]. Conággaib ainech ⁊ anmain dam-sa," ol sé, "in fer muintire ruccad úaim .i. [595] mo chú. Robo dín ⁊ dítiu díar feib ⁊ ar[3] n-indili. Ropo imdegail cacha slabra dún eter mag ⁊ tech."

' "Ni mór bríg sin trá," ol in gilla. "Ebéltair[4] culén din chúani[5] chétna lem-sa duit, ⁊ bíam[6] cú-sa do imdegail do chethra ⁊ dot imdegail féin colléic cor ása in cú hísin ⁊ corop ingníma. Ocus [600] imdíus[-s]a Mag Murthemne uile. Noc[h]o mbérthar úaim-se éit ná halma ass manip aurderg[7] lim-sa."

' "Bid Cú C[h]ulaind t'ainm-siu íarom," or Cathbad.

' "Maith lem cid ed mo ainm," ol Cú.

'Fer dorigni sin amdar lána a sé blíadna, nípu machdad cé [605] dorónad-side dagním ind inbuid sea in tan ata lána a secht mblíadna déc,' ol Conall Cernach.

[8]Aided trí mac Nechta Scéni inso sís[8]

'DOgéni fecht [n-]aile dano,' ol Fiacha mac Fir Febe. 'Boí Cathbad druí hi fail a meic .i. Conchobair meic Nessa. [610] Cét fer ndéinmech dó oc foglaim druídechta úad, is é lín doninchoisced Cathbad. Íarmifoacht araili dia felmaccaib[9] do sudiu cid díambad maith a llá sa. Asbert Cathbud ócláech no gébad gaisced and forbíad [10]a ainm Hérind co bráth ar gním gascid[10] ⁊ no mértaís a airscéla co bráth.   [615]

'Rochlunethar Cú Chulaind aní sin. Dothéit co Conchubar do chuingid gascid. Asbeir Conchobar:

---

[a] [*in marg.*] Nírbo é in tres cú ro boí i n-inchind Congánchnis in cú sin amal is cétfaid do foirind, ar is do dígail Con Roí for Ultaib dodeochaid Conganchnes ⁊ fota a haithli na Tána cid héside, ⁊ hi cind a secht mbliadna ro marb-som (.i. Cú Chulaind) coin na cerda. Conid bréc amlaid sin cétfaid na fairni út, ar is a hEspáin tucad cú na cerda amal innister hi curp in sceóil. [M], *not in* W

[1] tar Y, dar W   [2-2] *om.* U Y W (cf. is bethu immuig mo bethu, Táin 899)   [3] diar Y   [4] ébéltair U, ebeltair W, ebeltar Y   [5] chuain Y W [6] bidam W   [7] aúrderg U, aurrderg Y   [8-8] De gabail gaiscid do Coin Culaind inso W, *om.* Y   [9] *sic* Y W, felmaccaim U   [10-10] a ainm ar gnimaib gaiscip firu Erend Y, a ainm ar gnim ṅgaiscid firu hErenn W

' "Cia dorinchoisc sén[1] duit?"

' "Mo pobba Cathbath," ol Cú Chulaind.

620 ' "Rofetammar[2] ém," ol Conc[h]obar.

'Dobeir gaí ⁊ scíath dó. [3]Bertaigthus for lár in taige[3] conná ternó ní dona cúic gaiscedaib déc no bítís di imforcraid hi tegluch Conchobair fri maidm n-airm nó fri gabáil ngaiscid[4] do neoch. Co tardad dó gaisced Conchobair féin. Falloing-side immorro éseom 625 ⁊ bertaigthi hé[5] ⁊ bennachais in ríg bá gaisced, ⁊ asbert:

' "Céin mair túaith ⁊ cenél díanid rí in fer assa harm so."

'Dafic íarom Cathbad chucu ⁊ asbeir:

' "In gaisced gebes in gilla?" or Cathbad.

' "Ed," ol Conchobar.

630 ' "Ní sirsan do mac a máthar ém," ol sé.

' "Ced ón, nách tussu ém[6] donarchossaig?" ol Conchobar.

' "Nách mé écin," ol Cathbad.

' "Cid dochana duit [7]in bréc[7] do imbirt form, a siriti?" ol Conchobar fri Co[in] Culaind.

61[b] ' "A rí Féne[8], ní bréc," | ol Cú Chulaind.   "Is hé dorinchoisc 635 [sén] dia felmacaib imbúarach ⁊ rachúala-sa fri hEmain andess, dodeochad-sa chucut-su íarom."

' "Is maith ane in láa," ol Cathbad. "Is glé bid airdairc ⁊ bid animgnaid[9] intí gébas gaisced and acht bid duthain nammá."

640 ' "Amra brígi són!" ol Cú Chulaind. "Acht ropa[10] airderc-sa, maith lim cenco beind[11] acht óenlá for domun."

[12]'A lláa n-aile imchomairc araile fer dona druídib cid díambo maith a llá sin.

' "Nech no ragad hi carpat and," for Cathbad, " forbíad a ainm 645 Hérind co bráth."

'Roclunithar íarom Cú C[h]ulaind sin. Dothét-side co Conchobar co n-epert fris:

' "A popa Chonchobair[13]," ol sé, "carpat dam-sa."

'Dobeir-side carpat dó. Forrurim a láim eter dí fertais in 650 c[h]arpait co mmebaid[14] in carpat. Brissis in dá c[h]arpat déac in cruth sin. Doberar dó íarom carpat Conchobair. Foloing-side héseom.

---

[1] *sic* W, *sen added below line over word* em, *and something deleted between* dorinchoisc *and* duid Y, *om.* U   [2] Rafetamar W   [3-3] bertaigis forra (-ra *added in ras. and space left* Y   [4] *sic* Y W, ngasced U   [5] for lár hé W   [6] *erasure after* ém Y   [7-7] in mbréig W   [8] oc feini W   [9] *sic* MSS. *Read* anetargnaid? (*Strachan*)   [10] ropom (m-*stroke later*) Y, robadh-am W   [11] buan *add.* Y   [12] *prefaced by title* De techd Con Culaind i carpat inso W   [13] a Choncobair Y   [14] ina laim *add* Y

'Téit isin carpat iar sudiu ⁊ ara Conchobair leiss.　Imsoí in t-ara
.i. Ibor a ainm-side, in carpat foí-seom.

' "Tair asin[1] charpat fechtsa[2]," ol in t-ara.　"It cóema na [655]
heich."

'Am cóem-sa dano, [3]a maccán[3]," ol Cú Chulaind.　"Tair riun[n]
timchell nEmna nammá, ⁊ rot bía a lúag airi."

'Téit ón dano in t-ara ⁊ cotnéicnigidar[4] Cú Chulaind iar sudiu[5] co
dáirled forsin slige[6] do chelebrad dona maccaib, "ocus condam [660]
bennachtaís in meic."　Gáid dó dano co táirled in sligid dorísi.
Ó tháncatár ón dano, asbert Cú Chulaind frisin n-araid:

' "Indaig brot forsin n-echraid trá," ol sé.

' "Ced leth ón?" ol in t-ara.

' "Céin adindain[7] [8]in tslige[8]," or Cu Chulaind.　　　　　　[665]

'Tecait di sudiu co Slíab Fúait.　Forreccat Conall Cernach and.
Do Chonall dano dorala imdegail in chóicid a llá sin, fo bíth no
bíid cach láth gaile do Ultaib a láa hi Sléib Fúait fri snádud neich
dothíssad[9] co n-airchetul nó do chomroc fri fer, combad and sin
condrístá[10] fris arná téised nech dochum nEmna cen rathugud　　[670]

' "Do sonmigi sin trá," or Conall.　"Rob do búaid ⁊ choscor[11]."

' "Eirg-siu trá, a Chonaill, don dún ⁊ rom léic-sea oc forairi[12] sund
colléic," or Cú Chulaind.

' "Bid lór són," or Conall, "mád fri snádud neich co n-airchetul[13].
Mád do chomruc fri fer immorro, is rom són dait-siu co se béus."　[675]

' "Bés nípu hécen ón etir," ol Cú Chulaind.　"Tíagam etarphort,'
ol Cú Chulaind, "do déscin úan for fertais Locha Echtra. Is gnáth
airiseom [14]óc féne[14] and."

' "Is maith lim," or Conall.

'Tíagait ass íarom.　Focheird-seom cloich asa thábaill co mmebaid [680]
fertas carpait Conaill Chernaig.

' "Cid frisind rolais in cloich, a maccáin?" or Conall.

' "Do phromad mo lám ⁊ dírge mo urchair," or Cú Chulaind.
"Ocus is bés dúib-si far nUltaib ní réidid tar églinde[15].　Airc-siu do
Emain aridisi, a phopa Conaill[16], ⁊ rom léic-se sund oc forairi."　[685]

' "Maith lim dano," or Conall.

---

[1] isin MSS.　　　[2] a feachtsa Y W　　　[3-3] am (m- stroke added later)
maccam Y, a macain W　　[4] cotneignigestair Y W　　[5] im dula lais add. W
　　[6] sligid Y W　　[7] anindain Y, adinnam W; read adnindain　　[8-8] ar
intligi Y, (ar written in large red letters in rasura line-end, int with s written
under t in right margin)　　[9] dodisad Y　　[10] condrista Y, condrísta W
[11] sin or Conall add. Y　　[12] forairiri U　　[13] airchethul U　　[14-14] oc
fene Y, ocféne W　　[15] églindne (in ras. H) U, innglinde Y, anglinni W
[16] a Chonaill Y

62ᵃ 'Ni dechaid | Conall Cernach sech in magin [sin] iar sudiu.

'Téit Cú Chulaind ass íarom do Loch Echtra ⁊ ní fuaratar[1] nech and ara chiund[2]. Asbert in t-ara fri Coin Culaind ara n-urthaitís do
690 Emain co társitís ól and.

' "Acc," ol Cú Chulaind. "Ced slíab inso thall?" ol Cú Chulaind.

' "Slíab Monduir[n]d[3]," ol in t-ara.

' "Tiagam co rísam," ol Cú Chulaind.

'Tíagait íarum co rráncatár. Iar riachtain dóib in tslébe, im-
695 chomarcair Cú Chulaind íarom:

' "Cia carnd ngel inso thall ⁴i n-úachtor in tslébe⁴."

' " ⁊ indcharnd[5]", ol in t-ara.

' "Ced mag aní thall?" ol Cú Chulaind.

' "Mag mBreg," ol in t-ara.

700 'Adfét dó dano ainm cech prímdúne eter Themair ⁊ Cenandas. Adfér dó chétamus a n-íathu ⁊ a n-áthu, a n-airdirci ⁊ a treba, a ndúne ⁊ a n-arddindgnu[6]. Inchoscid[7] dó dano dún trí mac Nechta[8] Scéne[a] .i. Fóill ⁊ Fandall ⁊ Túachell[a] a n-anmand-aidi[9].

' "Indat éside asberat," or Cú Chulaind, "nách móo fil do Ultaib i
705 mbethaid oldás ¹⁰ro mbeótar-som¹⁰ díb?"

' "At ó écin," ol in t-ara.

' "Tíagom conda rísam," or Cú Chulaind.

' "Is gúais dúnn ém," ol in t-ara.

' "Ní día imgabáil ¹¹ ám tíagma," ol Cú Chulaind.

710 'Tíagait ass íarom ⁊ scorit a n-eochu oc commor mána ⁊ aba allandess úas dún a chéle. Ocus sréthe in n-id boí forsin corthe róut a láma isin n-abaind ⁊ léicthe la sruth dáig ba coll ng[e]isse do maccaib Nechta Scéne aní sin. Arigit-side íarom ⁊ dothíagat a ndochum,' Contuli Cú Chulaind íarom ocon chorthe iar lécud ind
715 ide frissin sruth ⁊ asbert frisin n-araid:

' "Ním dersaige fri úathad, nom díusca immorro fri sochaide."

'Ba himecal[12] immorro in t-ara colléic ⁊ indlid-side a c[h]arpat ⁊ dosrenga a fortgae ⁊ a forgaimniu ro bátár ¹³fo Choin¹³ Culaind úair nách rolámair[14] a dúscad. Dáig asbert Cú Chulaind fris-[s]eom ar
720 thús nách dúsced fri húat[h]ed.

---

[a] .i. ó Inbiur Scéne [H], [*in marg.*] Fer Ulli mac Lugdach a n-athair ⁊ Nechtan Scéne a mmáthair. Ulaid dano ro marbsat a n-athair. Iss air[i] ro bátár hi cocad faraib [H]; .i. o inber Scene W

---

[1] fuair W   [2] cind Y, *read* ciund   [3] Mondairn Y, Modairn W
[4-4] *om.* W   [5] na foraire *add*, Y   [6] mardingnu Y W   [7] incho-
saic Y   [8] Nechtain Y, Nechtan W   [9] nan[mandaíde H] U, nanmand
Y W   [10-10] *sic* W, ro beótarsom U Y   [11] nimgabail W
[12] himecail Y   [13-13] *sic* Y W, for Coin U   [14] *sic* W, rolamar U,
rolamadh Y

'Tecait íarom meic Nechta Scéne.

' "Cia fil sund?" ol fer díb.

' "Mac becc dochóid indiu ar esclu[1] hi carpat," ol in t-ara.

' "Nípo do ṡoinmige," ol in láech, "⁊ nírop do ḟechtnaige dó a chétgabáil gaiscid[2]. Ná bíd inar tír ⁊ ná gelat ind eich and ní as[3] mó," ol in láech. 725

' "Atát a n-éssi im láim-sea," ol in t-ara. "Nírbo lat-su tollem[4] écraite fris[5]," ol Ibar frisin láech, "⁊ attá dano in mac ina chotlud."

' "Nímda[6] mac écin," or Cú Chulaind, "acht is do chuingid chomraic fri fer dodeochaid in mac fil and." 730

' "Is sain lim-sa ón," ol in láech.

' "Bid sain duit-siu innossa issind áth ucut," ol Cú Chulaind.

' "Is tacair[7] dait trá," or in t-ara. "Foichle in fer dotháet ar do chend, Fóill a ainm," or sé, "ar mani thetarrais issin chétḟorgam, ní therarrais co fescor." 735

' "Tongu do dia toinges mo thúath, nocon imbéra-som for Ultu a cles sin dorísse | diano tárle mánaís mo phopa Conc[h]obair as mo láim-sea. Bid lám deóraid dó."

'Sréthis fair íarom in sleg co mmebaid a druim trít. Dobeir leiss a ḟodb[8] ⁊ a c[h]end íar sudiu. 740

' "Foichle in fer n-aile dano," ol in t-ara. "Fannall a ainm-side. Ní trummu do[n]essa[9] in n-usce oldás ela nó fandall."

' "Tongu-sa dano nocon imbéra-som for Ultu in cles sin doríssi," ol Cú Chulaind. "Atconnarc-su ém," ol sé, "indas imatíag-sa in lind oc hEmain." 745

'Condrecat íarom issind áth. Gonaid-som dano in fer sin ⁊ dobert a chend ⁊ a ḟodb lais.

' "Foichle in fer n-aile dotháet chucut," ol in t-ara. "Túachell a ainm. Ní lessainm dó dano ar ní thuit di arm etir."

' "Ondar dó-ssom in del chlis día mescad, conid nderna retherderg de," or Cú Chulaind. 750

'Sréthius fair íarom in sl[e]ig conid rallá ina chomsudiu[10]. Dolluid a dochum íarom ⁊ benaid[11] a chend de. Dobert Cú íarom a chend ⁊ a ḟodb laiss [12]dia araid[12] fadessin.

'Co cúala íar sudiu fóíd a mmáthar ina ndíaid .i. Nechta Scéne. 755 Dobeir a ḟodb di ṡudiu ⁊ dobeir na trí cind laiss inna charput, ⁊ asbert:

' "Ní fuicéb trá mo choscur," ol sé, "co rríus Emain Macha."

---

[1] oesclu Y [2] ngaiscid U [3] bus W [4] tuilled Y, tuillem W [5] sic W, om. U Y [6] nidam Y [7] sic W, tacar U, taccar Y [8] ḟoidb Y W [9] doessa with final letter almost deleted Y, doess W [10] chonsudi U, chonsuidiu Y, consuidiu W [11] bennaid U [12–12] sic Y W, diaraid U

'Documlat ass íarom cona coscor. Is and sin asbert Cú Chulaind
760 frisin n-araid:

' "Dorar[n]gertais-siu dagérim[1] dúnd," ol Cú Chulaind, "⁊ ros-
necam a less[2] indossa [3]di ág[3] in tressa[4] ⁊ inna íarra fil inar ndíaid."

'Imríadat íarom co Slíab Fúait. Ba hé lúas ind érma donucsat
[5]iar mBregaib[5] íar ngrísad ind arad[6] co togrennitís ind eich fón
765 charpat in [n]gaíth ⁊ inna heónu for lúamain ⁊ co táirthed Cú
Chulaind in n-urchur dolléced asa thailm ríasú rísad talmain.

'Iar riachtain dóib Slébe Fúait forrecat alma n-oss n-and ara
ciund.

' "Cissi slabrai [7]in díscer sa[7] thall?" ol Cú Chulaind.
770 ' "Oiss alta," ol in t-ara.

' "Cia de," or Cú Chulaind, "bad ḟerr la Ultu, a mmarb [8]nach áe[8]
do breith dóib nó a mbeó?"

' "Is inganto a mbeó," ol in t-ara, "dóib. Ní cach óen condric[9]
samlaid. A mmarb immorro ni fil úadib-seom [10]ónach ric[10]. [11]Ní
775 chumci-siu ón[11] a beó nach áe do br[e]ith," ol in t-ara.

' "Cumcim écin," ar Cú. "Indaig[12] brot forsna eochu isin mónai."

'Dogni in t-ara ón aní sin. Glenait ind eich isin mónai íarom.
Taurlaing Cú Chulaind ⁊ gabaid in n-oss ba nessom dó ⁊ bá caímem
díb. Slaittius sethnón na móna ⁊ dammainti fo chétóir. Cumrigis
780 eter dá[13] fert in c[h]arpait.

'Co n-accatár ní, éill ngésse ara ciund atheroch.

63ª ' "Cia de bad ḟerr la Ultu," or Cú Chulaind, "a mbeó nó | a mmarb[14]
dóib?"

' "Is a mbeó beres a n-as beódu ⁊ a n-as ségundo," ol in t-ara.
785 'Lát[h]raid Cú íarom cloich ṁbic forna[15] heónu co mbí ocht[16]
n-eónu díb. Inláa afrithisi cloich móir[17], co mbí dá én déc díib.
Tria tháithbémmend trá insin uli.

' "Tecmall na heónu dún trá," ol Cú fría araid. "Mád messe dig[18]
día tabairt," or sé, "conclichfe in dam allaid fort-so."
790 ' "Ní réid dam a t[h]echt ém," ol in t-ara. "Ro dássed imna
heochu conná dichtim seccu. Ní étaim dano techt sech nechtar

---

[1] dagimrim Y W   [2] cudnod add. W   [3-3] daig Y   [4] ⁊ na tóra
add. W   [5-5] dar Bregaib W   [6] do Choin Cudlaind add. W
[7-7] imdísciri si W (read imdíscir sea?)   [8-8] sic Y, no a mbeo written in
ras. (H) U, nach a mbéo W with nó a mbeó omitted at sentence end   [9] darric
with erasure before the word Y, ondarricc W   [10-10] onach ri Y   [11-11] ní
chumcison U, ni cumgisom on Y, ni cumcisi ón W   [12] indnaig Y, atnaig W
[13] dia Y, di W   [14] do brith add. Y W   [15] forsna W   [16] .uii. Y
[17] forru add. W   [18] theis Y

¹in dá roth*a* iarndae¹ in c[h]arpait ara fáebraige, ⁊ ni dichtim dano sech in dam ²ar ro lín² a c[h]ongna eter dí fert in c[h]arpait ule.''

' ''Cing-siu amend día c[h]ongno,'' or Cú. ''Tongu-sa do dia toingte Ulaid, clóenad clóenfat-sa mo c[h]end fair nó in tsúil dogén-sa ⁷⁹⁵ fris, nocon focher cor día chind riut ⁊ ³noco lémaither³ a glúasacht.''

'Dogníth són íarom. Conrig Cú Chulaind inna ésse ⁊ tecmalla⁴ in t-ara inna heónu. Conreraig Cú Chulaind íar sin inna heónu di thétaib ⁊ refedaib in c[h]arpait. Conid samlaid siu luid do Emain Macha: dam allaid i ndíaid a charpait ⁊ íall gésse oc⁵ folúamain ⁸⁰⁰ úassa ⁊ trí cind⁶ inna c[h]arput.

⁷'Recait iar sin co Emain.

' ''Carptech dorét far ṅdochum,'' ol in dercaid i nEmain Macha. ''Ardáilfe fuil laiss cach dune fil isind lis mani foichlither ⁊ mani dichset mná ernochta friss.'' ⁸⁰⁵

'Tossoí-som íarom clár clé a c[h]arpait fri hEmain ⁊ ba gess di aní sin. Ocus asbert Cú Chulaind:

''Tongu do dia toingte⁸ Ulaid mani étar fer do gleó frim-sa, ardáilfe fuil lim⁹ cach áein¹⁰ fil isin dún.''

''Mná ernochta ara chend!'' ar Conchobar. ⁸¹⁰

'Tothéit iarom bantrocht nEmna ara chend im Mugain*b*¹¹ mnaí Conchobair meic Nessa, ⁊ donnochtat a mbruinni friss.

''It é óic inso condricfat frit indiu,'' or Mugain*c*.

'Foilgis-[s]eom¹² a gnúis. La sodain atnethat láith gaile Emna ⁊ focherdat i ndabaig n-úarusci. Maitti immi-seom in dabach hísin. ⁸¹⁵ In dabach aile dano in ro lád, fichis dornaib de. In tress dabach i ndeochaid iar sudiu, fosngert-side combo chuimsi dó a tess ⁊ a fuacht. Dotháet ass íarom¹³ ⁊ dobeir ind rígan íar sudiu .i. Mugain¹⁴, bratt ngorm n-imbi ⁊ delg n-argit n-and ⁊ léne chulpatach. Ocus suidid fo glún Chonchobair íarom, ⁊ ba sí sin a lepaid do grés iar ⁸²⁰ sudiu.

---

a .i. fonnod [M]   *b* nó im Féraig secundum alios [M], nó im Feraich W
c nó or Férach [M], nó Ferach *written overhead* Y

1-1 in da roth .i. fonno iarnae Y, na da roth (.i. fonnad) iarṅde W   2-2 *sic* W, árolín U   3-3 nochonlinfaithir Y = nícon lilmaither   4 tecmalta *with punc. del. over* t U, tecmolta Y, tecmallta W   5 for W   6 mac Nechtain Scene *add.* Y   7 C *version begins here*   8 toigthe U, tongaid Y, tongte W, toinget C   9 lium C, *om.* U Y W   10 náen U, oen Y. aenduini W   11 Mumhain C   12 foilgisseom T *seconds* s *later over first.* folgissom W   13 ⁊ an rigan *add.* C   14 .i. Mumain no Ferach Y

'Fer dorigni sin inna śechtmad blíadain,' ol Fíachna[1] mac Fir
Ḟebe, 'nípo machdad cia chonbósad-side[2] for écomlond ⁊ cia nodragad[a3] for comlond in tan ata lána[4] a śé[5] blíadna déc indiu[6].'

825   Slicht sain so[b7] co aidid nŌrláím |

63[b] 'TÍagam ass trá hifechtsa,' or Ailill.
       Roecat[8] íarom Mag Mucceda. Benaid[9] Cú Chulaind omnae
ara ciund i sudiu ⁊ scríbais ogum ina taíb. Iss ed ro boí and :
arná dechsad nech sechai co ribuilsed err óencharpait. Focherdat a
830 pupli i sudiu ⁊ dotíagat día léimim ina carptib. Dofuit trícha ech
oc sudiu ⁊ brisiter[10] trícha carpat and.
       Belach nÁne íarom iss ed ainm na maigni sin co bráth.

[11]Aided Fraích[11]

Bíit and co ara bárach. Congairther Fráech[12] dóib.
835 'Tonfóir, a Ḟraích,' ol Medb. 'Díscart[13] dín[n] in n-écin fil fornd.
Eirg dúnd ar cind Con Culaind dús in comrasta[14] fris.'
       Tocumlai ass mattain muich nónbor co mboí oc Áth Fúait. Co
n-acca in n-óclaig ocá ḟothrucud isind abaind.
       'Anaid sund,' or Fráech fria muintir, 'conid rolur-sa frisin fer
840 n-uccut. Ní maith i n-usciu,' or sé.
       Tíscaid a étach de. Téit isin n-usci a dochum.
       'Ná tair ar mo chend-sa,' or Cú. 'Atbéla de, ⁊ is tróg lim do
marbad.'
       'Ragat óm,' ol Fráech, 'co comairsem isind usciu, ⁊ bad chert do
845 c[h]luchi frim.'
       'Committi són amal bas maith latt,' or Cú Chulaind.
       'Lám cechtar náthar immáraile,' or Fráech.
       Atnagait co céin móir oc imtrascrad forsind usci, ⁊ [15]bátir
Fráech[15]. Tanócaib súas aḟrithisi.

---

[a] .i. cia no érged [H]   [b] .i. sis [M]
[1] Fiacha Y W   [2] chonbosaide MSS.   [3] *sic* W, notragad U Y, no
ragad C   [4] slana C   [5] secht Y W C, *read* śecht   [6] It e maccerdda
Con Culaind andso annuas for Tain Bo Cuailṅge *add.* Y W C   [7] annso sis
Y, so sís W, so C   [8] roeca U, roecat Y W, ragait C   [9] bennaid U
[10] brister Y, C bristir W, *read* bristir   [11-11] *between columns* U, *om.* Y;
slicht sain so co comruc tri mac nGarach ⁊ bladh beag de ar daig dluthaigthe
in sceoil *prefixed* C   [12] mac Fidaig *add.* Y   [13] dichosctarad Y
[14] comrista W C   [15-15] contrascartar Fraech isin uisciu C

'In dul so,' or Cú, 'in [n]didma th'anacol? 850

'Noco didem[1],' or Fráech.

Atnaig Cú foí atherruch conid appad Fráech. Tocurethar for tír.
Berait a muinter a choland[2] co mboí isin dúnud.   Áth Fraích iss ed
ainm ind átha sin co bráth.

Coínti [3]a ndúnad n-ule[3] Fráech. Co n-accatar banchuri i n-inaraib 855
úanib for colaind Fraích [4]meic Idaid[4]. Focessat[5] úadib issa síd.
Síd Fraích ainm in tsída sin íarom.

Lingid Fergus darsin n-omnai ina charput[6]

[7]Tíagait co mbátar oc Ath Táiten[8]. Toscara Cú sessiur díb and
.i. [9]sé Dúngail Irruiss[9].   860

Tíagait ass íarom [10]co mbátar[10] hi Fornocht. Culén la Medb,
Baiscne a ainm. Lécid Cú irchor fair co mbert a chend de.
[11]Druim Baiscne[11] ainm inna maigni sin íarom ó sin immach.

[12]'Mór in cuitbiud dúib,' ol Medb, 'can tophund na erri angceóil
ucut fil [13]'co for nguin[13].'   865

Doberat-som íarom topund fair [14]iar sin[14] coro brisiset fertsi a
carpat oca.[12]

[15]Aided Órláim[15]

DOthíagat ass dano tar [16]Iraird Culend[16] ara bárach. Dosléci
Cú Chulaind ríam. Dofuric araid nÓrláim meic Ailello ⁊ 870
Medba i Tamlachtai Órláim fri Dísiurt Lóchait antúaid
bicán oc béim feda and.

—Mád iar n-araili slicht immorro is fertas carpait Con Culaind.
ro maid ⁊ is do béim fertas dochóid in tan cotránic fri araid nÓrláim.
[17]Is é in t-ara ros ben na fertsi mad íarsin tslicht sa[17].   875

64ᵃ 'Is nephnár a ndogníat Ulaid másat é file sund | t[h]all,' ol Cú,
'céin file in slóg fora tairr.'

Téit-seom cosin n-araid día chosc. Indar leis ba di Ultaib dó.
Co n-accai in fer oc béim feda .i. fertas carpat.

---

¹ didém U   ² leo add. W C   ³⁻³ inn dunad uile inti Y, isin dunad
huili W, an dunadh uile C   ⁴⁻⁴ meic Fidaid Y W C   ⁵ facesad Y,
facessat C   ⁶ feisin add. W   ⁷ words Iar slicht aile seo prefixed Y W
    ⁸ in ras. (hand H) U, Meislir Y, Taoidion C   ⁹⁻⁹ in ras. (hand H) U,
Meislir ⁊ reliqua Y W   ¹⁰⁻¹⁰ sic C, om. U Y W   ¹¹⁻¹¹ sic C, Druim
U Y, Druim B. W   ¹²⁻¹² in ras. (hand H) U, om. Y   ¹³⁻¹³ ca for
forguin W, agá bor forguin C   ¹⁴⁻¹⁴ iar sini U, iarsi W, om. C
    ¹⁵⁻¹⁵ between cols. U, om. Y C   ¹⁶⁻¹⁶ Airdd Y   ¹⁷⁻¹⁷ sic U C, om. Y W

880   'Cid dogní sund?' ol Cú.

'Fertse carpat do béim,' ol in t-ara.   'Ro brisisem ar carpat[1] oc
tofund na ailite ucut Con Culaind.   Congná[2] frim,' ol in t-ara[3]
'Déca nammá in bá teclaim na fertas dogéna [4]fa na n-imscot[h]ad[4].'
'Bid a n-imscot[h]ad ém,' ol Cú.[5]

885   Imscothis íarom na fertse culind tria ladra a glac [6]hi fíadnaissi a
chéli[6] conda cermnastar eter rúsc ⁊ udbu[7].

'Nip sí th'opar c[h]omadas dobiur fort,' ol in t-ara.   Bá-dn-
imomon-side.

'Can duit?' ol Cú Chulaind.

890   'Ara Órláim meic Ailella ⁊ Medba,' or sé.   'Ocus tussu?' ol in t-ara.

'Cú C[h]ulaind mo ainm-se,' ol sé.

'Romairgge són ém,' ol in t-ara.

'Ní ágither ní,' ol Cú Chulaind.   'Cáit atá do thigerna?' or sé.

'Atá isind fertai[8] ucut,' ol in t-ara.

895   'Coisle didiu as immalle frim[9],' ol Cú Chulaind, 'ar ní gonaim-sea
aradu etir.'

Téit Cú Chulaind dochom nÓrláim.   Gontai ⁊ benaid[10] a chend de
⁊ ros ecroth a chend frisin slúag.   Dobeir in cend for muin ind arad
íar sin ⁊ atbert:

900   'Beir latt sin,' or Cú, '⁊ tési don dúnud amlaid.   Manip samlaid
téis[11], roticcba cloch úaim-se asin tailm.'

[12]A ndochóid[12] i n-occus don dúnud tísca a cend día muin ⁊ adfét
a imtechta do Meidb ⁊ Ailill.

'Ní fríthid bid eissíne ém[a],' ol sí.

905   'Ocus asrubairt mini thucaind for mo muin dochom in dúnaid,
brisfed[13] mo chend form-sa co cloich[14].'

[15]Aided Trí Mac nGárach[15]

ANsait íar sin trí meic Gárach fora n-áth.   It é a n-anmand-
side .i. Lon ⁊ Úala ⁊ Díliu.   Mes Lir ⁊ Mes Láech ⁊ Mes
910   Lethan a[16] [17]trí n-araid[17].   Ba foróil leu a ndorigni Cú

---

[a].i. ní inund ⁊ én do gabáil [H] U id. C, .i. hi hinann so ⁊ éun do gabáil a sás W

[1] carpaid Y, car- W, *read* carptiu?   [2] congna Y, congnu W, congno C
[3] dodén ol C *add* W   [4-4] fa nimscothad Y, fo a nimscothad W, fa a
n-iomscothadh C   [5] int ara *written over* Cu Cul- Y   [6-6] fiadh a ceile C
[7] fudbu Y W C   [8] fert Y, ferta W C   [9] co hait a tta do thigerna *add*. C
[10] bennaid U   [11] *sic for* tési U, théis W, thes W, teis C   [12-12] an tar
dochoid an t-ara C   [13] *sic* U W, do brisfead Y C   [14] slicht sain so sis
co comruc tri mac Garach ⁊ blag bec de iarmo ar daig dluthaigi in sceoil *add*.
Y (*last five words added in marg. by a different hand*).   *This remark occurs in* C
just before Aided Fraích, *which seems the correct place.*   [15-15] *in marg.* U,
om. Y   [16] *sic* C, an U W, and Y   [17-17] *sic* Y, tri araid U

Chulaind .i. dá macdalca ind ríg do goin ⁊ a mac ⁊ crothad in chind
frisin slóg.   Co rubaitís Coin Culaind tara ési ⁊ co ndergabtaís a
n-óenur a n-imneth sin din tslóg.   Bentatar trí fidot día n-ar[a]daib
co róiltis glied fris a ssessiur.   Nos gegoin-seom uli ¹íarom úair¹
ro brisiset fír fer fair.   915

Ro boí ara Órláim in tan sin iter Ailill ⁊ Meidb.   Tanettat[a] Cú
cloich fair co mebaid a chend co tánic a inchind fora chlúasa .i. Fer
Tedil a ainm.   ²Ní fír trá amlaid sin ná marbad Cú aradu.   Ní
marbad ³ém cen chinaid³ ⁴cip innus⁴.²

⁵Aided in Togmaill ⁊ in Pheta Eóin⁵   920

BÁgais⁶ Cú Chulaind hi Méthiu port iar sin i n-acciged Ailill nó
Medb, fochichred⁷ cloich assa thábaill forru.   Dogní-som ón dano
.i. doléci cloich assa thailm co n-ort in togmall boí for gúalaind
Medba frisin n-áth andess.   Is de atá Méithe Togmaill.   Ocus ort in
n-én boí for gúalaind Ailella ⁸fri áth antúaid⁸.   Is de atá MéthenEóin. 925

64ᵇ   —⁹Nó dano is for | gúalaind Medba bátár immalle eter togán ⁊
én, ⁊ is a cind bentatár¹⁰ na urchora díb⁹.

Báite dano Reúin ina loch.   Is de atá Loch Reóin.

'Ní cían úaib atá far céle,' or Ailill¹¹ frisna Mane.

Ataregat-side súas ⁊ immusdécat.   In tan siasatár-som dano ⁹³⁰
atheroch, benaid Cú fer díb co mmebaid a chend fair.

¹²'Ní ma lodsaid¹² dó.   Níba adas¹³ far mbraisse,' or Máenén
drúth.   'Dobéraind-se¹⁴ a c[h]end de.'

Tolléci Cú cloich dó co mmebaid a c[h]end fair.

Is amlaid trá ¹⁵ro marbthá¹⁵ in luc[h]t sin: Órlám¹⁶ chétumus ina ⁹³⁵
dind; trí meic Gárach fora n-áth; Fer Tedil ina dedlib¹⁷; Máenán ina
dind.

'Tongu do dia toingthe¹⁸ mo t[h]úath,' ol Aillil, 'fer dogéna¹⁹ a
écnach sund, dagén-sa dá leth de.   Taít²⁰ ass eter láa ⁊ aidchi
chena dúnd,' or Aillil, 'co rísam Cúal[n]gi. Mairfid in fer sa dá trian ⁹⁴⁰
for²¹ slúaig fón n-innas sa.'

ᵃ .i. teilgid [M]; .i. srethis W; .i. telccid *suprascr.* C

¹⁻¹ *sic.* Y, iar núair U   ²⁻² *om.* W   ³⁻³ cen *foll. by erasure with* cinaid
in later hand in marg. Y   ⁴⁻⁴ *om.* Y, gided iss he in cert C   ⁵⁻⁵ *in marg.*
U, *om.* Y W C   ⁶ .i. eath *add.* W   ⁷ .i. caithem *add.* W   ⁸⁻⁸ *om.* Y
⁹⁻⁹ *om. here* W   ¹⁰ bertatar C   ¹¹ Medb C   ¹²⁻¹² *sic* C, bá mád
lodsaid U W Y   ¹³ ádas (*sic*) U   ¹⁴ do benfoindsi C   ¹⁵⁻¹⁵ ro
marbtha Y W, do marbtha C   ¹⁶ Órlámm (*sic*) U   ¹⁷ dedil Y, teidliuh C
¹⁸ toingi Y   ¹⁹ *page lost here* W   ²⁰ táet U Y, taod C   ²¹ ar C

Is and sin dosnáncatár cruitti Caínbili ó Ess Rúaid día
n-airfitiud. Indar leó ba du thoscélad forru ó Ultaib[1]. Doberat
toffund forru co llotár rempo i ndelbaib oss íarom isna coirthib
945 oc Líac Mór antúaid, ar roptar druíd co móreólas[2].

[3]Aided Lethain[3]

DAgéini[a] dano Lethan fora áth for Níth la Conailliu. Anais
cadessin ara chind Con Culaind. Bá sáeth laiss a ndogéni Cú
Chulaind. Ésgid dano Cú Chulaind a chend di šudiu; conid
950 fácab laiss. Is de atá Áth Lethan for Níth. Ocus memdaitir a
carpait léu oc comrac forsind áth inna farrad. Is de atá Áth
Carpat. Docer Mulcha, ara Lethain, isin gúala fil etarro. Is de
atá Gú[a]lo Mulchai.

Céin bátár didiu in tslóig oc tochim Maige Breg, forrumai[4]
955 Allechtu colléic, noch is í in Mórrígan són i ndeilb eúin co mboí
forsin chorthi hi Temair Cúalṅgi ⁊ asbert frisin tarb:

r.[5] In fitir in dub dušáim can eirc[b] n-echdaig[c] dál désnad fiacht
fíach nad eól [6]ceurtid namaib[6] ar túaith Brega bíth i ndaínib tathum
rún rofíastar dub día n-ísa maí muin tonna fér forglass for laich
960 lilestai áed ág asa mag meldait slóig scoith nía boidb bógeimnech
feochair fíach fir máirm[7] rád n-ingir cluiph Cualngi coigde[d] día[e] bás
mórmacni iar féic muintire do écaib.'

Luid in tarb íarom ⁊ cóeca samasca imbi co mboí hi Sléib Chulind, ⁊
luid a búachaill ina díaid, Forgemen a ainm. Focheird de na tri *cóecta*
965 mac no bítís oc[8] cluchiu fair do grés, ⁊ marbais dá trian a[9] macraide
⁊ concechlaid búrach hi Tír Marccéni hi Cúalṅgi [10]ré techt[10]. |

65[a] Ní rubai Cú Chulaind nech eter an Sailiu Imdorthi hi crích
Conailli co ráncatár Cúailngi. Baí Cú Chulaind íarom hi
Cuinc[h]iuf .i. arbágais íarom [airm][11] i n-acciged Meidb, no
970 tróistfed lais in cloich fria cend[12]. Nírbo réid dó-som ón, ar is
amlaid imthéged[13] Medb ⁊ leth in tslóig impe ⁊ amdabach[14] scíath
úasa cind[15].

---

[a] .i. tic [H]   [b] .i. cen bréic [H]   [c] .i. éca [M], .i. eca *written over-*
head Y   [d] .i. cach die [H]   [e] .i. laa [H]   [f] .i. slíab [H]

[1] donángador *add.* C   [2] móreólás (*sic*) U   [3-3] *between columns* U,
om. Y C   [4] fosrumaei Y, *leg.* fosrumai?   [5] *sic between columns* U, .l. *in*
marg. Y   [6-6] ecurtid namaib Y, cerdaid namait C, (cuardait námait LL)
[7] mairb Y C   [8] oca (ca *added under line*) Y   [9] na C   [10-10] *om.* Y   [11] *om.*
U Y, an airm C (íarom *a misreading of* airm?) *or read* airm iarom?   [12] *sic*
Y C, chend U   [13] no imtighed C   [14] damdabach Y C   [15] ceandaib Y

¹Aided Lócha inso¹

L Uid didiu inailt do Medb, Lóchu a ainm, do thabairt uisce, ⁊
  bantrocht mór impe. Indar la Coin Culaind bá sí Medb. ⁹⁷⁵
Sraíthius di c[h]loich a Cuinc[h]iu conda ort ina réid². Is de
atá Réid² Lócha hi Cúalṅgiu.

A Findabair Chúalngi fosdáilset in tslóig³ ⁊ adachtatár in crích hi
tenid. Doinólat a mbaí di mnáib ⁊ maccaib ⁊ ingenaib ⁴⁊ búaib⁴
hi Cúalngiu ⁵hi teclom⁵ co mbátár hi Findabair uli.   ⁹⁸⁰
'Ní ma lodsaid dó,' ol Medb. 'Ní acciu in tarb lib.'
'Ní fil ⁶isin chóiciud ᵃ⁶ etir,' or cách.
Congairther Lóthar dóib, búachaill do Medb.⁷
⁸'Cate⁹ in tarb,' or sí, 'in dóig latt?'
'Is⁸am ómun ara aisnéis,' ol in búachaill. 'Ind adaig,' or sé, ⁹⁸⁵
'dochótár Ulaid ina nóendin, dolluid¹⁰ ⁊ trí fichit samaisce imbi
conid fil i nDubc[h]airiu Glinne Gatt.'
'Ergid,' or Medb, '⁊ berid gatt eter cach ndís úaib.'
Dogníat ón íarom. Is de attá Glend nGat ¹¹forsin glind sein¹¹.
Doberat¹² íarom in tarb co mbaí in Findabair. Áit i n-accaiᵇ in ⁹⁹⁰
búachail .i. Lóthor, tofóbair¹³ cucai co mbert a inathar ass fora
bennaib ⁊ tofóbair cona t[h]rí cóectaib¹⁴ samaisce a ndúnad co
n-appad cóeca láech laiss.
Conid aided Lóthair ar Tána sin¹⁵.
¹⁶Luid úadib in tarb iar sin asin dúnud ⁊ ní fetatar cid dochóid ⁹⁹⁵
úadib ⁊ ba méla leó¹⁶. ¹⁷Ro íarfacht Medb in¹⁸ buachaill dóig leiss
cáit i mbaí in tarb.¹⁷
'Dóig lem bád i ndíamraib Slébe Culind no beth.'
Tintaíset íarom amlaid sin íar n-indred Chúalngi ⁊ ní fúaratár in
tarb n-and. ¹⁹Conéracht Glaiss Chruind friu i n-enna crand¹⁹ co ¹⁰⁰⁰
feótár fuirriᶜ, ⁊ asbert Medb fri drécht día muintir ara tístais taris.

ᵃ .i. isin chreich [H]   ᵇ .i. in tarb [M]   ᶜ .i. fora bru [H]

¹⁻¹ *between columns* U, *om.* Y C   ² ré C   ³ *overhead is written*
Erend fon coicid do cuindchid in tairb Y   ⁴⁻⁴ *om.* C   ⁵⁻⁵ *om.* Y, hi
tecluim C   ⁶⁻⁶ isin coiccrich *with* .i. in crech *written overhead* Y, isin
coicrich .i. isin chreich C   ⁷ slicht sain so sis *add.* Y   ⁸⁻⁸ *om.* Y
⁹ cáte U   ¹⁰ dochoid Y   ¹¹⁻¹¹ *in ras.* [H] U, iarsin slicht sin Y
¹² atchondcadar Y   ¹³ cofobair Y   ¹⁴ .l. ait Y   ¹⁵ ⁊ fagbail in
tairb iarsin slicht sin. Ni he lenfam sund beos *add.* Y   ¹⁶⁻¹⁶ *in ras.* (H)
U, *id.* C   ¹⁷⁻¹⁷ Cate in tarb? ol si, in doig lat? Issamomun ara faisneis ol
in buachaill Y   ¹⁸ din C   ¹⁹⁻¹⁹ *om.* Y

[1]Aided Úaland[1]

Uid láech amra ara bárach, Úalu a ainm.　Gabais liic móir
fri[a] ais do thecht darsin n-usce.　Dochorastár in glaiss for
1005　cúlu oss é cona liic fora thairr.　Atá a lecht ⁊ a lía forsin tsligi
ocon glais .i. Lía Úaland a ainm.

65[b]　　Lotar íarom timchell Glaisse Cruind co rrici in topor, ⁊ docóes | tis
eter a topor ⁊ slíab acht nád étad ó Meidb.　Ba ferr la sudi techt tar
slíab ara marad a slicht and co bráth ar sár for Ultu.　Ansait trí láa
1010　⁊ trí aidchi and sin co cechlatár a n-úir remib, Bernas Báu Cúalngi[2].

Is and sin geogain Cú Chulaind Crond ⁊ Cóemdele, ⁊ ro fer fuire
n-imnaise.　Atbath cét n-ánrod friss, rind ríg, im Roán im Roae im
dá senchaid na Tána.　Cethri ríg ar secht[3] fichtib ríg atbath laiss
forsin nglais chétnai.

1015　Dollotar íarom for[4] Bernas Bó Cúalngi co folodaib ⁊ indilib Cúalngi
co feótár hi nGlind Dáil Imda hi Cúalngi.　Botha a ainm in puirt sin
úair dogénsat botha forro and.　Do[th]íagat[5] árna bárach do
Cholptu.　Fanóprait[6] tri anfót.　Conéracht-side friu dano co
mbert cét cairptech[7] úadib dochom maro.　Iss ed ainm in tíre in
1020　robáte Clúain Carpat.

Lotár timchell Colbta íarom dochum a thopair do Bélut Alióin, co
feótár oc Líasaib Líac.　Iss ed ainm in puirt sin úair doringset
líassu fora lóegu and eter Chúalngiu ⁊ Conailliu.　Dollotár íarom dar
Glend nGatlaig.　Conérracht dano Glaiss Gatlaig friu.　Sechaire a
1025　ainm ríam.　Glas Gatlaig ó sein úair ba i ngataib dobertatar a
llóegu[8], co feótár i nDruim Féne la Conailliu.

It é sin trá a n-imthechta ó Chúalṅgi co Machairi iarsin tslicht sa.
Dogníat immorro augtair[9] ⁊ libair aile córugud aile fora n-imthech-
taib a Findabair co Conaille .i.

1030　　　　　　　　　[10]Orgain Chúalngi inso sís[10]

A　Tbert Medb iar torachtain cáich cona ngabáil[11] co mbátár uli
hi Findabair Chúalngi:
'Randtar in dúnad sund,' or Medb.　'Ní rucfaider ind imirgi
se for óenchoí.　Tíat Ailill la leith na immirgi for [Slige] Midlúachrae.
1035　Ragmai-ne[12] ⁊ Fergus[13] for [14]Bernas nUlad[14].'

[1–1] *in marg.* U, *om.* Y, Oigid Ualand inso C　　[2] a ainm o sein ille *add.* C
[3] sé Y　　　[4] dar C　　[5] dothiagad Y, dothiegait C　　　[6] fanópaīt U,
fanopart Y, fonoprat C　　[7] carpat Y C　　　[8] tarrsia *add.* C, *read* tairse
[9] in dana sa *add.* Y, W *resumes here*　　　10–10 *in marg.* (*hand* H) U, *om.*
Y W C　　[11] ngabalaib Y W　　[12] ragmaitne Y C　　[13] ⁊ in tarb
add. W　　14–14 Bernas Bo nUlad Y C (bó *added overhead* Y)

'Ní ségda,' or Fergus, 'in leth donroacht dind imirgi. Ní rucfaiter
na baí tarsin slíab cen raind[1].'

Dogníth ón, conid de atá Bernas Bó nUlad.

Is and sin asbert Ailill fria araid Cuillius:

'Finna dam indiu Meidb ┐ Fergus. Ní fetur cid rodanuc don [1040]
choibdin[2] se, ┐ bid fó lim donísed[3] comartha n-úait.'

Dotháet Cuillius in tan bátar hi Cluichrib. Ansait ind lánamain
fo deóid ┐ lotar ind óic remib. Dotháet **chucu** Cuillius ┐ ní for-
chúalatár in fer forcsi. Ecmaic boí a chlaideb hi farrad Fergusa.
Tánísca Cuillius[4] asa thrúaill ┐ fófácaib[5] in trúaill fás. Dotháet [1045]
Cuillius co Ailill.

'Ameind,' or Ailill.

'Amne dano,' or Cuillius. 'Undar dait sund comartha.'

[6]'Is maith sin trá,' or Ailill.

Tibid cechtar de fria chéle[6]. [1050]

'Amal dondruimin-so,' or Cuillius, 'is amlaid fosfairnec-sa hi
comlepaid.'

'Is dethbir disi,' or Ailill. 'Is ar chobair ocon táin dorigni. |
Bá maith bláth in c[h]laidib lat,' or Ailill. 'Atnaig fót ṡuide isin
carput ┐ anart léined imbi.' [1055]

Atraig Fergus día chlaidiub íarom.

'Aill amai!' or sé.

'Cid no taí?' ol Medb.

'Olc gním dorignius fri Ailill,' or sé. 'Indnaidid sund co tísa asind
fid,' or Fergus, '┐ níp machdad lib cid cían co tísor.' [1060]

Ecmaic ní fitir Medb tesbaid in c[h]laidib. Téit ass ┐ berid
claidiub a arad laiss ina láim. Dogní claidiub craind isind fid. Is
de atá Fid Mórdrúalle[7] la Ultu.

'Tiagam ass i ndíaid ar céle,' or Fergus.

Cotrecat isin maig a slógaib ulib. Arrócbat a pupli. Congairther [1065]
Fergus do Ailill do imbirt fidchille. In tan dolluid Fergus don
phupull, gabaid Ailill gári fris. Asbert Fergus:

[8].r. Fergus dixit[8]

'Fó fer fris tibther | manip sceó mera mórgnímo merthar | airbiur
mo chlaidib mache[9] mind | mosdísem calga de Galión[10] gáir | manip [1070]
ed búaid mná misrálastar | di dáil dondlecht | sceó gaib genin almi |

66ᵃ (marginal, left of line 1053)

---

1 comrainn Y (com *added later over the line*)   2 coibdinil Y C, coibdil W
3 tomissed Y, domissed W C   4 Cuillesc (*plene*) C   5 forfacaib W
6–6 *om. here and inserted after* comlepaid Y   7 Morthruailli Y, Mortrualle
W, Mortruailliu C   8–8 *in marg.* U, *in marg. without* .r. Y, Feargus dixit W,
ut dixit Fergus C   9 macha Y W C   10 gaileonchaib Y, Gáleon W,
gaileon C

ét ar mórslúag murechaib | fester do sléib auí Nessa níth | do slóg
co mbríg | cosrife medrathu fer.'

    [1].r. Ailill dixit[1]

1075 'Ná fer báig,' or Ailill, 'dit dith claidib sceó airdib áth brond rig
menmonfait [2]ces sóe fére[2] frit gallnai gáir dait deim Medb ar iltúatha
dothoing fíad ni fairis lim de debuid ar mnáib étsechaib ar cía
denat torruídet sceó thadet di cach airm ar céo mórglonnaib fechat.

    'Suid sís trá,' or Ailill, 'co n-imberam fidchell. Is fo chen do
1080 thíchtu[a].'

    [3].r. Ailill dixit[3]

    'Imbeir fidchill sceó búanbach ar bélaib ríg sceó rígnai cluche
arafuiretár fo mórslúagu dulecha níbecaumu[4] frit cia thochill berae
ar is di íarnantaib cungnas ar rignaib ingenaib am mareóla bés ni
1085 gáubu cétchinta for mnaib meldrígi sceó chara Findabair Fergus
rodanae ar búaib búrechaib co slógaib móraib timchella di thuataib[5]
techtmóirib co n-ilcruth ríg co mbruth dracon co n-anáil n-athrach
co mbéim léoman[6] dethairith tossaig [7]Fergus mac Rossa Róich[7].'

    Gabsait[8] imbirt na fer fithchille íarom. Adrethsat na firu óir ⁊
1090 argait tarsin clár crédumae.

    [9].r. co clos Ailill[9]

    'Ní cóir ríg cóel caíni tria rind umae báis berair is aldu sceó clár
airbule islú ataurrid a Medb mórglonnach sceó fer sanais fri Fergus
ar imdígirt cliche cíambre[10].'

1095   [11].r. co cloth ní Medb[11]

    'Léic [12]de bríathra[12] athig ní déroig[13] ruben sceó atúar atmib
macrath mín in éri chuairm nita cailtech esbrethach fritoing di
thúatha nitat neúit éiti ar buaib sceó foicherthar di gnússi glanfidir
Fergus.'

66[b]   [14]Co cloth Fergus[14]. |[15].r. Fergus dixit[15].

    [16]'All amai[16],' or Fergus, [17]na bríathraib[17] ilib imgonm[18] ar bélaib
iltúath sceó anassaib[19] ailfitir sceó sétaib sebortir sceó[20] gáib glanfitir
sceó rígaib imgenaiter deraga rofír .i. dogéntar do ríar.'

---

[a] ní ágais ní *sdd. in marg.* [H]

[1-1] *in marg.* U, Ailill dixit *without* .r. W C   [2-2] cessoe fera Y, cesso fero W
[3-3] *in marg.* U, *in marg. without* .r. Y   [4] ni becacumma C   [5] thuathaib
Y W C   [6] leomain W C   [7-7] m̅c̅ Roeich Fergus hua Rosa inrig ruire Y
[8] gaibid Y, gabait W, gabaitt C   [9-9] *in marg.* U, concloth Ailill *in
marg.* Y, conclos Ailill, Ailill dixit W C   [10] cíaimbre Y W, cia imbre C
[11-11] *in marg.* U, *in marg. without* .r. Y, Concloth ni Medb. Medb dixit W C
[12-12] de becc briathra Y W, dod beg briatra C   [13] deoraid W, deoraig run C
[14-14] Concloth Fergus *in marg.* Y   [15-15] *between columns* U, *om.* Y W C
[16-16] iall a m̅c̅ Y   [17-17] niambriathraib Y   [18] imgonaim Y, imgonib
W, imgonaid C   [19] sanesaib Y, sanasaib W, anasaib C   [20] sceó
added above line U, *om.* Y W, sceo C

Anait and ind aidchi sin.   Co cúalatár Ailill isin matin ara bárach.

[1].r. Ailill dixit[1].   1105

'Tofil mórglond ar bélaib mórslúaig fri Cruind uisci uí Nessa
níthu donteilgfet[2] Fir Ol nÉcmacht ar fir fuilglassa de fulib méderath
fri dáil dondlechtaig [3]sceó mórfer[3] taurcbat iltonna fri níach
n-amaulach di Ultaib ticfa[4].'

[5]Medb dixit[5].   [6].r. Medb dixit[6].   1110

'Ná fer immoráin a meic Máta mórúallaig sceó gres erreth a ardaib
auralig drongtar fir fertar mná búaib remib cennaib slúag demensatár
claidib cech uí muinter céochlessaib imbret sceó damaib ágat sceó
mnaib berat arbertat mórslúaig di roí Chúalngi contolat in tslúaig.'

[7].r. co cloth Fergus[7].   1115

'Gremmaigther mórchend for bruinniu drochol tíagait ria ríagaib[8]
in braiss mórmenmnaig di thúathaib toinget di rígnaib báiget fri
namte agat[9].'

Co cloth ní Medb: 'Déntar, dentar a n-asbeir.'

[10].r. Medb dixit[10].   1120

'Fót mám midedar de ilsluagaib cengat cen bá Ailill fót chommus
tabairther.'

Tocumlat ass do [11]Glaiss Cruind.   Co cúalatár[11] Mane mac Ailella:

[10].r. Mane dixit.[10]

'Díam dían léicthir ar fir find cless sceó máthair athair ar búaib   1125
bennachaib arciuchlais co rrís mod [12]de carp–[12], arscin di búaib
ardchles no silis roí.'

.r. Co cloth ní Fergus.

'Na téig a meic mórglonnaig ni bad chomarli berat co ticfa dit[13]
chend dit muníul berthair la gilla n-amulach totáet imarrda fri   1130
roí búrethar fortoing glaiss boccit cuillte ar silestár i rrichtu airchecht
mórglond usci [14]for bádfae di dameib[14] mórslúag [15]ar Ailill[15] guinfa
dimecfiter Medb ilgnússi archel a rroib rindechaib.'

'Rom lécid-sa com loingis hi tossuch,' or Fergus, 'ar náro brister
fír fer forin gillae, ⁊ na baí riund ⁊ in slúag inar ndeóid ⁊ na mná ina   1135
ndíaid-side.'

Co cloth ní Medb.

1–1 *between columns* U, *om.* Y   2 dondotelcfet Y   3–3 sceo decc
morfer Y, sceo dec mor fer W, sceo dec morfer C   4 sa tress *add.* Y
5–5 *om.* Y, *omitt.*   6–6 *between cols.* U, *om.* Y W C   7–7 *between cols.*
U, *in marg. without* .r. Y, Concloth Fergus, Fergus ait W, Conclos Fergus C
8 rigaib W C   9 sceo mnaib berat *add.* C (*taken from preceding speech*)
10–10 *om.* Y W C   11–11 *sic* W C, do Glaiss Cruind*con* co cualatár U, do
Glais Chruind*chon* co cualadar Y   12–12 decar*n* Y C, de carn W   13 dith
Y, di W C   14–14 forbadfae didamib Y, forbádfae di do Meidb W, for
badfae dimeidb C   15–15 *sic* W C, ari⅃ U

[1].r.[2] Medb dixit[1].

'Cluinte[3] a Fergus dit inchaib anmain ar búaib aurscaig[4] cot
1140 slúagaib maithib ní thelce Ultu di thnutaib tairbertha tarcoba a gári
i mMag nAí forberi dáil slicht.'

[5].r. Fergus dixit[5].

'Aill amai,' or Fergus, 'a Medb co mbaísse nat guth cluniur fo
thúathaib nim thorais ar nimthá mac moethlig fri gailte ar Emuin.
1145 Mórbulli for túathaib ni biu rom léic dit leccaib nam iarrair[a6]
[7]cosin nalaide[7] cúlaid di maith[b] lessa ar fechtaib.' |

67[a]   Tothét Cú Chulaind co mboí oc Áth Chruind ara cind[8].
'A popa Loíg[9],' ol sé fria araid, 'dofil [10]na sluagu[10] dún.'
[11].r. Lóeg dixit[11].

1150 'Artung-sa déu,' ol in t-ara, 'firfassa ardchless ar bélaib eirred hi
cocill chumucc[12] for echaib sengaib co cungaib argit co ndrochaib
órdaib for búada bertair cichis ar chennaib ríg a conicim toberat
búaid aráu scindairecht.'

[13].r. Cú C[h]ulaind dixit[13].

1155 'Émde, a Laíg,' or Cú Chulaind, 'co ngaba eissi fri mórbúaid Mache
[14]ni srengat[14] tar drong fri umed mná muidme tíarmaig derúich
mac sceó aitti ailmi fri etnai eocrith sceó Ailill Medba melleth fri
imt[h]echt di éiss roslúagaib.

'Adeochosa[c15],' or Cú Chulaind, 'inna husci[16] do chongnam frim.
Ateoch nem ⁊ talmuin ⁊ Cruinn in tsainrethaig.'

1160   Gaibid Crón[17] cóidech[18] friu
          nís léicfe [i][19] Muirthemniu[20]
          co rroisc[21] monar[22] Féne
          isin tSléib túath Ochaíne.

La sodain cotnóccaib in t-usci súas co mboí i n-indaib crand.

---

[a] .i. nan tiagar [M], .i. nontiagar W   [b] .i. dirorben [M], diroirben
suprascr. Y, .i. dirosben W   [c] .i. atgim [H]

[1-1] *between cols.* U, *om.* Y W   [2] *om.* C   [3] Cluinti lat C   [4] aursclaich
Y, aursclaig W C   [5-5] *between cols.* U, *om.* Y W C   [6] numtiagar *add.* Y
[7-7] cosin dala nde Y *and put after* fechtaib   [8] *sic* Y W C, chind U   [9] a
Laig Y W C   [10-10] menma na sluagh C   [11-11] *in marg.* U, *om.* Y W C
[12] cumaing C   [13-13] *in marg.* U, *om.* Y W, Cu Culaind dixit (.r. *om*) C
[14-14] nit srengat Y C, nith srengat W   [15] Ateochsa W C, *sic leg.*
[16] huisceda W C   [17] cron Y W, Crand C, *read* Cronn   [18] foítech W,
faoitioch C; *read* coídech U ?   [19] a W, *om.* U Y C   [20] Muirthimiu U
[21] *sic* Y W C, rroirc U   [22] monar fer Y, opair fer W, monur bfer C, *read*
monar fer

Téit Mane mac Ailella ⁊ Medba ria cách. Araslig Cú Chulaind [1165]
forsind áth ⁊ bátir trícha marcach día muintir isind usci. Toscara
Cú Chulaind dá šé ndéc ndagláech[1] díb aitherroch immon n-usciu.
Focherdat a puiple icond áth sin. Totháet Lugaid mac Nóis [2]uí
Lomairc[2] Allchomaig[a3] do acallaim Con Culaind trícha marcach.

'Fo chen dait, a Luigid,' ol Cú Chulaind. 'Dia foigela énlaith[4] [1170]
Mag Murthemni rot bía caud[b5] co lleith alailiu día tomna[c6] dano
iasc indbiru rot bía [7]éu .i. bratán[7] co lleith arailiu rot bíat na tri
gaiss .i. gass biroir, gass fochluchta, gass trechlaim. Rot bía fer
i n-áth tart chend.'

'Is torisse,' or Lugaid. 'Feba túathe don mac dodúthracar[8].' [1175]

'It caíni for slúaig,' or Cú Chulaind.

'Níbu[9] dirsan dait do úati ara cind,' or Lugaid.

'Imgéna fír lim-sa ⁊ dagláechdacht,' or Cú Chulaind. 'A popa
Lugaid[10], inim áigetar-sa [11]in tslúaig[11]?'

'Tongu do dia[12],' or Lugaid, 'ní laimethar óenfer ná días úadib [1180]
tabairt a fúail i n-imechtur in dúnaid mani bet fíchtib nó tríchtaib[13].'

'Bid sain ní dóib-som ón,' or Cú, 'diand ragba-sa díburgud[14] asin
tailm.'

'Bid adas dait, a Lugaid, in chocéli-si fil dait la hUltu dianom
tí-sse bríg cach fír. Apair-seo trá cid as áil dait,' ol Cú. [1185]

'Conom raib cairte lat frim budin.'

'Rot bía acht ro pé comarthae furri. Ocus apair frim popa
Fergus bíd comardae fora mbudin. Apair frisna legi bíth comardae
fora mbudin ⁊ toinget anmchomét frim ⁊ domiced bíad cach
n-óenaidche úadib.' [1190]

Téit Lugaid úad. Ecmaic buí Fergus hi pupaill la[15] Ailill.

67[b] Cotgair Lugaid imach hé ⁊ ráti fris insain.

Co cloth ní Ailill.

[16].r. Ailill dixit[16].

[17]'Cáir iss i sanassaib ferthair hi meltmuigib nimrath mórslúagaib[18] [1195]
diar tuathaib ticset[19] fo bíth fir Róich aisnethar díndethar fíadon
falnathair ar Meidb[20] meldulig tonfáir mórchobair. Tíagam

---

[a] .i. techt taidecht [H]   [b] .i. cadán [?H]   [c] .i. día tí [H]

[1] laech Y W C   [2-2] om.. Y   [3] .i. techt ocus toidecht add. C   [4] ónflaith
U   [5] cadan Y, caud W, cadhath C   [6] tonna Y, tonda W C   [7] iech
W, eo C   [8] doduthracair Y, duthracair W, dotnuthraccair C   [9] nib W C
[10] a Lugaid Y W   [11-11] om. Y   [12] et reliqua add. Y, atonncai mo
thuath add. C   [13] ocai add. Y W C, sic leg.   [14] doip add. C   [15] sic Y
W C, l U   [16-16] between cols. U, om. Y W C   [17] .l. prefixed Y W
[18] morsluagaich Y, mórslúagid W C   [19] Ticcfet W   [20] Meidm U

úathad slúaig co pupaill móirscoith ⁊ scor anacol di leccaib artuirb[1]
imfóit ar dálaib díamraib tascnae tánicc.'

1200　'Tongu do dia nimthá,' ar Fergus[2], 'cen athchomarc don gillu.
Tomair, a Lugaid[3], eirg cuici dús in raga[4] Ailill trícha cét cucum-sa
im budin. Beir dam co tinni dó ⁊ taulchuma fína.'

Téit chuci íarom ⁊ ráti fris.

'Fó lim-sa ón,' or Cú Chulaind, 'cia théis.'

1205　Cotrecat a ndí budin íarom. Bít and cot adaig[5]. Brisid Cú
Chulaind *trícha* láech díb cosin tailm.

[6]Nó co mbetís fiche aidchi and sin amal itberat araili libair[6].

'Bit olca íar n-imt[h]echta,' ol Fergus. 'Toficfat Ulaid assa
noíndin ⁊ cotomélat[7] ar[8] Múr[8] ⁊ grian. Is olc in chúl catha inonfil.

1210　Taít ass do Chúil Aiithir.'

Ecmaic dochúaid Cú Chulaind in n-aidche sin do acallaim Ulad.

'Scéla lat?' or Concobar.

[9].r. Cú C[h]ulaind dixit[9].

[10]'Mná brataitir,' ol Cú Chulaind, 'éti agatair, fir gonaitir.'

1215　'Ciche[11] brata, ciche[11] áig, ciche[11] goin?'

'Bertius buchae fuile fuirtbe gainne .i. cend fuirtbi áir berthius
Ailill mac Mátae ⁊ Fergus mac Róich rodána roda clecht claideb
[12]conda *coscar*[12] eochridi Conchobair cáich ⁊ codescarfa.'

'Ní mor torbai dait,' or Conchobar. 'Indiu tonánic ar tinorcain
1220　in chétnae.'

Téit ass iar sudiu úadib co n-accai na slúagu oc[13] scuchud[a] ass.[14]
[15]Ailill dixit[15].

[16]'Aill amai,' or Ailill. [17]'Atchíu carpat condathrind táuthat
slúagu is bodbdae ardibi firu i n-áthu argéba bú[18] curetha bith a
1225　tríchait imbera iar tudecht slúag dí búanaib .i. di Laignib sreithfid
fuil a mméderad dofóetsat oc imorráin ar búaib Ulad issin n-áth,'

---

[a] .i. oc techt [H], *not in* W

---

[1] arthuirb Y W, ar túirib C　　[2] *sic* Y W C, Lugaid U　　[3] aitherrach
add. C　　[4] rága U　　[5] ádaig U　　[6-6] no co mbeidis tricha aidche
andsud Y (*added after* adaig), no co mbetis .xx. aidqi and sút W, no co
mbadiss fiche aidchi ann sin C　　[7] *sic* U Y C, cotmelat W. *Read.*
cotobmélat *or* cotonmélat?　　[8-8] itir uir C　　[9-9] *om.* Y W C　　[10] .i.
prefixed Y　　[11] cisi C　　[12-12] conda- coscar Y, conda scara C　　[13] o U
[14] iar sodain *add.* Y　　[15-15] om. Y W C　　[16] .l. *prefixed in marg.* Y
[17] l. *prefixed in marg.* W　　[18] .i. Ulad *overhead* Y

Gonaid Cú Chulaind *tricha* laéch díb for Áth Duirn.　¹Ní ro
ansatar¹ íarom conid adaig ráncatár Cúil nAirthir.　Gonaid²
trícha³ díb ⁴i sudiu⁴ ⁊ focherdat a pupli and.

Buí ara Ailella .i. Cuillius oc nigi na fondad issind áth mattain. ¹²³⁰
Benti-seom co cloich conid ro marb.　Is de attá Áth⁵ Cuillne hi
Cúil Airthir.

Rosagat trá co feótár i nDruim Féine la Conailliu amal atrubrumar
remoind.

Dosnethat Cú Chulaind ⁶iar suidiu⁶.　Orggaid⁷ cét fer cacha ¹²³⁵
aidche díib na trí aidchi mbátár and.　Gabais tabaill dóib a hOch-
aíniu⁸ inna farrad.

'Bid dimbúan ar slóg la Coin Culaind in cruth sa,' ol Ailill.　'Berar
imarchor comai úan dó .i. ra mbía comméite Maige Murt[h]emne di
68ᵃ　Maig Aíi ⁊ carpat bas dech | bess i nAíi ⁊ timthacht dá fer déac. ¹²⁴⁰
Airg mad ferr laiss in mag sa in ro halt ⁊ trí secht cumal, ⁊ adgig-
nethar dó cach ní atbath airi dia thribi ⁊ indili ⁊ imgéntar laiss immi
ocus táet im gélsine-sea⁹.　Is ferr dó oldás célsine óctigernd.'

'Cia ragas fris sin?'¹⁰

'Mac Roth sund ucut.'　　　　　　　　　　　　　　　　　¹²⁴⁵

Luid ¹¹for sin¹¹ do Delga Mac Roth, techtaire Ailella ⁊ Medba—is é
timchellas Hérind i n-óenló.　Is and bad¹² dóig la Fergus bith Con
Culaind i nDelga.

'Atchíu fer chucund,' or Láeg fri Coin Culaind.　'Berrad bude
fair.　Fethal línda imbi.　Lorg anfaid inna láim.　Calg dét fóa ¹²⁵⁰
choim.　Léne c[h]ulpatach co ndergintliud imbi.'

'Cia do láechaib ind ríg sin,' or Cú Chulaind¹³.

Imcomairc Mac Roth do Láeg cia díambo chéli.

'Céle dond fir uccut tís,' or Láeg.

Boí Cú Chulaind i¹⁴ sudiu isin tsnechtu co rrici a dí leiss cen ¹²⁵⁵
mether imbi oc escaid a léine.　Atbeir dano Mac Roth fri Coin
Culaind cia díarbo chocéle.

'Céle Conc[h]obair meic Nessa,' or Cú Chulaind.

'Indad fil slondud bas derbu?'

'Is lór sin,' or Cú Chulaind.　　　　　　　　　　　　. ¹²⁶⁰

'Anáu cia airm sund hi tá Cú Chulaind?' ol Mac Roth.

---

¹⁻¹ *sic* C, ni ro*ach*tatar Y, ni roachtatar U W　　² cu chul- *add.* Y　　³ laech
add. Y W C　　⁴⁻⁴ sudiu U, oc suidiu Y, hi suidiu W C　　⁵ *om.* Y
⁶⁻⁶ suidiu U, iar suidiu (iar *add. under line*) Y, hi suidiu W, ierom C
⁷ orggait Y, orguin W, oircte C　　⁸ Fochaine C　　⁹ chellsinesa Y,
célsine W, ceilsinesi C　　¹⁰ or cach *add.* W C　　¹¹⁻¹¹ frissin W C, *sic leg.*
¹² *sic* U *with* d *partly expunged,* ba W C, *sic leg.*　　¹³ Rann Meic Roth ocus
an aradh *add.* C (*intended as title to foll. passage*)　　¹⁴ ina *overhead* Y, ina W

'Cid [1]asbérthá[1] fris?' or Cú.

Adfét dó in n-imarchor n-ule amal asrubartmár.

'Cía no beth Cú in n-occus, ní dingned insein.   Ní rriri[2] bráthair
1265 a máthar ar ríg n-aile.'

Doéth[3] chucai afridisi ⁊ asbreth friss doléicfithe[4] dó a mbad
soírem na mban ⁊ a mbad seisc dind folud arná imbreth in tabaill
forroib i n-aidchi cía nos gonad fri dé.

'Ní dingén,' or Cú.   'Dia ructhar ar mná dóera úan, bíait ar mná
1270 sáera for bróntib, ⁊ beim-ni[5] cen blicht má ructhar ar mbaí blichta
úain.'

Doéth[3] cucai afridissi ⁊ asberar friss ra mbíat na mná dóera ⁊
na baí blichta.

'Ní dingén,' or Cú Chulaind.   'Dobérat Ulaid a mná dóera chucu
1275 i llige[6] ⁊ bértair dóermaicni dóib íarom ⁊ imbérat a mblichtach do
feólaib hi [n]gaimred.'

'In fil na aill didiu?' ol in techtaire.

'Fil,' ol Cú Chulaind, '⁊ ní epér frit-su. Dothíasar fair má
atchosse[7] nech dúib.'

1280 'Rafetar-sa,' or Fergus. 'Dam-sa ararocles[8] in fer a foilsigud, ⁊
immorro ní less dúib-si[9]. Ocus iss ed inso in choma,' or Fergus.
'.i. áth forsi ngénathar a gléo ⁊ a chomrac fri óenfer arná ructhar
ind éit de sin láa co n-aidchi dús in táir cobair Ulad[10] fóo. Ocus
machdad lim-sa,' ol Fergus, 'a fot co tecat-side assa cessaib.'

1285 'Is assu ém dúinni,' or Ailill, 'in fer cech laí andás a cét cach
n-aidchi.'

[11]Aided Etarcomail ⁊ imarchor n-athisc fer nÉrend i mbeólo Fergusa
do C[h]oin Chulaind[11]

Luid Fergus íarom forsin[12] n-imarchor n-ísin.   Lil[a][13] di sudiu
1290 dano Etarcomol mac Eda ⁊ Lethrinne,[14] macdalta Ailella ⁊
Medba.

'Ní haccobor lem do thecht,' or Fergus, '⁊ ní ar do miscais.   Scíth
lim namá comrac dúib ⁊ Cú Chulaind.   Do sotlacht[15] ⁊ do saisle,

---

[a] .i. lenaid [M] *not in* W

[1-1] ros berthá U, asbertsa Y, isbertha W, asberthai C   [2] rirse Y,
rirfed W C   [3] *sic* U = doeth   [4] *sic* Y W C, om. U   [5] beimmi
Y, bemi W, beimne C   [6] llege U *with* i *written over first* e, lligi Y W C
[7] *read* atchossed?   [8] araroithcleastar Y, araroichlestair W, araroiclistar C
[9] doibsi U   [10] o Ultaib Y W C   [11-11] *om.* Y, Imarchor n-athisc fer
nErenn i mbeolu Ferguso so W   [12] lasin W, frisin C   [13] lilis C
[14] létrinne U   [15] shotlasu Y C

68ᵇ luinne | ⁊ ansirce, drús ⁊ tarp[th]ige ⊣ dechrad do chéli .i. Con
Culaind.   Ní bía maith do for comruc.'   1295
'Cani sétir lat-su mo snádud airi?' or Etarcomol.
'Sétir dano,' ol Fergus, 'acht nammá ní tharda ¹a rád fri díardain
[dó]¹.
Tecait de² i ndíb carptib do Delga.   Baí Cú Chulaind ind úair sin oc
imbirt búanfaig fri Láeg a dí chúlaid-seom friu ⊣ enech Laíg³.   1300
'Atchíu dá charpat chucund,' or Láeg.   'Fer mór dond isin
carput toísech.   Folt dond cráebach⁴ fair.   Brat corcra imbi, eú
óir and.   Léni chulpatach co ndergintliud imbi.   Cromsciath co
fáebur chondúala⁵ fair di findruini.   Manaís bréfech⁶ ó mimusc eo
hadairc ina láim.   Claideb sithidir loí churaig fora díb slíastaib.'   1305
'Is fás ind laí mór sin doberar lam popa Fergus,' ol Cú Chulaind,
'ar ní fil claideb ina intiuch inge claideb craind.   Atchoas dam
dano,' ol Cú Chulaind, 'ro gab Ailill a mbáegul inna cotlud, héseom
⊣ Medb, ⊣ dorétlaistir a c[h]laidiub ar Fergus ⊣ dorat día araid dia
t[h]oscaid, ⊣ doratad claideb craind ina intech.'   1310
Tic Fergus fó sodain.
'Fo chen sin, ⁷a phopa Fergus⁷,' ol Cú.   'Dia tí⁸ íasc ⁹i n-inbera⁹,
rot bía hé¹⁰ co lleith, araile dia tí íall a mmag, rot bía caúth co
lleith, alaili dor[n]d birair nó femair, dornd fochlochta, deog de
ganim.   Techt i n-áth ar cend fir má thecra¹¹ t'imaire co comthala 1315
rat bía.'
'Is tarise lim,' ol Fergus.   'Ní do biad dorochtamar.   Rofetamar
do threbad sund.'
Arfoím Cú Chulaind íarom in n-imarchor ó Fergus.   Téit Fergus
ass íarom.   1320
¹²Anaid Etarcomol oc déscin Con Culaind.
'Cid dofécai?' ol Cú.
'Tussu,' ol Etarcomol.
'Mós tairchella ém súil tar sodain,' ol Cú Chulaind.
'Is ed ón atchíu,' ol Etarcomol.   'Ní fetar¹³ ní ar[n]dott¹⁴ áighte 1325
do neoch.   Ní acim di gráin ná herúath¹⁵ ná forlond líno latt.
Maccáem tuchtach amne co ngaisciud do [f]id ⊣ co clesaib ségdaib
atotchomnaic.'

---

¹⁻¹ a rad fri (.i. ri) diardain dó W, a roth fri diertain doua C   ² didiu C
³ *lacuna here in* C   ⁴ craaebach U   ⁵ condualach Y   ⁶ brefnech
Y W   ⁷⁻⁷ a popa a Fergáiss Y   ⁸ tonna Y W   ⁹ isna haibnib no
isna hindberaib Y, isna hinderaib W   ¹⁰ eú W, *read* éo   ¹¹ *read* thecma ?
¹² *Title to foll. passage* Comrac Etarcomail ⊣ Con Culand inso *inserted here* W
¹³ feicim Y (icim *overhead*)   ¹⁴ arṅdot Y, arnot W   ¹⁵ héruath U

'Cia nom cháne,' ol Cú Chulaind, 'nít gén-sa fo bíth Fergus[a].
1330 Manipad do snádud immorro[1], roptís do renga rigthi ⁊ do chet[h]ra-
main scaílte ricfaitís úaim dochom in dúnaid i ndegaid do charpait.'
'Náchim thomaid im sodain,' ol Etarcomol. 'In cor amra
[2]ro nenaisc[2] .i. comrac fri óenfer, is messe cíatacomraicfe frit di
feraib Hérend i mbárach.'

1335 Téit ass íarom. Tintaí afrithisi ó Méthiu ⁊ Cethiu, a n-asbert fria
araid:

'Ro bágus,' ol sé, 'fíad Fergus, comrac fri Coin Culaind i mbárach.
Ní hassu dún didiu a i[n]dnaide. Toí forsna heochu asin telaig
dofrithisi.'

1340 Atchí Láeg aní sin ⁊ asbeir fri Coin Culaind:
'Dofil in carpat afrithisi ⁊ dorala clár clé frinn.'
'Ní fíach opaid,' ol Cú. [3]'Ara chind dún sís dond áth co fiasmar,'
or Cú Chulaind[3].
'Ní accobor lem,' ol Cú, 'a condaigi form.' |
69[a] 'Is écen dait-siu ón,' or Etarcomol.
Benaid Cú Chulaind in fót baí fó chossaib co torchair ina lige ⁊ a
fót fora t[h]airr.
'Airg úaim,' or Cú Chulaind. 'Is scíth lem glanad mo lám
inniut. Fotdáilfind i n-ilpartib ó chíanaib acht manibad[4] Fergus.'
1350 'Ní scarfom in cruth sa,' ol Etarcomol, 'co rruc-sa do chen[d]-su
nó co fárcab-sa mo chend lat-su.'
'Is ed ón ém bías andsom,' ol Cú Chulaind.
Bentaí Cú Chulaind cona c[h]laidiub asa[5] díb n-axalaib co
torchair a étach de, ⁊ ní forbai ima c[h]nes.
1355 'Colla trá,' ol Cú Chulaind.
'Aic,' ol Etarcomol.
Danaidle Cú íarom co fogaid in c[h]laidib co sebaind a folt de
amal bid co n-altain [6]no ber[r]thá[6]. Ní forroim cid drisiuc for
toind dó. Ó ropu tromda íarom ⁊ ropo lenamnach in t-ait[h]ech,
1360 bentaí hi fossud a mullaig[7] conid rorand co rrici a imlind.
Co n-acci Fergus in carpat secha ⁊ in n-óenfer and. Tintaí
Fergus do debuid fri Coin Culaind.
'Olc dait, a siriti,' ol sé, 'mo díguin. Is garit mo lorg latt,' ol sé.
'Nába lond frim, a popa Fergus,' ol Cú Chulaind:
1365 .r.[8] 'Fri[9] baga benai fri náimtiu ascada cen claideb fa allud is hé
tororáid ar Ulad aigid sceó slechtfa ailtu tairbirt fo mám Etarcomol[10]

---

[1] mo popa Fergus add. W   [2-2] ronenasc fort W   [3-3] sic Y W, om.
U   [4] mbad U, nipad Y W (misreading)   [5] isa Y W   [6-6] no
bertha Y, no berrtha W   [7] mullaid U   [8] in marq. U, .l. in marg. Y
[9] frim Y   [10] Etarconail W

úallaig dimrén esbláthaib [1]in neoch nam accae ar bail uallchas fo
chemdib[1] fíalum forsaid[2] ligu fortchi for carpat cotlud ná longud ní
sám lam balcbrain. Ná fer aithber form, a popa Ḟergus.'

Talléci inna śléchtain co ndechaid carpat Fergusa taris co fo thrí. **1370**
'Iarfaig día araid in mé fódrúar.'

'Náthú[3] écin,' ar a ara-som.

'Asrubairt,' ol Cú Chulaind, 'ní regad co rrucad mo chend-sa nó
co fárcbad-som dano a chend lem-sa. Cia de bad assu lat-su, [4]a popa
Ḟergus[4]?' or Cú Chulaind. **1375**

'Is assu ém lem-sa a ndorónad,' ar Fergus, 'úair iss éseom ropo
úallach[5].'

Atnaig Fergus íarom id n-erchomail tria a dí pherid ⁊ berthi[6] i
ndead a c[h]arpait fadessin don dúnud. In tan no théiged tar
carrce, no scarad a leth ó [a]lailiu. In tan ba réid, conrictís affrissi. **1380**
Danécai Medb.

'Ní boíd ind imbert moíthchulióin sin, a Ḟergus,' ol Medb.

'Ní tocrád dam dano in t-at[h]echmatud,' ol Fergus, do[7] glieid
frisin coin móir nád n-argarad.'

Cladar a ḟert íarom. Sátir a lia. Scríbthair a ainm n-ogaim. **1385**
Agair a gubae.

Nís dibeirg Cú Chulaind dano d'adaig[8] assa thábaill[a9].

[10]Aided Nath Crantail inso sís[10]

'Ia fer fil lib ar cend Con Culaind i mbárach?' or Lugaid[11].
'Dabérat dait-so i mbárach,' or Mane mac Ailella. **1390**

'Ní étom nech ara chend,' or Medb. 'Ro bíth[12] essemon
laiss co comthastar[13] fer dó.'

Atchotad ón dano.

'Ced leth ragthar úaib,' or Ailill, 'do chuingid ind ḟir sin ar cend
Con Culaind?' **1395**

'Ní fil i nHére,' or Medb, 'adchotar dó mani thuicther Cú Roí mac
Dáre nó Nad Crantail fénnid[14].

---

[a] ⁊ dobertar a mna ⁊ a ingena do ⁊ leth a bó ⁊ doberthe biad do fri dei [*add.*
between cols. H]

[1-1] *om.* Y   [2] um forsaid Y   [3] na tú W, nad thú C (C *resumes after*
loss of leaf)   [4-4] a popa a Fergus Y W, a mo popa Fergus C   [5] uallcho W
[6] berid Y, bert C   [7] *om.* U W, *written overhead* Y, *in text* C   [8] dádaig U
[9] Oighid Etarcomail co sin *add.* C   [10-10] *om.* Y, Comrac Nat Crandail fri
Coin. W, Incipit do chomracc Nad Crandail ⁊ Con Chulaind C   [11] fri Mane
mac Ailella ocus Medbe *add.* C   [12] ronbith Y W C   [13] comthastár U
written betwee cols.   [14] nó Nad Cardil *add.* Y

Boí fer di muintir Con Ruí isin phupaill.

'Ní therga Cú Roí,' or sé. 'Is leór leiss dodeochaid[1] día muintir
1400 and.'

'Tíagar co Nad Crantail didiu.' |

69[b] Téit Mane Andoí cuci. Adfiadat[2] a scéla dó.

'Tair lind di giull di inchaib Connacht.'

'Ní rag-sa[3],' ol sé, 'inge má doberthar Findabair dam.'

1405 Totáet leó íarom. Doberat a gaisced hi carr a hairthiur Chonnacht
co mboí isin dúnud.

'Rotbía Findabair,' or Medb, 'ar dul ar cend ind fir uccut.'

'Dagén,' or sé.

Totháet Luigid[4] co Coin Culaind in n-aidchi sin.

1410 'Dotháet Nad Crantail ar do c[h]end-so i mbárach. Is dirsan
duit. Ní fáelais.'

'Ní bá sin,' or Cú Chulaind.

—[5]Combad and sin no chanad Cú Chulaind:

'Má dofóetsad Nath Crandtail[5]'—

1415 Téit Nad Crandtail arna bárach asin dúnud ┐ berid noí mbera
culind fúachtai[6] follscaidi laiss. Is and boí Cú i sudiu oc foroim én
┐ a c[h]arpat inna farrad. Sríd[7] Nad Crantail biur for Coin
Culaind. Clissis Cú Chulaind for rind in bera hísin ┐ ní nderbai di
forimim[8] inna n-én. A chumut na hocht mbera aili. In tan
1420 focheird a nómad mbir, techid ind íall ó Choin Chulaind i sudiu.
Luid Cú Chulaind íarom for slicht na hélle. Cingid íarom for rindris
na mbera amal én di cach biur for araili i n-iarmóracht na n-én
arnách élaitís. Glé la cách immorro ba for teched luid Cú Chulaind
remi-seom.

1425 'For Cú Chulaind uccut,' ol sé, 'dochóid reom-sa for teched!'

'Deithbir són,' ol Medb, 'má ranistaís dagóic, ní gébad in siriti
fri féta.'

Ba sáeth la Fergus [9]co nUltaib[9] aní sin. Dotáet Fiacha mac Fir
Feibe úadib do chosc Con Culaind.

1430 'Apair fris,' ol Fergus, 'bá fíal dó buith arnaib ócaib céin dogéni
calma. Is féli dó immorro,' ol Fergus, 'a imfolach in tan teches ría
n-áeniur, ol nípo[10] móo a gress dó andás do Ultaib archena.'

'Cia ro maídi sin?' ol Cú Chulaind.

'Nad Crantail,' ol Fíacha.

---

[1] i ndodechaid C   [2] atfet C   [3] rágsa U   [4] Lugaid Y W C
[5-5] Comad and sin adbathadar ┐ adberad Cu Chulaind ma dafoesad Nad
Crantail et reliqua Y, *om.* W C   [6] fuaigthi Y W   [7] sreid Y W, sreithid C
[8] foraim Y W C   [9-9] *id.* Y *but altered by* do *above line and* o *made into* u
to read do Chuin cul, co nUltaib W, co nUltaib imbi C   [10] ni W, nip C

'Ced ed no maíded-som a cless dorignius-[s]a fíada, nípu anféliu [1435]
dó,' or Cú Chulaind. 'Nícon maídfed-som acht [1]no beth[1] arm ina
láim. Rafetar-su ém ní gonaim-se nech cen arm. Táet trá i
mbárach,' ol Cú Chulaind, 'co mbé eter Ochíne ⁊ muir, ⁊ cid moch
donté, fomricfa-sa and ⁊ ní téis[2] ríam.'

Tairnic Cú Chulaind íarom a dáil, ⁊ focheird fáthi n-imbi íar [1440]
cathais na haidchi, ⁊ ní airigestár in corthe már baí ina farrad
comméte friss fessin. Daratailc etir ⁊ a brat, ⁊ saidid inna farrad.

Tic Nad Crandtail fo sodain. Hi fénai bretha arm la suide.

'Cate[3] Cú Chulaind?' ol sé.

'Undse sund tall,' or Fergus.   [1445]

'Nípu samlaid domarfás indé,' ol Nad Crantail. 'In tú Cú
Chulaind?'

'Ocus mássu mé dano?' or Cú Chulaind.

'Másu thú ém,' ar Nad Crandtail, '[4]noco rucaim-se[4] cend úain bic
don dúnud, ní bér do chend ngillai n-amulaig.'   [1450]

'Nícon messi etir,' ol Cú Chulaind. 'Eirg a dochum timchell
ind aird.'

Totháet Cú Chulaind co lLáeg.

70ᵃ   'Commail uilchi smerthain[5] dam-sa latt. Ní hétar | forsin
trénfer comrac frim cen ulchi.'   [1455]

Dogníthe[6] dó. Téit ara chend forsin taulaig.

'Córu lim ón,' or sé. Déne cóir ngascid frim trá,' ol Nad Crantail.

'Rot bía són co[7] fesamar,' or Cú Chulaind.

'Fochichur-sa aurchor dait,' or Nad Crantail, '⁊ ní n-imgaba.'

'Ní n-imgéb acht i n-arddai,' or Cú Chulaind.   [1460]

Focheird Nad Chrantail aurchor dó. Lingid Cú Chulaind i
n-arddi ríam.

'Is olc dait a imgabáil ind aurchora,' or Nath Crantail.

'Imgaba-so[8] mo aurchor-sa i n-ardda dano,' or Cú Chulaind.

Légid Cú Chulaind in ngáe fair acht bá i n-ardda conid anúas [1465]
tocorastár inna mullach co lluid trít co talmain.

'Amai ole! Is tú láech as dech fil i nHérind,' or Nath Crantail.
'Atáat ceithre meic fichet dam-sa isin dúnud. Tiaga-sa[9] co n-écius
dóib a fil lim [10]di foilgib[10], ⁊ dorag-sa co nderna-so mo díchennad
air atbél-sa dia talltar in gáe as mo chind.'   [1470]

'Maith,' or Cú Chulaind. '[acht][11] dotéis doríssi.'

[1-1] co mbiad C   [2] *sic* U, theis Y, teis W C; *read* tess   [3] cáte U,
codde Y, cadde W, caitti C   [4-4] nochor rucais Y, no cu ruccuindse W, cu
ruccaimsi C   [5] smertha Y, smérthain W, smerthan C   [6] dognithide
Y W, *read* dogníth-ide   [7] ? = acht co   [8] imgabsa W C   [9] tiagso Y,
tiagsa W C, *sic leg.*   [10-10] d'imfhailccib C   [11] *sic* C, *om.* U W Y

Téit Nath Crantail íarom don dúnud. Dotháet cách ara chind.

'Cate[1] cend ind riastarthi lat?' or cách.

'Anaid, a láechu, co n-écius mo scéla dommo maccaib ꝉ co ndeochus
1475 doríssi[2] co ndernar comrac fri Coin Culaind.'

Tiat ass di ṡaigid Con Culaind ꝉ dolléci a c[h]laideb for Coin
Culaind. Lingid-side i n-arddae co mbí in corthe co mmebaid in
claideb i ndé. Siabartha[3] im Choin Culaind amal dorigni frisna
maccu i nEmain, ꝉ lingid Cú Chulaind fora scíath-som la sodain co
1480 mbí a c[h]end de. Bentai aitheroch inna méde anúas co imlind.
Dofuitet a cethri gábaiti[4] for talmain.

Is and sin íarom asbert Cú Chulaind inso:

'Má dorochair Nath Crantail
bid formach dond imargail.
1485 Apraind cen chath isind úair
do Medb co tríun in tṡlúaig.'[5]

[6]Fagbáil in Tairb iarsin slicht sa so sís[6].

IS and sin luid Medb co tríun in tslóig lé hi Cuib do[7] chuingid in
tairb ꝉ luid Cú Chulaind ina ndíaid. For Sligi Midluachra didiu
1490 dochóid-si do indriud Ulad ꝉ Cruthne co dice Dún Sobarche.

Co n-accai ní intí Cú Chulaind: Bude mac Báin ó Ṡléib Chulind
cosin tarb ꝉ cóic samaisci déac imbi. Sesca láech a lín de muintir
Ailella[8]. Brat hi forcebul im cach fer. Dotháet Cú Chulaind
chucu.

1495 'Can tucsaid[9] a folad?' ol Cú Chulaind.

'Ón tsléib ucut,' ol in láech.

'Ceist cate a mbúachaill?' ol Cú Chulaind.

'Atá amal fóndráncamár,' ol in láech.

Focheird Cú Chulaind trí bidcu ina ndíaid oc saigid acallma forro
1500 co tice in n-áth. Is and sin asbert frisin toísech:

'Cia t' ainm-siu?' ol sé.

'Nachit aiss, nachit chara—Bude mac Báin,' ol sé.

'Are in gaí se for Bude,' ol Cú Chulaind.

Sraithe[10] din chertgaí co lluid i nderc a oxaille co mmebaid i ndé
1505 ind óe altarrach resin gaí.

Gontai sin fora áth. Is de atá Áth mBude.

---

[1] cáte U, cade Y W, caiti C   [2] morisi Y W, mofrithisi C   [3] siartha
U Y W, siabharthi C   [4] gabaidi Y W, gabaitte clis C   [5] Aided Nad
Cranntail sin add. in space above last line Y   [6-6] om. Y, Fagbail in tairb W
[7] dó U   [8] ꝉ Medba add. W C   [9] asa tuccsaid W   [10] sraite Y, sráite W

70ᵇ Berair in tarb isin | dúnad la sodain.

Imráidset íarom nípád ansu Cú Chulaind acht tuctha a c[h]letíne airi.[1]

[2]Aided Redg Cáinte inso[2]

1510

IS íarom luid [3]Redg Cáinte a comarli Ailella[3] chucai do chuingid in c[h]letíne .i. gaí Con Culaind.

'Tuc dam-sa do gaí,' or in cánte.

'Acc óm,' or Cú, 'acht dabér seótu dait.'

'Nád géb-sa ón,' ar in cáinte.

1515

Gegna-som dano in cáinte úair nad fáet a targid dó, ⁊ asbert in cánte na[4] bérad a enech mani berad in cletíni. Focheird Cú Chulaind íarom in cletíne dó co lluid triana chend forstarsnu[5].

'Is [6]tolam[a] in sét se[6] ém!' ol in cánte.

Is de ata Áth Tolam Sét.

1520

Atá dano áth friss anair airm i n-arrasar a n-uma don c[h]letíniu. Humarrith ainm ind átha sin dano.

Is and sin trá geguin Cú Chulaind inna hule sea asrubartmar hi Cuib .i.[7] Nath Coirpthe [7]occá chrannaib, Cruthen fora áth, Maccu Búachalla ocá carnd, Marc ina thelaig, Meille ina dind, Bodb ina [1525] thur, Bogaine ina grellaig.

Tintaí Cú Chulaind aitheruch i mMag Murthemne. Ba diliu laiss imdegail a mennato fessin. Iar tíachtain íarom geogain firu[8] Crochine[b9] .i. Focherda. Fiche fer focherd de. Dosnetarraid oc gabáil dúnaid dóib, deich ndeogbaire ⁊ deich fénnide.

1530

Tintaí Medb aitheruch atúaid ó ro an coícthiges oc inríud in chóicid, ⁊ ó ro fich cath fri Findmóir[10] mnaí Celtchair meic Uthidir[11], ⁊ dosbert cóecait ban iar togail Dúin Sobarchi furri hi crích Dáil Ríatai. Nach airm trá i Cuib in ro sáidi Medb echfleisc, is Bile Medba a ainm. Cach áth ⁊ cach dingnai ocár fíu, is Áth ⁊ Dindgna [1535] Medba a ainm.

Condrecat uli íarom oc Focheird eter Ailill ⁊ Medb ⁊ in fiallach [12]timacht in tarb[12]. Acht gabais [13]a búachaill[13] a tarb díb [14]conid timachtatár[14] taris i mbernai cumaing[15] la crand for scíathu. Conid

---

[a] .i. sét talman [H]   [b] nó Croiniche [M]

[1] .i. gai Con cCulaind add. C   [2-2] between cols. U, om. Y W C   [3-3] sic C, Redg cainte Ailella a comairle U Y W   [4] = no   [5] fortharrsu Y, fortharsnu W, fortarsnai C   [6-6] talam set se Y W, tolamh set C   [7-7] na tri Coirpthiu C   [8] om. W   [9] Croiniche Y W, Croinice no Croinichiu no Crochine C   [10] fri add. U (H)   [11] Cuitheochair Y, Guthidir W   [12-12] timtacht in tarb U, timthacht in tarb Y, thimthacht in tarb W, timtachtai an tairp C   [13-13] sic Y, a mbuachaill U W C   [14-14] conid timtachtar Y, conitimachtatar W, conid timthachtatar C   [15] nimchumaing Y W C

[1540] bertatar cossa na slabrai triasin talmain. Forgemen ainm in búachalla. Atá[1] and iarom [2]conid hé[2] ainm in c[h]nuic Forgemen[3].

Ni baí [4]imneth foraib[4] trá isind aidchi sin acht adchota[5] fer do dingbáil Con Culaind for áth namá úadib.

[1545] [6]'Guitter cardi chlaidib úand for Coin Culaind,' or Ailill.

'Tíat Lugaid fris,' ol cách.

Téit íarom Lugaid día acallaim.

'Cinnus atú-sa innosi ocon tslóg?' for Cú Chulaind.

'Mór ém in cuitbiud condiachtais forro,' for Lugaid, '.i. do mná [1550] ⁊ t'ingena ⁊ leth do bó duit. Ocus is trummu leó [7]a nguin ⁊ do bíathad indá cach ní[7].'

Dothuit fer cach laí leis co cend sechtmaini and sin. Bristir fír fer for Coin Culaind. Láitir fichi[8] i n-óenḟecht dia ṡaigid ⁊ nos geogain-sium uli.

[1555] 'Eirg cuci, a Ḟergus,' for Ailill, [9]'conda raib[9] cláemchlód[10] magni lais.'

Tíagait íarom co mbátár hi Crónig. Iss ed dorochair leiss ar galaib óenḟir[11] isin magin sin .i. dá Roth, dá Lúan, dá banteolaid, deich ndrúith, deich ndeogbaire, deich Fergusa, seser Fedelmthe, sé [1560] Fiacraig. Ro bítha trá sin uli les-[s]ium ar galaib óenḟir[11]. Ó ro
71ᵃ láiset íarom a pupli hi Crónig, ro imráidset cid dogén | tais [12]fri Coin Culaind[12].

'Rofetur-sa,' ol Medb, 'a n-as maith and. Tíagair úaind día ṡaigid conda raib carti claidib úad frisin slóg, ⁊ ra mbía leth na mbó [1565] fil sunda.'

Berair íarom in fis sin chuci.

'Dogén-sa aní[13], or Cú Chulaind, 'acht [14]nár mil[l]ter úaib-si a n-árach[14].'

[15]Comrac Con Culaind fri Findabair inso[15]

[1570] 'Immarchuirther fris,' or Ailill, 'Findabair do thabairt dó ⁊ a dingbáil dona slógaib.'

Téit Mani Aithramail a dochum. Téit-side co lLáeg hi tossiuch.

---

[1] Notta Y, *read* Atá cnoc?   [2-2] conid de Y C   [3] Ro fásastoir em Forgaimoin de sin *add.* C   [4-4] fortha d'imneadh C   [5] adcotad Y C, atchotar W   [6] *here begins* H *interpolation to l.* 1712   [7-7] ina sin do biathad acus a nguin W C   [8] nó tricha *add.* C   [9-9] condon raib W, *sic leg.*, condom raib C   [10] cláechlad W, caomclodh C   [11] oenfer U, oinḟir W   [12-12] *om.* W C   [13] ám W, eimh C   [14-14] na millter uaibsi imbarach W, na ro millter uaibhsiu a marach C   [15-15] *in marg.* U

'Cia díandat céli-siu?¹' ol sé.

Ní n-arlasair Láeg dano. Asbert Mani fris fo thrí in cruth sin.

'Céli do Choin Culaind,' for sé, '⁊ nacham forraig nád n-ecma nád ¹⁵⁷⁵
benur² do chend dít.'

'Is lond in fer so,' ol Mani la sóud úad.

'Téit iarom do acallaim Con Culaind. Is and ro boí Cú Chulaind
iar [m]béim dei a léned ⁊ in snechta immi ina ṡudiu co rici a cris, ⁊
ro lega in snechta immi fercumat fri méit brotha in míled. Asbert ¹⁵⁸⁰
Mani dano ón mud chétna fris-side fo t[h]rí cia díambo chéli.

'Céli Conchobair³, ⁊ nacham forraig. Díanam forgea immorro ní
bas síriu, bíthus di chend dít amal tíscar di lun.

'Ní réid,' ol Mani, 'acallaim na desi seo.'

Téit Mani úadib íarom ⁊ adfét do Ailill ⁊ do Medb a scéla.   ¹⁵⁸⁵

'Táet Lugaid chuci,' ⁴or Ailill⁴ '⁵⁊ ara n-airlathar dó in n-ingin⁵.'

Téit Lugaid iar sudiu ⁊ adfét do C[h]oin Chulaind aní sin.

'A poba Lugaid⁶,' ol Cú Chulaind, 'is bréc sin.'

'Is bríathar ríg assidrubairt,' for Lugaid. 'Ní bía bréc de.'

'Déntar amlaid,' ol Cú Chulaind.   ¹⁵⁹⁰

Luid Lugaid úad la sodain ⁊ adfét do Ailill ⁊ do Medb a n-at[h]esc
sin.

'Táet in drúth⁷ im richt-sa,' or Ailill. '⁊ mind ríg fora c[h]ind, ⁊
⁸fasisidar di chéin Coin Culaind⁸ arnacha n-aithgné. Ocus téiti ind
ingen leis⁹ ⁊ ara naiscea dó hí, ⁊ tecat ass ellom¹⁰ fón cruth sin. Ocus ¹⁵⁹⁵
is dóig ¹¹immérthai ceilg¹¹ fón cruth sin fair¹² conná fostba sib céin
co tí la hUltu don chath.'

Téit íarom in drúth cuci ¹³⁊ ind ingen lais¹³ ⁊ ba di chéin arlastar
Coin Culaind. Téit Cú dia saigtin. Ecmaic atgeóin-sium for
erlabrai ind ḟir combo drúth. Srethis liic telma boí ina láim fair con ¹⁶⁰⁰
sescaind ina c[h]end co tuc a inc[h]ind ass. Tic dochum na ingini.
Benaid a dí trilis di ⁊ sádid liic tríana brat ⁊ tríana lénid, ⁊ sádid
corthe | tría medón in drúith. Atát a ndí chorthi and .i. corthi
Findabrach ⁊ corthi in drúith. Fácbais Cú Chulaind fón cruth
si[n] íat.   ¹⁶⁰⁵

Tiagair ó Ailill ⁊ ó Medb do iarmóracht a mmuntiri ar ba fota leó
ro mbátár. Co n-accassa íarom isin tunidi sin. Atchlos íarom fón
dúnchaire uli aní sin. Ní baí trá carti dóib la Coin Culaind iar tain.

71ᵇ

---

¹ céliusiu U   ² benadh W, mbenae C   ³ meic Nessa *add.* W C
⁴⁻⁴ or siat W   ⁵⁻⁵ *sic* U, ⁊ ara narlathar W, ⁊ ara n-airlathor do an ingen C
⁶ a Lugaid C   ⁷ draí C   ⁸⁻⁸ ⁊ fosissethar do chein Coin Culaind W,
⁊ fosisidhar do cein Co[i]n gCulaind C   ⁹ ⁊ ba do chein o Coin cCulaind
arnach n-arrlathorsom ⁊ arnach n-aithgne *add.* C   ¹⁰ co hollam C
¹¹⁻¹¹ imbertha ceilg W, imberthar celg C   ¹² *sic* W C, *om.* U   ¹³⁻¹³ *om.*
W, ⁊ an ingen ina ferrad lais C

¹Comlond Munremair ⁊ Con Roí inso¹.

¹⁶¹⁰ A mbátár in tslóig and tráth nóna co n-accatar docurethar in lía forru anair ⁊ a chéli aníar ara cend.   Condrecat isind aer. No thuititis eter dúnad Fergusa ⁊ dúnad nAilella ⁊ dunad nÉrand. Ro both ocond reib sin ⁊ ocond ábairt ón tráth co 'raile, ⁊ ro bátár in tslúaig inna seseom ⁊ a scéith fora cennaib día sáerad for ¹⁶¹⁵ barnib² na cloch combo lán a mmag dina lecaib.   Is dé atá Mag Clochair.

Ecmaic immorro iss é Cú Ruí mac Dáiri dorigni insin.   Dodeochaid do chobair a muntiri ⁊ boí hi Cotail for cind Munremair³ meic Gerrcind⁴.   Doluid-side ó Emain Macha do chobair Con Culaind co ¹⁶²⁰ mboí i nArd Róich.   Rofitir Cú Roí ní boí fer fulaing Munremair insin tslóg.   It é didiu dorigénsat ind ábairt sin etorro a ndís.

Guitter ón tslóg forro bith 'na tost.   Dogníat córai íarom Munremur ⁊ Cú Ruí, ⁊ téit Cú Ruí dia thig ⁊ Munremur do Emain Macha. Ocus ní thánic Munremur co lá in chatha⁵.   Ní thánic dano Cú ¹⁶²⁵ Ruí co comrac Fir Diad.

'Apraid fri Coin Culaind,' ol Medb ⁊ Ailill, 'conda[n] rab-ni cláemchlód magni leis.'

Doberar dóib íarom ⁊ cláemchlóit inad.

Ro scáich noínnin Ulad fo šodain, ar in tan dofiuchtraitís asa cess, ¹⁶³⁰ tictis drécht díb béus forsin slóg conos gabad a tindorcain doridisi.

⁶Aided na Macraidi inso⁶

R O imráidset íarom macrad Ulad i nEmain Macho oco. 'Tróg dún,' ar siat 'ar popa Cú Chulaind cen chobair dó.' 'Ceist ém,' ol Fiachna Fulech mac Fir Febi—derbráthair ¹⁶³⁵ side do Fiachaig Fíaldána mac Fir Febi—'rom bía-sa cethern lib co ndeochsaind-sea do ⁷thabhairt cobra dó de sin⁷.'

72^a   Tíagait trí cóecait mac leis cona lorcaib áni, ⁊ ba⁸ sé sin trían macraidi Ulad.   Atcít⁹ in slóg cucu tarsa mag.

'Tofil slóg mór tarsa mag cucund,' or Ailill.

¹⁶⁴⁰   Téit Fergus día ndéscin.

'Araill do macraid Ulad inso,' for sé, '⁊ do c[h]obair Con Culaind tecait.'

'Eirged buden ara cend,' or Ailill, 'cen fis do Choin Chulaind, ar di[a] comairset fris, ní fáelsaid íat.'

---

¹⁻¹ *in marg.* U   ² bairnioch C   ³ *sic* W, Munremar U, an Munrembar C
⁴ *a folio missing after this point* W   ⁵ morcathae C   ⁶⁻⁶ *in marg.* U,
om. C   ⁷⁻⁷ cobair dó codesin C   ⁸ *sic* C, be U   ⁹ atací U, atcíd C

Tíagait trí cóecait láech ara cend. Immacomthuit dóib conná [1645]
tadchith[1] nech díb i mbethaid ass do gléri na mmac oc Liic Tuill.
Is de sin atá Lía Fiachrach meic Fir Ḟebi, ar is and sin ro thuit.

'Dénaid comarli,' for Ailill. 'Gudid Coin Culaind imófor lécud
asind inud sa, ar ní ragaid ar écin tairis úair rod leblaing a lón
láith.'   [1650]

Ar bá bés dó-som in tan no linged a lón láith ind, imréditis a
t[h]raigthi iarma[2] ⁊ a escata remi ⁊ muil a orcan fora lurgnib, ⁊
indala súil ina chend ⁊ araili fria chend anechtair. Docoised ferchend
fora beólu. Nach findae bíd fair ba háthithir delc sciach ⁊ banna
fola for cach finnu. Ní aithgnéad cóemu ná cairdiu. Cumma no [1655]
slaided ríam ⁊ iarma[2]. Is de sin doratsat Fir Ól[3] nÉcmacht in
ríastartha [4]do anmaim[4] do C[h]oin C[h]ulaind.

[5]Bánchath Rochada inso[5]

FOídis Cú Chulaind a araid co Rochad mac Fat[h]emain di
    Ultaib co tísad dia chobair. Ecmaic dano ro carastar Finda- [1660]
    bair Rochad ar iss éside ócláech as áildem ro boí la Ultu ind
inbaid sin. Téit in gilla 'na dochum Rochad[a] ⁊ asbert fris techt[6]
do ḟórit[h]in Con Culaind, má dodeochaid asa nóennin[7], co tartaitis
ceilc immon slóg fri tarrachtain dréchta dib día n-airlech. Dotháet
Rochad atúaid cét láech dó.   [1665]

'Décaid dún a mmag indiu,' for Ailill.

'Atchíu dírim tarsa mag,' ol in dercaid, '⁊ máethócláech etarro.
Ní thacmainget dó ind óic acht co rici a gúalni.'

'Cia sút, a Ḟergus?' for Ailill.

'Rochad mac Fathema[i]n,' for sé, '⁊ is do c[h]obair Con Culaind [1670]
dotháet. Rofetur-sa a n-as maith dúib fris,' ol Fergus. 'Táet
cét láech úaib lasin | n-ingin út co ria medón in maigi ⁊ téit ind[8]
ingen remán[9] remib, ⁊ téiti marcach día acallaim co tí a óenur do
acallaim na ingini, ⁊ tabraiter láma tairis, ⁊ immacurfi sin fogail a
muntiri dínd[10].'   [1675]

Dogníther íarom amlaid sin. Téit Rochad ar cend in marcaig.

'Dodeochad-sa ó Ḟindabair ar do chend-so co ndechais día
hacallaim.'

Téit íarom día hacallaim a óenur. Mutti don tslóg immi di cach
leith. Nos gabar ⁊ fochertar láma tairis. Maidid dano día muntir- [1680]

72[b] (margin left)

---

1 tadcth U *with* i *above line*, taithrith C   2 iarom C   3 nÓl U
4–4 do anm U, d'ainm C   5–5 in *marg.* U, *om.* C   6 toigecht C
7 ces C   8 in | ind U   9 *om.* C   10 don tsluagh C

seom for teched. Lécair-sium íarom ass ⁊ fonascar fair can tudecht
forsin slóg co tísad ar óen fri Ultu uli[1]. Dorairngired dó dano
Findabair do t[h]abairt dó, ⁊ immásoí[2] úadib íar sudiu.

Conid Bánchath Rochada insin.

1685   [3]Aided na Rígamus inso[3]

'GUitter dano cairdi chlaidib dún for Coin Culaind,' for
   Ailill ⁊ Medb.
    Téit Lugaid fris sin ⁊ [4]dobeir Cú Chulaind in cartini [dó].[4]
'Tabar fer for áth dam-sa i mbárach,' for Cú Chulaind.
1690   Bátár sesiur rígamus la Meidb .i. sé rígdomnai do chlannaib
Dedad .i. trí Duib Imlig ⁊ trí Deirg Sruthra.
    'Cid dún,' ar siat, 'can techt i n-agid Con Culaind?'
    Tíagait íarom arna bárach ⁊ geogain Cú Chulaind a sesiur iat.

                         [5]Aided Cáuir[5]

1695   Guitter dano Cúr mac Da Láth dóib im dula for cend Con Culaind.
Intí assa teilced-side fuil [6]is marb re cind nomaide[6].
    [7]'Mad dia ngona'[7], ol Medb, 'is búaid. Gid hé gontair and dano,
is dingbáil tromma[8] don[9] tslóg. Ní réid bith fris [10]im longud nó im
ligi.[10]'
1700   Téit ass dano. Nírbo maith les-side íarom techt for cend siriti
amulaig.
    [11]'Ní gó ém,' ol sé[11], '[12]is cert in bríg doberid dún[12]. Má rofesind
combad ar cend ind fir se nom faíte, ním foglúasfind féin [13]día
saigid[13]. Ropad leór lem gilla a chomadais[14] dom muntir 'na agid.'
1705   [15]'Ecca sin!'[15] for Cormac Cond Longas. 'Ba hamra dúnni día
ndingbaitea fessin hé[16].'
    'Cipé cruth trá,' ol sé, 'ol is form-sa féin doberar imthésid-si isin
matain i mbárach día saigid.   [17]Ním erchoisse guin[18] na erri ucut[18].'
    Téit íarom matain muich ara bárach ara chend[17] ⁊ asbeir frisin
1710 slóg tarrgraige[19] n-imtechta [20]a séta rempo[20] ar ba suba sliged
dogénad-sum di t[h]echt ar cend Con Culaind.   [20]Luid dó íarom[20].

---

[1] don cath add. C   [2] imsaoi C   [3-3] add. in marg, U, om. C   [4-4] doberar
an cairdine do C   [5-5] between cols. U   [6-6] ba marb re ndé nomaide Y C
[7-7] Ma rongona Y, Ma rod gona C   [8] dromma U, truim Y   [9] dom U
[10-10] im shuide ná ligi na longu(u)d Y C   [11-11] Ní có ém ol se U, ni
caomh ol se C, om. Y   [12-12] ⁊ isbert fria Meidb is cert in brig doberi
dom add. at foot of page Y   [13-13] om. Y C   [14] chomais Y   [15-15] é cé
sin C   [16] om. Y C   [17-17] ⁊ dognith tengraidhe a n-imtechta ⁊ asmbert
add. C (misplaced)   [18-18] na eirreille ucut Y C   [19] tengraige Y W
[20-20] om. Y W C

Boí Cú Chulaind ac imbert chless isin uair sin .i.[1] |

73ᵃ [2]Turim na cless inso sís[2]:

[3]in t-ubullchless[3] ⁊ fáeborc[h]less ⁊ fáenc[h]less ⁊ cless cletenach
⁊ tétc[h]less ⁊ corpc[h]less ⁊ cless caitt ⁊ ích n-erred ⁊ cor ndeled ⁊ [1715]
léim dar néib ⁊ filliud erred náir ⁊ gaí bolga ⁊ baí brasse ⁊ rothchless
⁊ ochtarchless[4] ⁊ cless for análaib ⁊ bruud gine ⁊ sian caurad ⁊
béim co commus[a] ⁊ táithbéim ⁊ dréim fri fogaist co ndírgiud crette
fora rind [5]co fornadmaim níad náir[5].

Ro boí dano Cáur oc airimbert[6] gascid hi túamaim a scéith co [1720]
rrice trían ind laí fris-seom, ⁊ nícon tetarraid béim ná forgab fair la
dechrad inna cless ⁊ nícon fitir-seom in fer i n-imforgub friss co
n-epert Fiacha mac Fir Ḟebe fri Coin Culaind:

'Fomna in láech fodotben!'

Danécai Cú secha. Sraíthi [7]in n-ubullchless[7] tarraid ina láim co [1725]
lluid iter chobrad ⁊ bróin in scéith co lluid tríana chend ind athig síar[8].

[9]Combad[10] i nImślige Glendamnach dano dofáethsad Cáur [11]iar
n-araile slicht[11].[9]

Tintaí Fergus frisin slóg.

'Mánop gaib far nglinne[12],' ol sé, 'anaid sund [13]co bárach[13].'   [1730]

'Níp and,' ol Ailill. 'Regmai diar sostaib afrithisi.'

Guitter dano Láth mac Da Bró ara chend amal ro ngess Cáur.
Datuit-side dano cadessin. Dointáth[14] dano Fergus béus do chor
a nglinni[15] forru. Ansait and sin trá corrubad and Cáur mac Da
Láth ⁊ Láth mac Da Bró ⁊ Foirc mac Trí nAignech ⁊ Srubgaile mac [1735]
Eóbith. Ar galaib óenḟir[16] [17]ro gáeta[17] uli.

[18]Aided Fir Baíth inso[18]

'COllaa[b] dún, a popa Loíg[19], issa ndúnad co n-airlither[c]
Lugaid mac Nóiss uí Lomairc dús cía dotháet ar mo chend i
mbárach. [20]Iarfaigther co lléir ⁊ a imchomarc lat[20].'   [1740]
[21]Rosoich iarom Láeg[21].

---

[a] nó co fomus [M]   [b] .i. erig [M]; .i. eirg W   [c] .i. co n-iarfaigea
[M]; .i. co ro accille W

[1] H· *interpolation ends*   [2-2] *in marg.* U; *list in three cols.*   [3-3] *itir*
ubullcleas Y W C   [4] *sic* Y, otar U, ocharcless W, otharcles C   [5-5] co
fonnad maidm niath Y, cona fonaidm niadh nair C   [6] airbert Y W C
[7-7] in nubaillcleasa Y, don certgai nó don ubullcles C   [8] combo marb
add. W   [9-9] *om.* W, *om. here* C, *inserted later after* afrithisi   [10] nó comad
Y C   [11-11] *om.* Y   [12] *sic* Y W C, glinne U   [13-13] *sic* U W, co
arabarach (ara *under line*) Y, co a barach C   [14] *sic* U Y W, doinntaid C
[15] glinni U C   [16] óenfer U Y   [17-17] ron bithae C   [18-18] *in marg.* U,
om. Y C   [19] a Laig Y   [20-20] ⁊ a fiarfaidhedh co lleir ⁊ a imchomarc lat et
reliqua Y C, iarfaigh co lleir ⁊ a imchomarcc lat et reliqua W   [21-21] *om.*
Y W, rosoich Laocch co Lugaid C

'Fo chen dait,' or[1] Lugaid. 'Ní sirsan do Choin Chulaind a n-imned i tá a óenur fri firu Hérend.'

[2]'Cia dot[h]aet ar cend Con Culaind amárach?'[2]

1745 'Ar cocéle[3] díb línaib amin, mallacht a gascid fair, is é théte ara chend i mbárach, Fer Báeth. Doberar Findabair dó airi ⁊ rígi a cheniúil.'

[4]Sóid Láeg afrithisi co airm i mboí Cú Chulaind[4].

'Ní forbáelid mo popa Láeg dia athiusc,' or Cú Chulaind.

1750 Adfét Láeg dó uile[5] aní sin[a5]. Ro congrad Fer Báeth hi pupull do Ailill ⁊ Medb, ⁊ asber fris suide for láim Findabrach ⁊ a tabairt dó ar ba hé a togu ar chomrac fri Coin Culaind. Ba hé fer a dingbála[6] leó ar ba cuma[7] dán díb línaib la Scáthaig. Doberar fín dó íarom corbo mesc, ⁊ asber fris bá cáem leó-som a llind sin, ní tobrad acht 1755 ere cóecat fén leó. Ocus ba hí ind ingen no gebed láim fora c[h]uit-seom de.

73ᵇ 'Ní haccobor lem,' or Fer Báeth. 'Comalta ⁊ fer | bithchotaig dam Cú Chulaind. Ragat-sa ar apa ara chend i mbárach co topach-tur a chend de.'

1760 'Bid tú dogéna[8],' or Medb.

Asbeir Cú Chulaind fri Láeg techt ar cend Lugdach dó co tísad día acallaim. Dotháet Luigid chucai.

'Fer Báeth ane dotháet ar mo chend-sa i mbárach,' or Cú Chulaind.

'Éseom ón óm,' ar Lugaid.

1765 [9]'Olc dia sin[9],' or Cú Chulaind. 'Nícon beó-sa i mbethaid di śudiu. Dá chomaís sind, dá chomśolam, dá chutrummae, co comairsem. A Lugaid, celebor[10] dam. Apair friss dano ní fír láechdachta dó tuidecht ar mo chend-sa. Apair fris táet ar mo chend-sa innocht dom acallaim.'

1770 Ráti Luigid friss. In tan nád rimgaib Fer Báeth, luid in n-aidchi sin do athchor a chairdessa for Coin Culaind ⁊ Fiacha mac Fir Ḟebe lais. Attaich Cú Chulaind friss a chomaltus ⁊ a mummi díb línaib Scáthaig.

'Isim égen trá,' ol Fer Báeth. 'Darindgult[b11] [12]do Meidb[12].'

1775 'Doselba[13] do chotach didiu,' ol Cú Chulaind.

Luid Cú Chulaind fo luinni úad. Fornessa sleig culind isin glind hi coiss Con Culaind co túargab ocá glún súas a cend. Dasrenga ass.

ᵃ .i. a athesc [M]   ᵇ .i. ro gellus [M]

---

[1] sic U W, a Y, al (= ol) C   [2-2] om. U W C, written overhead between lines Y   [3] coicle C   [4-4] om. Y W   [5-5] a aithesc Y W C   [6] sic Y W C, ndingbala U   [7] dorighensat add. W   [8] sic Y C, dogénad U W   [9-9] alcco dia sin Y W C   [10] celebair Y   [11] doringiull .i. do gellus C   [12-12] sic Y added later above line   [13] sic Y W C, dośella U

'Ná téig, a Fir Baíth, co n-aicther in fríthi fónúar-sa.'

'Tochrae úait,' ar Fer Báeth.

Focheird Cú Chulaind in sleig n-íarom i ndegaid Fir Baíth co [1780]
n-érrmadair áth a dá chúlad co ndeochaid fora beólo sair co
torchair tara aiss issa nglend.

'Focherd sin ém!' or Fer Báeth.

Is de atá Focherd Murthemne.

Nó iss é Fíacha asrubairt: [1785]

'Is beóda do feocherd indiu, a C[h]ú Chulaind,' or sé.

Conid de attá Foc[h]erd Murthemne.

Atbail fo chétóir Fer Báeth isinn glind.   Is de atá Glend Fir
Baíth.

Co cloth ní, Fergus co n-epert: [1790]

    'A Fir Baíth is báeth do fecht
    'sin magin i tá do fert
    rosiacht coll [1]do chombár[1] and
    is crichid hi Cróen Chorand.

    F[r]íthi[2] ainmnigther a n-ard   [1795]
    co bráth bid Cróenech i mMuirthemniu
    ó'ndiu bid Focherd a ainm
    ind airm i torcha(i)r, a Fir,'
        [3]a Fir Baíth ⁊c.[3]

'Tarrochair far céle,' or Fergus. 'Eprid in n-ícfa in fer sin [1800]
i mbárach?'

'Ícfa écin,' or Cú Chulaind.

Foídid Cú Chulaind atheroch Láeg do fis scél dús [4]cia cruth imthá-
thar[4] isin dúnud ⁊ in bo beó Fer Báeth.

Asbert Luigid: [1805]

'Atbath Fer Báeth ⁊ tiat[5] Cú Chulaind iar n-úair [6]dom acallaim[6].'

       [7]Comrac Láríne meic Nóis inso[7]

'N Ech úaib i mbárach co ellom ar cend far céle,' or Lugaid.
    'Ní faigébthar-side etir,' or Ailill[8], 'acht má dorónaid[9] céill[a]
occai[10].   Nách fer dotháeti chucaib, tabraid fín dó corop [1810]

---

[a] .i. ceilg [M]

[1-1] do com bar *last word written over erasure* Y, do combar W, do combra
rann C   [2] Fíthi U W, fichi Y, Fichti C   [3] a Fir et reliqua Y W, a
Fir C   [4-4] cia cruth mbotha Y W, ciabo cruth botha C   [5] tiad C.
dotháet U Y W   [6] *sic* Y W C, do chomacallaim U   [7-7] *between
columns* U, *om.* Y W C   [8] Medb C   [9] doronad *with* o *added under* n Y,
doronta C   [10] .i. ceilcc *add.* C

maith a menma, ⁊ asbert[h]ar friss "iss ed nammá fil[1] dond fín tucad a Crúachnaib, rosáeth linni do bith-siu for uisciu isin dúnad," ⁊ doberthar Findabair fora desreth ⊓ asberthar "ragaid chucut día tuicce cend ind ríastairthe dúinni." '

[1815] [2]No foíté[2] co cach láth ngaile a aidche, ⊓ [3]ro ráté[3] fris aní sin.

74ª No gonad-som | cach fer díb a úair. Ní féta nech leó ara chend assennad.

Congairther dóib Láríne mac Nóiss olla n-aile bráthair side do Lugaid ríg Muman. Ba mór a úallchas. Doberar fín dó ⊓ doberar [1820] Findabair fora desraid. Tossécai Medb a ndís.

'Is mellach lim ind lánamain ucut,' ol sí. 'Ba coindme[4] a comrac.'

'Ní géb-sa[5] dít ém,' or Ailill. 'Ra mbia día tuca cend ind ríastairthe dam-sa.'

'Dobér immorro,' ar Láríne.

[1825] Tic Lugaid fo sodain.

'Cate lib i mbárach fer i n-áth?'

'Téite Láríne,' or Ailill.

Dotháet Lugaid íarom do acallaim Con Culaind. Conrecat[5a] i nGlend[5a] Fir Baíth. Ferais cechtar de comráichne[6] fri araile.

[1830] 'Is dó dodeochad dot acallaim,' or Lugaid. 'Atá at[h]echmatud drúth sotal sund ucut,' ol sé. 'bráthair dam-sa, Láríni a ainm. Dober bréc[7] immón ingin cétnai. Fort chotach didiu ní ruba é, nacham fácba-sa cen brát[h]air. [8]Ár is airi doberar-som chucut-su ar dáig co forgénmaís ar ndís debuid[8]. Maith lem chena cé no slaiss co [1835] léir ar is dar mo therthogu théite.'

Téit Láríne ara bárach ar cend Con Culaind ⊓ ind ingen inna farrad día nertad. Danethat[9] Cú Chulaind íarom cen arm laiss. Tallaid-side[10] a arm n-airi ar écin. Gabaid íarom eter a dí láim ⊓ cotmeil ⊓ fochrotha con sephaind a channebor ass combo búadartha [1840] in t-áth día chacc ⊓ combo thrúallnethe aér na cethararda dia dendgur. Ocus focheird co mbaí iter dá láim Lugdach.

Céin robo beó ní thaudchaid a brú for cóir. Ní robai cen clíabgalar. Níro loing cen airchissecht. Iss é óenfer ar apaide adroinni drochtérnam[11] úad-som di neoch cotránic friss ar Tána[12].

---

[1] and *add.* Y W C   [2-2] no faidti t *added overhead* Y, No foidhtiu C
[3-3] no raiti Y C   [4] condme (*mark over first stroke of* m *might suggest reading* contine *as printed in TBC*[2]) Y, coindfe C   [5] gebasa Y   [5a-5a] *sic* C
im Glend U Y   [6] comraichne failte Y   [7] uimbi *add.* C   [8-8] *om.* Y
[9] donetat Y, donetha C   [10] *sic* C, dolodside U, doloidsidi Y
[11] drochernam Y C   [12] Tana Bo Cuailge Y, an Tana C

[1]Imacallaim na Mórígna fri Coin Culaind inso[1]　　　　1845

CO n-aca Cú in n-ócben chuci[2] co n-étuch cach datha impe ⁊ delb roderscaigthe furri.

'Cé taí-siu ?' or Cú Chulaind.

'Ingen Búain[3] ind ríg,' or sí. 'Dodeochad chucut-su[4]. Rot charus ar th'airscélaib, ⁊ tucus mo šeótu lim ⁊ mo indili.'　　　　1850

'Ní maith ém ind inbuid tonnánac, nachis olc ar mbláth, amin gorti. Ní haurussa dam-sa dano comrac fri banscáil céin no mbeó isind níth so.'

[5]'Bidim chobair-se dait-siu[a] oc sudiu.'[5]

'Ní ar thóin[6] mná dano gabus-sa inso.'　　　　1855

'Bid[7] ansu dait-siu,' or sí, 'in tan dorag-sa ar do chend oc comruc frisna firiu. Dorag-sa i rricht escongan fót c[h]ossaib issind áth co taíthis.'

'Dóchu lim ón oldás ingen ríg. Not géb-sa,' or sé, 'im ladair [8]co mmebsat t'asnai[8] ⁊ bia fónd anim sin coro secha bráth bennachtan 1860 fort.'

'Timorc-sa[9] [10]in cethri[10] forsind áth do dochum-sa, i rricht soide glaisse.'

'Léicfe-sa cloich dait-siu asin tailm co commart[11] do šúil it
74[b] c[h]ind, ⁊ bía fónd anim [sin] coro | secha bráth bennachtan fort.'　　　　1865

'Dorag-sa[12] dait i rricht samaisci maíle derce riasind éit co memsat ort forsna iláthu ⁊ forsna háthu ⁊ forsna linniu ⁊ [13]ním aircecha-sa[13] ar do chend.'

'Tolécub-sa cloich deit-siu,' or sé, 'co mmema do fergara[14] fót, ⁊ bia fóind anim sin coro secha bráth bennachtan fort.'　　　　1870

La sodain téit úad.

[15]Combad sechtmain dó-som for Áth Grencha ⁊ dofuitted fer cach laí i nÁth Grencha laiss .i. i nÁth Darteisc.[15]

---

[a] .i. dogén-sa congnom latt [M]

[1-1] *in marg.* U, *om.* Y C　　　　[2] cuchi U　　　　[3] *om.* C　　　　[4] cuchutsu U
[5-5] bid *in* chobairse daitsiu oc sudiu U, bia achobera daitseo oc suidiu
Y, bidhim cobraisi doitsi occ suidhiu .i. dogénsa coboir .i. congnamh C
[6] oin, *which looks very like* ain, *foll. by long erasure* Y　　　　[7] *sic* Y C.
bi U　　　　[8-8] co mbebois t'asno innat C　　　　[9] *sic MSS.: read* timorr-sa ?
[10-10] na ceithri Y, na cetro C　　　　[11] *sic* U, ma Y, mmuidhe C　　　　[12] *sic*
C, Torach U, Torrachsa Y　　　　[13-13] ní n-airccébhasa C　　　　[14] gerrgaire C
[15-15] *om.* Y

6

[1]Aided Lóich meic Mo Femis inso sís[1]

1875 GEssa[2] Lóch dano [3]mac Emonis[3] amal a chéliu ⁊ dorairngired dó comméte Maige Murthemne di mín Maigi Aí ⁊ timtacht dá fer déac ⁊ carpat secht[4] cumal, ⁊ nírbo fíu[5] laiss comrac fri gilla[6]. Baí bráthair laiss, Long mac Ebonis cadessin. Dobreth do ṡudiu a tinscra cétna iter ingen ⁊ dechelt ⁊ carpat ⁊ tír.

1880 Téit-side[7] ar cend Con Culaind. Gontai Cú Chulaind co tobrad a marb ar beólu a bráthar .i. Lóich.

Asbert-side dano dá fessed acht combad[8] fer ulc[h]ach[9] nod ngonad, [10]no mairfed-som hé[10] ind.

[11]'Berid grem catha chuci,' ar Medb fria muintir, 'tarsin n-áth 1885 aníar co ndigsid taris, ⁊ brister fír fer fair.'

Tíagait na secht Mane mílid i tosoch conid n-accatar for brú ind átha aníar. Gabaid-som a díllait n-óenaig imbi in láa sin. Iss and fordringtís na mná na firu día déscin.

'Is sáeth dam,' or Medb, 'nách accim in gilla imma n-ágar sund.'

1890 'Níba sláiniu de latt do menma,' or Léthrend echaire Ailella, 'día n-aicigther.'

Dotháet íarom dochum ind átha [12]amal buí:[12]

'Cía fer sucut, a Ḟerguis?' or Medb.

r.[13] 'Gilla araclich claideb co scíath ar búaib mór serig ar mnáib 1895 feraid fodil di fer lessaib ar óenathib Ulad imgóet caín fera fodil di fobaid ríg than m̄c̄ dían día ngarar Muirthemne Mag másu Cháuland Cú.'

Fordring Medb dano na firu la sodain día déscin.[11]

Is and sin asbertatár na mná fri Coin Culaind dogníthe a c[h]ut-1900 biud isin dúnud úair nád baí ulcha laiss ⁊ nícon téigtís dagóic acht siriti ara chend. Ba hassu dó ulcha smérthain do dénam leiss. [14]Conid gní-som[14] aní sin [15]ar dáig cuingthi[15] comraic fri fer .i. fri Lóch.

[16]Gabais íarom Cú C[h]ulaind lán duirnd dind ḟeór ⁊ [17]dichac[h]ain[a] 1905 fair[17], combo hed domuined cách combo ulc[h]a baí lais[18].

_____

[a] .i. bricht [H]

[1-1] Comrac Lóich annso C   [2] Dogeassa Y, geisi C   [3-3] mac Mo Fefis Y   [4] tri _secht_ C   [5] uisiu, ui _written overhead_ Y, fiú C [6] namulcach _add._ C   [7] Téitsidé U   [8] bid Y, bad C   [9] ualach Y, ulach .i. ulcach C   [10-10] not muirfidsamh C   [11-11] _om._ Y [12-12] amal mbui C, aṁ _deleted by l.h. and a added with caret mark_ [13] _between cols._ U, _om._ C   [14-14] conid gnidsom U, conid dignisom Y, conit ngnisiṁ C   [15-15] do chuinchid Y C   [16] H _interpolation begins_ [17-ᵢ7] docachain bricqt fair C   [18] fair C

'Fír,' or in bantroc[h]t, 'is ulc[h]ach Cú Chulaind. Is cubaid do niaid comrac fris.'

Oc gressacht Lóich ón dorigénsat-som aní sin.

'Ní digéon-sa[1] comrac co cend [2]secht lathi[2] ó 'ndiu fris,' for Lóch.

'Ní cubaid dúinni cen fóbairt ind fir frisin ré sin,' ol Medb.   1910

'Tabram [3]fían láech[3] cach n-aidchi do ṡeilc fair [4]dús in tairsimmis | a báegal.'

75ᵃ

Dogníther íarom samlaid. Dothéged fían láech cach n-aidchi do ṡeilg fair-sium[4] ⁊ nos gonad-som uli. It é seo immorro anmand na fer dorochratar and: secht Conaill, secht nÓengusa, secht nÚargusa 1915 secht Celtri, ocht Féic, deich nAilella, deich nDelbaíth, deich Tasaig. It é insin gníma na sechtmaine sin dó-som i nÁth Grencha.

Conniacht[a][5] Medb comarli dús cid dogénad fri Coin Culaind ar ba aincis mór lei an ro bíth leis día slógaib[6]. Is í comarli arránic áes féig forúallach do chor i n-óenfecht día ṡaichthin[7] in tan ticfad i 1920 n-airis dála [8]día accallaim-si[8], ar baí [9]aires[b] dála[9] dissi ara bárach fri Coin Culaind do dénam sída celci fris día t[h]arrachtain. Foíti-si techta úadi dia ṡaig[thin] [10]arco[10] tíasad 'na coinni, ⁊ bad amlaid tíasad ⁊ sé anarma fo déig ní[11] ragad-si acht sí cona bantrocht dia áil-seom.   1925

Ludi in techtairi .i. Traigt[h]rén co airm i mboí Cú C[h]ulaind ⁊ adfét do ait[h]esc Medba. Bágais Cú Chulaind co ndingned samlaid.

'Ced ón, cinnas as áil duit-siu tec[h]t i ndáil Medba i mbárach, a C[h]ú Chulaind?' or Láeg.   1930

[12]Amal conniacht[c] Medb dano[12], ol Cú Chulaind.

'At móra glonna Medbi,' ol in t-ara. 'Atágur lám ar cúl aci.'

75ᵇ

| 'Cinnas as dénta dún samlaid?' for sé.

'Do chlaideb fót choim,' ol in t-ara, 'arnachat fagthar i mbáegul, ár ní dlig láech a enecland dia mbé i n-écmais a arm. Conid cáin 1935 midlaig no ndlig fón samail sin.'

'Déntar amlaid íarom,' ol Cú Chulaind.

Is and íarom baí in chomdál i nArd Aignech frisi ráter Fóchaird indiu.

Tic íarom Medb isin dáil ⁊ inlis [13]cethri firu déc[13] dia sainmuintir 1940 fessin do neoch [14]as dech engnomma baí[14] díb fora chind. At iat

---

ᵃ .i. arranic [H]   ᵇ .i. comdal [H]   ᶜ .i. ro cuinnig [H]

1 dingensa C   2-2 sechtmoine C   3-3 fíallach C   4-4 om. by homveoteleuton C   5 coniacht .i. ranic C   6 muintir C   7 saighid C   8-8 diaccallaimsi U, die soightin C   9-9 aires .i. comdal C   10-10 ara C   11 nad C   12-12 Amal condíacht Medb .i. ro cuindig C   13-13 fiche fer C   14-14 ba ferr engnamh C

so iat-side: dá Glas Sinna dá mac Buccridi, dá Ardáin dá mac Licce,
dá Glas Ogma dá mac Cruind, Drúcht ⁊ Delt ⁊ Dathen, Téa ⁊
Tascur ⁊ Túalang, Taur[1] ⁊ Glese.

1945 Tic íarom Cú Chulaind ina dáil. Ataregat ind fir dó. Srethait[2]
[3]cethri goí déac[3] i n-óenfecht fair. Nos dítin Cú íarom conná riacht
toind nó fóescham[4] fair. Imsoí fóithib íarom ⁊ [5]marbthus íat a
cethri firu déac. Conid íat sin cethri fir déac Fócherda[5], ⁊ is iat fir
Chrónige ar isin Chrónig oc Foc[h]eird ro bíta.

1950 Conid de asbert Cú Chulaind:

.r.[6]

76ª

'Fó[a] mo cherd láechdachta |
benaim béimend ágmara
for slóg síabra sorchaidi.
Certaim ág fri ilslúagaib
1955 im díth erred anglondach
sceó Medbi ⁊ Ailella..
[7]altai drochrún derchoblid
gossa dubrúin banmassa[7]
cengait celga úargossa
1960 fri[8] ág erred anglonnach
congeib dagrún degmessa
oc fir dia ndich dagarliud[8]
im anglonna fó.'

fó .m.

1965 Combad de sin dano rod lil a n-ainm as Focherd dond inud .i.
fó cerd .i. maith in cherd gascid[9] donecmaic do Choin Culaind and
sin.

Tánic dano Cú Chulaind ⁊ dosnetarraid oc gabáil dúnaid ⁊ bíthus
dá Daigri ⁊ da Ánli ⁊ cethri Dúngais Imlich díb. Gabais dano Medb
1970 for gressacht Lóich andaide.

'Mór in cutbiud dait,' for sí, 'in fer ro marb do bráthair do bith
oc díthugud ar slóig cen techt do chomrac fris, ar is derb lind ní
déma siriti bras birda [10]na letheti út[10] fri bruth ⁊ feirg niad [11]do
let[h]eti-siu[11], ⁊ dano is óenmummi forcetail conrotacht dán dúib.'

76ᵇ

| [12]Tánic dano Lóch i n-agid Con Culaind do dígail a bráthar
[13]fair, ar donadbacht dó ba ulcha boí lais[13].

---

[a] .i. maith   [7] .i. oca mbí degbríathar [H]

[1] Tortor C   [2] sretais U, srethitt C, [srethaid Rec. III]   [3-3] fiche
gai C   [4] faoscal C   [5-5] marbius fiche fer Focherdai C   [6] between
cols. U, om. C   [7-7] Altaie drochrun dercoiblead | gosai dibruin banmassa
C, [Rec. III]   [8-8] om. C   [9] laochdachta C   [10-10] na a leithéit
sút C, [mar é Rec. III]   [11-11] amar tusae C, [Rec. III]   [12] Y resumes
[13-13] om. Y

'Tair dond áth úachtarach,' or Lóch. 'Nípá isind áth escomon sa condricfem, ¹áit hi torchair Long.'

Ó thánic íarom do saigid ind átha,¹ bibsat² ind fir na bú tairis.

'Bíaid tart eisc sund indiu,' or Gabrán fili.   1980

Is de atá Áth Darteisc³ ┐ Tír Mór Darteisc³ ⁴ó sin forsin phurt sin.⁴

⁵Ó ro chomraicset íarom ind fir forsind áth ┐ ó ro gabsat oc glíaid ┐ oc imesorcain and ┐ ó ro gab cách díb for trúastad a chéli⁵, focheird ind escongon trí olᵃ im c[h]ossa Con Culaind co mboí ⁶fáen fortarsna⁶ isind áth ina ligu. Danautatᵇ⁷ Lóch cosin chlaidiub ⁸combu 1985 chróderg in t-áth día fulriud⁸.

⁸'Olc ón óm,' for Fergus, 'a ngním sin hi fíadnaisi námat⁸! ⁹Gressed nech úaib, a firu,' for sé fria muintir, 'in fer nár tháeth i n-ascid⁹.'

⁸Atraig Bricriu Nemthenga mac Carbatha ┐ gabais for gressacht 1990 Con Culaind⁸.

'Ro scáich do nert¹⁰,' ol sé¹¹, ⁸in tan is⁸ bratán bec dattrascair in tan dofil Ultu asa ces chucut. ¹²Dolig duit gním n-erred do gabáil fort hi fíadnaisi fer nÉrend ┐ láech ansa do¹³ dingbáil a gaisciud fón samail [sin]¹².' ¹⁴ | 1995

La sodain atraig ┐ benaid in n-escongain co mebdatár a hasnai indi ┐ comboing in cethri darsna slúagu sair ar écin co mbertatár a puple inna n-adarcaib lasa torandcless darigénsat in dá láth gaile isind áth.

Tanautat-som¹⁵ in tsod meic tíre. Doimairg na bú fair síar. Léicid-som cloich asa tailm co mebaid a súil ina cind.   2000

Téite i rricht samaisce maíle derge¹⁶, Muitti riasna búaib forsna linni ┐ na háthu. Is and asbert-som:

¹⁷'Ní airciuᶜ¹⁷ a n-átha la linni¹⁸.

Léicid-seom cloich don tsamaisc maíl deirg co memaid a gergara¹⁹ foí.   2005

²⁰Cachain laíd la sodain:

    'M'óenurán dam ar étib

    sech nís n-étaim nís léicim

    atú ar tráthaib úaraib²¹

    m'óenurán ar iltúathaib.   2010

77ᵃ (margin)

ᵃ .i. tri curu [H]   ᵇ .i. búalis [H]   ᶜ .i. ni rochim

¹⁻¹ om. Y   ² bibsad Y with a faint letter (d?) over the second b, bidgsat C
³ Tarteisc Y C   ⁴⁻⁴ om. Y C   ⁵⁻⁵ om. Y, O ro gabsat occ gliaid ┐ acc imesarccain and C   ⁶⁻⁶ om. Y C   ⁷ danuatat Y, tanuat .i. buailis C
⁸⁻⁸ om. Y   ⁹⁻⁹ gresid in fer or Fergus fria muinter Y   ¹⁰ bruth Y C
¹¹ Bricriu Y   ¹²⁻¹² om. Y   ¹³ dod C   ¹⁴ H interpolation ends
¹⁵ Donautatsom Y   ¹⁶ riasin eit add. C   ¹⁷⁻¹⁷ ní airciu .i. ni rochim C
¹⁸ ┐ rla add. C   ¹⁹ gergairi Y, gerrgairiu C   ²⁰ This passage not here
in C which instead places Rec. II version later after death of Lóch   ²¹ moraib Y

Aprad nech fri Conchobar
cía domíssed níbo rom
rucsat Meic Mágach a¹ mbú
conda randsat etarru.

2015   Ro bíi cosnom im óenchend
acht nád lassa nach óenc[h]rand
día mbetis a dó nó a trí
lasfaitis a n-athinni.

   ²Bec nárom nítsat ind fir
2020   ar imad comlaind óenfir
ní rubaim níth n-erred n-án
immar atú m'óenurán.²

                      m'óenurán .d.

    Is and sin trá dogéni Cú Chulaind frisin Mórrígain a tréde dorairn-
2025 gert di hi Táin Bó Regamna, ⁊ fichid Lóch ³isind áth³ cosin gaí bolga
doléic in t-ara dó lasin sruth. Gaibthi dó co lluid hi timthirecht a
chuirp, ar ba conganchnes oc comruc fri fer ⁴boí la Lóch.⁴

   'Teilg traigid dam!' or Lóch.

   ⁵Doléici-seom⁵ Cú Chulaind combo tharis docer. Is de atá Áth
2030 Traiged i Tír Mór^a⁶.

   Is and sin conbocht fír fer fair-seom a llá sin día lotar in cóicfer
cucai-seom fón oínme .i. dá C[h]rúaid, dá Chalad, Derothor. Nos
ngeogain Cú Chulaind a óenur. Is hé sin Cóicsius Focherda ⁊
Cóicer Óengoirt. Nó is cóic lá déc iss ed ro boí Cú Chulaind hi
2035 Focheird, conid de atá Cóicnas⁷ Focherda isin Tána. Dosmbidc⁸
Cú Chulaind a Delga conná cáemnacair anmanna de duniu ná
cethir ronucad a ainech secha fadess iter Delga ⁊ muir.

       ⁹Slánugud na Mórrígna inso⁹

O Cond ai[th]scís mór sin trá do C[h]oin Culaind, danarraid in
2040   Mórrígan i ndelb na sentainne caillige ⁊ sí cáech losc, oc
   blegon bó triphne. Coniacht-som dig furri. Dobert-si
blegon sini dó.

ᵃ benaid Cu Chulaind a c[h]end de iar sudi [add. between cols. H]

¹ ar Y   ²⁻² om. Y   ³⁻³ cusan claidim ⁊ Y, isin ath cosin claidhem
no C   ⁴⁻⁴ om. Y C   ⁵⁻⁵ daleici son Y, doleicte C   ⁶ conadh i
aghaidh co nuige sin add. C   ⁷ Coicsnas Y, Coicndes C   ⁸ sic Y C,
dosmídc U   ⁹⁻⁹ in marg. U, om. Y

'I n-iam[1] bid slán doduc!' ol Cú Chulaind. 'Bennacht dé ⁊ andé
fort!' ol sé.

Déi leó-som in t-áes cumachta, andéi immorro in t-áes trebtha[2].   2045
Íctha a cend-si íarom combo slán[3].

Dobeir blegon indala sini combo slán [4]a súil[4].

77ᵇ   Dobeir blegon in tress sini combo slán | [5]a fergaire[5].

[6]Combad ed atberad-som in [7]cech ní díb sin :

'Bráth bennachtan[8] fort!' or sé[6].   2050

'Atbirt frim trá,' or in Mórrígan, 'ním bíad íc lat co bráth.'

'Acht rofessin[d] combad tú,' ol Cú Chulaind, 'nít ícfaind [9]tria
bith sír[9].

—Combad[10] Ríamdrong Con Culaind [11]for Tarthesc[11] ainm in
sceóil sea isin Tána[12].   2055

Is and sin dosiacht[13] Fergus fora glinne arná bristé fír fer [14]for
Coin Culainn[14]. Is and sin íarom etha[15] ar galaib oenḟir[16] cuici [17]co
ngeogain cóicer[17] Cind[18] Coriss nó Dúin Chind Coross .i. Delgu Murthemne ind inbuid se.

Geogain Cú Chulaind and sin Fota ina roí, Bó Mailce fora áth, 2060
Salach ina imliuch, Muinne ina dind, Lúar i lLethberaib, [19]Fer
Toíthle hi Toíthlib[19]. Hit é a n-anmand na tíri sin co bráth, cach
bale i torc[h]air cach fer díb sin.

Geogain Cú Chulaind dano Traig ⁊ Dornu ⁊ Dernu, Col ⁊ Mebul ⁊
Eraise, for Áth Tíre Móir de síu oc Méthiu ⁊ Cheithiu. Trí[20] druíd 2065
insin ⁊ a teóra mná.

Iar sin tra foídis Medb cét fer día sainmuintir do guin Con Culaind.
Nos geogain-seom uli íarom for Áth Chéit Chúile.

Is and asbert Medb:

[21]'Is cuillend[a][21] dúnd ém guin ar muintire.'   2070

Is de atá Glaiss Chráu ⁊ Cuillend Cind Dúin ⁊ Áth Céit Chúle.

ᵃ .i. is col lind [H]

---

[1] *om.* C, aniam Y   [2] No dombertsom brath bennachtan furi sic in ceteris
add. Y   [3-3] i suil (= a súil) *add.* C   [4-4] a gerrgare C   [5-5] a hasnai C
[6-6] *om.* Y   [7] fiad C   [8] de ⁊ andee *add.* C   [9-9] *om.* Y C
[10] no comad Y, conidh C   [11-11] for Tartescc Y, *om.* C   [12] agus
a Tarteisc tucath *add.* C   [13] *sic* Y siacht U C   [14-14] forsin
ngilli C   [15] Cú *add.* U (*scribal misreading of* cuci)   [16] óenfer U
[17-17] coicer U, cuici *added above line* Y, *and after this a long omission to*
l. 2311, ara cenn co ngeogoin coiccer C   [18] *sic* C, Cend U   [19-19] Fer
Tóithle hi Tóithlib U   [20] *sic* C, Di U   [21-21] Is cuillend .i. is col
leind C

¹In Carpat Serda ⁊ in Breslech Mór Maige Murthemne inso¹

RO gabsat trá cethri chóiced Hérend dúnad ⁊ lonngport isin
Breslig Móir i mMaig Murthemne, ⁊ ro láiset a n-ernail búair
2075 ⁊ braite seoc[h]o fodess hi Clithar Bó Ulad.

Gabais Cú Chulaind icond fert i lLercaib i comfocus dóib, ⁊ ataís a
ara tenid dó tráth nóna na haidchi sin .i. Lóeg mac Ríangabra.
Itchonnairc-seom úad grístatinem na n-arm nglanórda úas chind
cethri cóiced nÉrend re funiud néll na nóna. Dofánic ferg ⁊ luinni
2080 mór ic aicsin in tslóig re hilar a bidbad [⁊] re himad a námat. Ro gab
a dá sleig ⁊ a scíath ⁊ a c[h]laideb. Crothis a scíath ⁊ cresaigis a
slega ⁊ bertnaigis² a chlaidem, ⁊ dobert a srem³ caurad asa brágit
coro recratár bánánaig ⁊ boccánaig ⁊ geniti glinni ⁊ demna aeóir re
úathgráin na gáre ⁴dosbertatár ar aird⁴. ⁵Cordas mesc ind
2085 Némain forsin tslóg⁵. Dollotár i n-armgrith cethri chóiced Érend
im rennaib a sleg ⁊ a n-arm fodessin co n-erbaltatár cét láech díb do
úathbas ⁊ cridenes ar lár in dúnaid ⁊ in longpairt in n-aidchi sin.

Dia mbaí Láeg and co n-acca ní, in n-óenfer dar fíartharsna in
dúnaid fer nÉrend anairtúaid cach ndíriuch ina dochum.

2090 'Óenfer sund chucund innossa, a Chúcán,' or Láeg.
78^a 'Cinnas | fir and sin?' or Cú Chulaind.

'Ní handsa. Fer caín mór and dano. Berrad lethan laiss.
⁶Folt casbude fair⁶. Brat úanide i forcipol immi. Cassán gelairgit
isin brot úassa bruinne. Léne de sról ríg fo dergindliud do dergór i
2095 custul fri gelcnes co glúnib dó. Dubscíath co calathbúali findruni
fair. Sleg cóicrind ina láim. Foga fogablaigi inna farrad. Ingnad
ém reb ⁊ ábairt ⁊ adabair dogní, acht ní saig nech fair ⁊ ní saig-seom
for nech feib ⁷nachas faiced nech hé⁷.

'Is fír sin, a daltán,' for sé. 'Cia dom chartib síthc[h]aire-sa sein
2100 dom airchiseacht-sa dáig ar bíth foretatár-som in t-imned már inam
fuil-sea m'óenur i n-agid cethri n-ollchóiced nÉrend ar Táin Bó
Cúalngi don chur sa.'

Ba fír ém do Choin Chulaind anní hísin. A nad-ránic in t-ócláech
airm i mboí Cú Chulaind, argládais ⁊ airchissis de.

2105 'Ferda sin, a Chú Chulaind,' ar sé.
⁸'Ní mór side etir⁸,' for Cú Chulaind.
'Dabér-sa dano cobair dait,' ar in t-ócláech.

---

¹⁻¹ *between cols.* U   ² bertaiges C   ³ srém U, reim C   ⁴⁻⁴ *sic*
U, dosmbertatar C [do-rinde St. doberadh ar aird Rec III]   ⁵⁻⁵ cor
mebaid ind [N]emuin forsin sluagh C   ⁶⁻⁶ os e casbuide C   ⁷⁻⁷ nachat
n-acathar nech isin dunath cehtre n-oldcoiced nErenn C   ⁸⁻⁸ Ferdai
eiccein C, [nim fhóir sidhe Rec. III]

[1]'Cía tai-siu[1] eter ?' or Cú Chulaind.

'Iss messe do athair a ssídib .i. Lug mac Ethlend.'

'It tromda dano na fuli form-sa. Ba héim dam [2]mo íc[2].'   2110

'Cotail-siu sin bic, a Chú Chulaind,' or in t-ócláech, 'do throm-
thort[h]im cotulta hicond ferta Lerga co cend teóra láa ⁊ teóra
n-aidchi, ⁊ firfat-sa[3] forsna slógaib in n-airet sin.'

Canaid a chéle ferdord dó, contuli friss co n-accae nách crecht
[4]and ropo glan[4].   2115

Is and asbert Lug:

        [5].r. Éli Loga inso sís[5]

       'Atraí, a meic mór Ulad

       fót sláncréchtaib curetha

       fri náimtiu fer melldarath   2120

       móradaig todonathar

       dia ferragaib sligethar

       slúaig immenard nerethar

       fortacht a síd sóerfudut

       issin mruig ar conathaib   2125

       cot anmuim arfucherthar

       fóchiallathar óengillae

       arclith ar búaib báifedae

       slig delb silsa ríut.

       [6]Ni fil leó do nertsáegul   2130

       fer do baraind bruthaigte

       co niurt for do lochtnamtib

       [7]cing it charput[7] comglinni

       is iar sin atrai.'

                atrai .a.m.[6]   2135

Teóra lá ⁊ teóra n-aidchi baí Cú Chulaind ina chotlod. Bá dethbir
són ém ce ro baí do mét in chotulta boí do mét na a[th]scísi. Ón
lúan íar samain sainrud cosin cétaín íar n-imolg níro chotail Cú
Chulaind frisin ré sin [8]acht mad maní[8] chotlad fithisin mbic fria gaí
íar medón midlaí ⁊ a chend fora dor[n]d ⁊ a dor[n]d ima gaí ⁊ a gaí   2140
fora glún, acht ic slaidi ⁊ ic slechtad ⁊ ic airlech ⁊ ic esorcain cethri
n-ollchóiced nÉrend frisin ré sin. Is and sin focherd in láech síde
lossa ⁊ lubi íci ⁊ slánsén i cnedaib ⁊ i créchtaib, i n-áladaib ⁊ i n-ilgonaib
78[b] | Con Culaind, co ternó Cú Chulaind ina chotlud cen ráthugud dó etir.

1-1 Cia tusae C, [Cía thusa eter Rec. III]   2-2 ind ic (= a n-ícc) C
3 fífatsa U, firfatsai C, [firbat-sa LL]   4-4 ron both pa hoghslan C, [ann
rob oghlan Rec. III] *read* and ropa ógslán   5-5 *in marg.* U, [éle Lugha
andso sís inasdech Rec. III]   6-6 *in ras.* H [*also in* Rec. III]   7-7 cingith
earpat U cing at carput C   8-8 mina C, [acht mádh mini Rec. III]

²¹⁴⁵ Is í sein trá amser i llotár in macrad atúaid ó Emain Macha trí
choícait mac ríg do Ultaib im Follamain mac Conchobair ⁊ dosberat
teóra catha dona slúagaib co torchratar a trí comlín leó ⁊ torcratár
in macrad dano acht Fallamain mac Conchobair. Bágais Fallamain
ná ragad ar cúlu co hEmain co bruinni mbrátha ⁊ betha co mberad
²¹⁵⁰ cend Ailella leiss cosin mind óir boí úaso. Nírbo réid remi-seom¹
aní sin, úair dofairthetár dá mac Bethe meic Báin, dá mac mumme
⁊ aite do Ailill, ⁊ rod gonsat co torchair leó.

Conid Aided na Macraide Ulad insin ⁊ Fallamna meic Conchobair.

Cú Chulainn immorro baí ina śúantairthim cotulta co cend teóra
²¹⁵⁵ láa ⁊ teóra n-aidchi hicond ferta i lLergaib. Atracht Cú Chulaind iar
sin asa chotlud ⁊ dobert láim dara agid ⁊ dorigni rothmúal² corcra de³
ó mulluch co talmain, ⁊ ba nert leiss a menma ⁊ tíasad i n-óenach nó
i tochim nó bandáil nó i cormthech nó i prímóenach do priméonaigib
Érend.

²¹⁶⁰ 'Cia fot atú-sa isin chotlud sa innosi, a óclaích?' ar Cú Chulaind.

'Trí lá ⁊ trí aidchi,' for in t-ócláech.

'Ron⁴ mairg-sea de side!' or Cú Chulaind.

'Cid de ón?' or in t-ócláech.

'Na slóig cen [ś]ópairt frisin ré sin,' ar Cú Chulaind.

²¹⁶⁵ 'Ní filet-som ón óm etir,' or in t-ócláech.

'Ceist, ⁵cia arránic⁵?' ar Cú Chulaind.

'Lotar in macrad antúaid ó Emain Macha trí choícait mac im
Follomain mac Conchobair do maccaib ríg Ulad ⁊ dobertsat teóra
catha dona slúagaib ri hed na trí lá ⁊ na trí n-aidchi hi taí-siu it
²¹⁷⁰ chotlud ⁶innossa, ⁊ torcratár a trí comlín leó ⁊ torchratár in macrad
acht Follomain mac Conchobair⁶. Bágais Follomain ⁷co mbérad
cend Ailella ⁊ nírbo réid dó-som ón ar ro marbad⁷.'

'Apraind ná bá-sa for mo nirt de side, úair día mbeind-se for mo
nirt ni tóethsitís in macrad feb dorochratár ⁊ ní tóethsad Follomain
²¹⁷⁵ mac Conchobair.'

'Cossain archena, ⁸a Chúcán⁸, ní haisc dot inchaib ⁊ ní táir dot
gasciud.'

'Airis-[s]iu sein innocht dún, a óclaíg,' or Cú Chulainn,' arco
ndíglom malle in macraid forsna slúagaib.'

²¹⁸⁰ '⁹Nád anéb om ale⁹,' for in t-ócláech, 'uair cid mór do chomramaib
gaili ⁊ gascid dogné nech ¹⁰hit arrad-so¹⁰ ní fair bías a nós nách a allud
nách a irdarcus acht is fort-so. Is aire sin nád aniub-sa. Acht

---

¹ do som C   ² rothnuall C   ³ om. U, nde C, [dhe Rec. III]   ⁴ rom C
⁵⁻⁵ cia rodos fuaipre C   ⁶⁻⁶ om. C   ⁷⁻⁷ ⁊rla C   ⁸⁻⁸ a Chu Chulaind
uair cidat maithe C   ⁹⁻⁹ Nit ainub C   ¹⁰⁻¹⁰ at fochairsi C

imbir-seo féin do gním gascid t'óenur forsna slúagu úair ní leó atá commus t'anma don chur sa.'

'Ocus in carpat serda, a mmo phopa Laíg[1]?' ar Cú Chulaind. 'In [2185] coemnacar a innell [2]ᄀ innatá a threlom[2]? Má cotnici a innell ᄀ má dotá a threlom, [3]na n-innill[3], ᄀ mani fil a t[h]relom, nacha n-innill etir.'

Is and so[4] atracht in t-ara ᄀ ro gab a fíanerred aradnachta immi.

79ª Bá dond fíanerred aradnachta | sin ro gabastár-som immi a inar [2190] bláith bíannaide is é étrom aerda is é súata srebnaide, is é úagthe osslethair[5] [6]conná gebethar[6] ar lúamairecht lám dó anechtair. Ro gabastar-som forbrat faind taris anechtair dorigni Simón Druí do Dáir do ríg Rómán conda darat Dáir do Chonchobar conda darat Conchobar do C[h]oin Culaind conda rairbert Cú Chulaind día araid. [2195] Ro gabastar in t-ara cétna sin dano a chathbarr círach clárach cethrochair co n-ilur cach datha ᄀ cach delba dara midgúallib sechtair. Bá somassi dó-som sin ᄀ nírbo thortromad. Taraill a lám leiss in gipni ndergbudi mar bad land dergóir do brondór bruthi[7] dar or n-inneóni fri[a] étan dó [do] indchomartha a arad- [2200] nachta sech a thigerna. Ro gabastár idata[8] aurslaicthi a ech ᄀ a del intlassi ina desra. Ro gabastár éssi astuda a ech ina thúasri .i. aradna a ech [9]ina láim chlí[9] re imchommus a aradnachta.

Is and so[10] focheird a lúrecha iarnaidi intlassi immó echaib con- gebethar dóib ó thul co aurdornd[11] do gaínib ᄀ birínib ᄀ slegínib ᄀ [2205] birc[h]rúadib corbo birfocus cach fonnod isin charpat sin, corbo chonair letartha[12] cach n-ulind ᄀ cach n-ind ᄀ cach n-aird ᄀ cach n-airc[h]ind don charput sin. Is and sin focheird bricht comga dara echraid ᄀ dara chomalta connárbo léir do neoch isin dúnud ᄀ corbo léir dóib-seom cách issin dúnud. Bá deithbir ém cé focherded-som [2210] inni sin dáig ar bíth bátár teóra búada aradnachta forin n-araid in lá sin .i. léim dar boilg ᄀ foscul ndírich ᄀ imorchor ndelind.

Is and so[10] ro gab in caur ᄀ in cathmílid ᄀ in t-indellchró bodba fer talman, Cú Chulaind mac Súaltaim, ro gab a chatherred catha ᄀ com- raic ᄀ comlaind imbi[13]. Bá don c[h]atherred catha sin ᄀ chomraic ᄀ [2215] chomlaind ro gab-som immi secht cneslénti[14] fichet cíartha clártha comdlúta bítís bá thétaib ᄀ rothaib ᄀ refedaib hi custul fri[a] gelc[h]- nes dó arnacha ndec[h]rad a chond nach a chíall ó dofíced a lúth

---

[1] a Laig C   [2-2] *om.* C, [ᄀ inata a threlum leat Rec. III]   [3-3] noniinnill U
[4] sin C   [5] *sic* U, osslethar *Dipl. Ed.*   [6-6] conna gebeth C, *sic leg.*
[conach gebhedh Rec. III]   [7] brúthi U, bruintie C   [8] id fodui C
[9-9] ina láim in chli U   [10] sin C   [11] co n-egar *add.* C, [lan *add.*
Rec. III]   [12] duine *add.* C   [13] *sic* C, *om.* U [imbi LL, uimi Rec.
III]   [14] cneslesti U, cneislenti C

láthair. Ro gabastár a chathcriss curad taris anechtair do chotut-
2220 lethar crúaid choirtchide[1] do formna secht ndamseched ndartada co
ngabad dó ó thana a thaíb co tiug a ochsaille ro bíth immi ic díchur
gaí ⁊ rend ⁊ err[2] ⁊ sleg ⁊ saiget. Dáig is cumma focherditís de ⁊ mar
bad do chloich nó charraic nó congna [3]ro chíulaitís[3]. Is and sin ro
gabastár a [f]úathroic srebnaide sróill cona cimais do bánór bricc
79[b] fria fri móethíchtur a medóin. Ro ga | bastár a dond[f]úathróic
ndondlethair ndegsúata do formna cethri ndamseched ndartada cona
chathchris do cholomnaib ferb fua dara fúathróic srebnaide sróill
sechtair. Is and so ro gabastár in rígnia a chatharm catha ⁊
comraic ⁊ comlaind. Ba don chatharm chatha sin íarom[4] ro
2230 gabastar a ocht claidbíni ima [5]arm dét[5] ndrechsolus. Ro gabastar
a ocht slegíni ima sleig cóicrind[a]. Ro gabastar a ocht ngothnatha
'má goth néit[6]. Ro gabastar a ocht cletíni 'ma deil cliss. Ro
gabastar a ocht scíathu cliss imma chromscíath ndubderg ina
téged torc taiselbtha ina tul tárla[7] cona bil áithgéir ailtnidi imgéir
2235 ina hurtimcheull contescfad finna i n-aigid srotha ar áthi ⁊ ailtni-
decht ⁊ imgéri. Inbaid fogníth [8]ind óclaig[8] fáeborchless di, is
cumma imthescad dá scíath ⁊ dá sleg ⁊ dá chlaideb. Is and so[9] ro
gab a chírchathbarr catha ⁊ comraic ⁊ comlaind ima chend asa
ngáired gáir chét n-óclách do sírégem cecha cúli ⁊ cecha cerna de,
2240 dáig is cumma congáirtis de bánánaig ⁊ boccánaig ⁊ geniti glinne ⁊
demna aeóir ríam ⁊ úaso ⁊ ina imt[h]imchiull cach ed no téged re
testin fola na mmíled ⁊ [10]na n-anglond[10] sechtair. Ro chress a
c[h]eltar comga taris don tlachtdíllat Tíre Tair[n]gire dobretha
[dó][11] ó aiti druídechta.
2245 Is and so[9] cétríastartha im Choin Culaind co nderna úathbásach[12]
n-ílrechtach n-ingantach n-anaichnid de. Crithnaigset a charíni
imbi imar crand re sruth nó imar bocsimin fri sruth cach mball ⁊
cach n-alt ⁊ cach n-ind ⁊ cach n-áge de ó mulluch co talmain. Ro
láe sáebglés[13] díberge dá churp i mmedón a chrocind. Táncatár a
2250 t[h]raigthe ⁊ a luirgne ⁊ a glúne co mbátár dá éis. Táncatár a sála
⁊ a orcni ⁊ a escata co mbátár ríam remi. Táncatár tulféthi a orcan
co mbátár for tul a lurgan combá métithir muldor[n]d míled cech
mecon dermár[14] díbide. Srengtha tollféthe a mullaich co mbátár for
cóich a muineóil combá métithir cend meic mís cach mulchnoc

---

[a] ⁊ a saigetbolg [add. in marg. H]

[1] coirtighti C   [2] [iaernn LL]   [3-3] [do chiuchlaidis Rec. III]   [4] in
ras., perhaps by H, U, [om. LL]   [5-5] [cholg ndét LL]   [6] [ndét LL]
[7] [tárla LL]   [8-8] [in t-óclách LL sic leg.]   [9] [sin LL, Rec. III]
[10-10] na nananglond U, [na n-anglond LL]   [11] [sic LL] om. U, [in
asgaidh dho-son Rec. III]   [12] úathbásách U   [13] [sáebchless LL]
[14] dérmár U

dímór dírím dírecra dímesraigthe díbide. And sin dorigni cúach cera [2255]
dá gnúis ⁊ dá agid fair. Imslo[i]c indara súil dó ina chend; iss ed
mod dánas tairsed fíadchorr [a] tagraim do lár a grúade a hia[r]thor
a c[h]locaind. Sesceing a sétig co mboí fora grúad sec[h]tair.
Ríastartha a bél co úrtrachta[1]. Srengais in n-ól don fidba chnána
comtar écnaig[2] a ginchróes[3]. Táncatár a scoim ⁊ a t[h]romma co [2260]
mbátár ar etelaig ina bél ⁊ ina brágit. Benais béim n-ulgaib
leóman[4] don charput úachtarach fora forcli comba métithir molt-

80[a] chracand[5] cech slamsrúam thened doniged | ina bél asa brágit.
Roclos bloscbéimnech a chride ré chlíab imar glimnaig n-árchon hi
fotha nó mar leómain ic techta fó mathgamnaib. Atchessa [6]na [2265]
coinnli bodba ⁊[6] na cithnélla neme ⁊ na haíble tened trichemrúaid
i nnéllaib ⁊ i n-áeraib úasa chind re fiuchud na ferge fírgarge[7]
hitrácht úaso[8]. Ra chasnig a folt imma c[h]end imar craíbred
ndergscíach i mbernaid at[h]álta. Ce ro crateá rígaball fó rígthorad
immi iss ed mod dá rísad ubull díb dochum talman taris acht ro sesed [2270]
ubull for cach óenfinna and re frithchassad na ferge atracht dá
fult úaso. Atracht in lúan láith asa étun comba sithethir remithir
airnem[9] n-óclaích [10]corbo chomfota frisin sróin coro dechrastár oc
imbirt na scíath, oc brogad ind arad, oc taibleth na slóg[10]. Ardithir
immorro remithir talcithir tresithir sithidir seólc[h]rand prímlui[n]gi [2275]
móri in buinne díriuch dondfala atracht a fírchléthe a chendmullaig
hi certairdi, co nderna dubchíaich ndruídechta de amal chíaig do
rígbrudin in tan tic rí día tincur hi fescur lathe gemreta.

Iarsin ríastrad sin ríastarda im Choin Culaind is and sin doreblaing
ind err gascid ina chathc[h]arpat serda [11]co n-erraib[11] iarnaidib, cona [2280]
fáebraib tanaidib, cona baccánaib ⁊ cona birc[h]rúadib, cona thair-
birib níath, cona nglés aursolcdi, cona thair[n]gib gaíthe bítís ar
fertsib ⁊ íallaib ⁊ fithisib ⁊ folomnaib don charpat sin. [12]Is amlaid boí
in carpat sin cona chreit chróestana chróestirim chlesaird clangdírig[13] caurata ara taillfitís ocht n-airm n-indflatha co lúas faindle nó [2285]
gaíthe nó chliabaig dar róe maige. Ro suidiged in carpat sin for
dá n-echaib díana dremna dásachtacha cendbeca cruindbeca
corrbeca biruích bascind bruinnederg sesta suachinte sogabálta
sodain fo grinnib áillib a fén. Indara hech díb-side ocus sé lugaid
lúathlémnech tresmar túagmar traigmar fótmar fochorsid. In [2290]
t-ech aile ocus sé casmongach cascháel coseng seredchóel airgdech.[12]

---

[1] [urthrachda LL]   [2] [inécnaig LL Rec. III]   [3] sic U, [ginchrais
Rec. III], inchróes LL, sic leg.   [4] [leomain LL, Rec. III]   [5] [teóra
mblíadan add. LL, Rec. III]   [6-6] na kine bodba U[LL, om, St. na
coindli bodhbha Rec. III]   [7] [fírgaírbe LL]   [8] úasto U, [úaso LL]
[9] sic U[LL, airtimh St]   [10-10] [om. LL St Rec. III]   [11-11] [cona
erraib LL, cona searraib St, cona earraibh Rec. III]. Read cona serraib
[12-12] [om. LL St Rec. III]   [13] sic; read colgdírig

Is and so[1] focheird torandchless cét ⁊ torondc[h]less dá chét ⁊
torandchless trí cét ⁊ torandchless cethri cét, ⁊ tarrasair aice for
torandchless cúic cét, úair nírbo furáil less in comlín sin do thotim
²²⁹⁵ leiss ina chétchumscli ⁊ ina chétchomling catha for cethri chóiced
Hérend. Ocus dotháet ass fón cumma sin d'insaigid a námat ⁊
dobretha[2] a charpat mórthimchull cethri n-ollchóiced nÉrend
80ᵇ ammaig anechtair, ³⁊ dosbert | fóbairt bidbad fó bidbadaib foraib[3]
⁊ dobreth seól trom fora charpat ⁴⁊ dollotar rotha íarnaidi in c[h]ar-
²³⁰⁰ pait hi talmain[4] corbo leór do dún ⁊ do daingen[5] feib dollotár rotha
íarnaide in charpait hi talmain, uair is cumma atrachtatár cluid ⁊
cairthe ⁊ carrce ⁊ táthleca ⁊ murgrían in talman aird i n-aird frisna
rothaib íarndaidib súas[6] sell sechtair. Is aire focheird in circul
m[b]odba sin[7] mórthimchull cethri n-ollchóiced nÉrend ammaig
²³⁰⁵ anechtair arná teichtis úad ⁊ ná scaíltís immi coros tairsed fri
tendta fri tarrachtain na macraide forro. Ocus dotháet isin cath
innond ar medón ⁊ fáilgis fálbaigi móra do chollaib a bidbad mór-
thimc[h]oll in tslóig ammaig anechtair ⁸fo thrí[8] ⁊ dobert fóbairt
bidbad fo bidbadaib forro co torchratár bond fri bond ⁊ méde fri
²³¹⁰ méde, ba sí ⁹tiget ind árbaig[9]. Dosrimchell aridisi fa thrí in cruth
sin co farcaib cossair sessir impu fá mór- ¹⁰thmichull .i. bond trír fri
méde trír fó chúaird timchill immón dúnad. Conid Sesrech Breslige
a ainm issin Táin, ⁊ iss ed tres ndírime na Tána .i. Sesrech Breslige
⁊ Imslige Glennamnach[11] ⁊ in cath for Gárig ⁊ Irgárig. Acht ba
²³¹⁵ cumma cú ⁊ ech ⁊ dune and.

—¹²Iss ed atberat araili ro fich Lug mac Eithlend la Coin Culaind
Sesrig mBreslige[12].

Nícon fes immorro a árim ⁊ ni cumangar a rím cía lín dorochair
and do dáescorslúag, acht ro rímthé a tigernai nammá. It é seo
²³²⁰ ¹³a n-anmand-side[13] inna rurech ⁊ inna taísech .i. .r.[14] Dá Chrúaid, dá
Chalad, dá Chír, dá Chíar, dá Ecell, trí Cruim, trí Caurith, trí
Combirgi, cethri Feochair, cethri Furachair, cethri Caiss, cethri
Fotai, cúic Caurith, cúic Cermain, cúic Cobthaig, sé Saxain, sé Dáich,
sé Dári, secht Rocháid, secht Rónáin, secht Rurthig, ocht Roc[h]-
²³²⁵ laid, ocht Rochtaid, ocht Rindaich, ocht Corpri, ocht Mulaich, náe
nDaigith, náe nDári, náe nDámaig, deich Féic, deich Fiacaich, deich
Fedelmid.

---

¹ [sin LL]   ² drobretha U, [dobreth LL]   ³ [om. LL St]   ⁴⁻⁴ omitt. ?
[om. Rec. III]   ⁵ [dóibh add. Rec. III]   ⁶ súas Depl. Ed.   ⁷ [sic
LL C Rec. III], om. U   ⁸⁻⁸ [om. LL St Rec. III]   ⁹⁻⁹ [tiget a colla
LL], tiug a n-armaich C   ¹⁰ Y resumes   ¹¹ Glennammach U   ¹²⁻¹² om. Y
¹³⁻¹³ sic Y, amandside U, a n-anmand-side LL, anmann C   ¹⁴ in marg.
between cols. U, om. Y, names in three cols. U

Deich ríg ar secht[1] fic[h]tib ríg ro bí Cú Chulaind i mBresslig
Móir Maigi Murthemni.   Dírime immorro olchena di chonaib ⁊
echaib ⁊ mnáib ⁊ maccaib ⁊ mindaínib ⁊ drabarṡlóg, ar nír érno in tres ²³³⁰
fer do feraib Hérend cen chnáim lessi nó lethc[h]ind nó lethṡúil do
brisiud nó cen bithanim tria bithu betha.   ²Ocus dotháet úadib iar
sin iar tabairt in tressa sin forro, cen fuligud cen fordercad fair
féin ná fora gillu ná for ech dia echaib². |

81ᵃ   ³Túarascbáil Delba Con Culaind so³   ²³³⁵

D Otháet Cú Chulaind arna bárach do t[h]aidbriud in tṡlóig ⁊
     do thaisbénad a chrotha álgin álaind do mnáib ⁊ bantrochtaib
     ⁊ andrib ⁊ ingenaib ⁊ filedaib ⁊ áes dána, úair nír⁴ míad ná
mass leiss in dúaburdelb druídechta tárfás dóib fair ind adaig sin⁵
reme.   Is aire sin tánic do thaselbad a chrotha álgin álaind ⁶in lá sin⁶. ²³⁴⁰
    Álaind ém in mac thánic and sin do t[h]aselbad⁷ a chrotha dona
slúagaib .i. Cú Chulaind mac Soaldaim.   ⁸Faircsi trí folt⁸ fair: dond
fri toind cind, cróderg ar medón, mind órbude ardatugethar.   Caín
cocarsi ind fuilt sin co curend teóra imsrotha⁹ im c[h]lais a chúlaid,
comba samalta ⁊ órṡnáth cach finna fathmainnech forscáilte forórda ²³⁴⁵
dígrais dúalfota derscaigt[h]ech dathálaind dara formna síar sell
sechtair.   Cét cairches corcorglan do dergór órlasrach imma brágit.
Cét snáthéicne don charmocol cummascda hi timthacht fria chend.
Cethri tibri cechtar a dá grúad .i. tibre buide ⁊ tibre úane ¹⁰⁊ tibre
gorm¹⁰ ⁊ tibre corcra.   Secht ngemma do ruthin ruisc cechtar a dá ²³⁵⁰
rígrosc.   Secht meóir cechtar a dá choss, secht meóir cechtar a dá
lám co ngabáil ingni sebaic, co forgabáil ingne griúin ar cach n-aí
fo leith díib-sin¹¹.
    Gabaid-seom dano a díllat n-óenaig n-imbi in láa sin.   Baí dá
étgud immi .i. fúan caín cóir corcorglan¹² corthorach cóicdíabuil. ²³⁵⁵
Delg ¹³find findargit¹³ arna ecor d'ór intlassi úasa bánbruinni gel
imar bad lóc[h]rand lánsolusta nád chumgaitis súili doíni déicsin¹⁴ ar
gleóraidecht ⁊ glainidecht.   Clíabinar ¹⁵sróil sirecda ré chnes¹⁵
congebethar¹⁶ dó co barrúachtar a dondfúathróci donddergi ¹⁷míleta
do ṡról ríg¹⁷.   Dondscíath dondderg dondchorcra co cóicroth óir, ²³⁶⁰

¹ sé Y [LL]   ²⁻² in ras. M, om. Y [LL]   ³⁻³ in marg. U, om. Y C
[LL]   ⁴ nír uo C   ⁵ riam add. Y [LL]   ⁶⁻⁶ om. here Y   ⁷ in
la sin add. Y (misplaced)   ⁸⁻⁸ Tri fuilt batar Y [LL Rec. III]   ⁹ imrotha
Y, himsrethae C, [sretha Rec. III]   ¹⁰⁻¹⁰ om. Y   ¹¹ in ras. M, dib Y
¹² corcardai Y, [om. LL]   ¹³⁻¹³ fiudruine nó findarcaid Y   ¹⁴ a dexin
C, [a désgain Rec. III]   ¹⁵⁻¹⁵ siric srethnach Y   ¹⁶⁻¹⁶ co ngeibed C,
[condriced LL]   ¹⁷⁻¹⁷ om. C

co mbil finddruini fair. Claideb órduir[n]d intlasi co torceltaib[1] óir
derg i n-ardgabáil gaili fora chris. Gaí fota fáeborglas re faga féig
fóbartach co semmannaib[2] óir órlasrach inna farrad issin charpat.
Naí cind isindala láim dó. Deich cind isind láim aile. Ros ecroth
2365 úad frisna slúagaib. [3]Conid comram aidchi do Choin Chulaind
sin[3].

Is and sin frisócbat mná Connacht forsna buidne ┐ fordringtís
mná[4] firu do déscin crotha Con Culaind. Follaig immorro Medb a
hainech ┐ ní lámair taidbsin a gnúsi, acht boí fo damdabaig scíath ar
2370 omon Con Culaind.

Conid de sin asbert Dubthach Dóel Ulad:

.r.[5]   'Masu hé in ríastartha
                          bíait collai duíne de. |
81[b]   Beite[6] éigme im lissu
2375   bíait fuind fri airisiu.

                          Biait corthi i llechtaib
                          bid formach do rígmartaib.
                          Ní maith no fichid in cath
                          i lleirg frisin n-oennenach[7].

2380   Adchíu [8]in cruth immondnaig[8]
                          ocht cind inna chuillsennaib.
                          Adchíu fodb leiss i mbrétaib
                          deich cind ina rosétaib[9].

                          Adchíu dofócrat[10] far mná
2385   a ngnúis tarsna ergala.
                          [11]Adchíu far rígna in móir[11]
                          ní toccair dond imforráin.

                          Díambad mé bad chomarlid
                          bíad slóg imme di cach leith.
2390   [[12]coro gartigtis[13] a ré
                          mása é in ríastarde.[12]']'
          Conid and ro chan Fergus inso co n-ebairt:

---

[1] toircetlae C   [2] *sic* U, semmanaib *Dipl. Ed.*   [3-3] conid fobairt aidchi
do Choin C[h]ulaind for ceithre coicedaib hErenn dosin Y, Conid fuabairt
aidchi di Choin Culaind annsin for cetribh coiccedhoib Erenn C, do chomartha
a gascid ┐ a engnama LL   [4] Muman *add.* Y, Ulad *add.* C   [5] *in marg.* U
[6] biait Y C betit LL   [7] fóendelach LL   [8-8] in cruth imonaig Y, in
cruth imondaigh C, [chruth inn fóendelaich LL cruth inaenellaigh Rec. III]
[9] [rothedaibh Rec. III]   [10] dofócbat C *sic leg.*   [11-11] atchíu-sa far rígain
máir LL, *part of line in ras.* U   [12-12] *om.* U Y, *sic* C [LL Rec. III]   [13] gairdis C

.r.[1]   Ber ass Dubthach nDóeltengaid
                     iar cúl in tslóig na srengaid.
                     Nícon dergéni nach maith   2395
                     ó geogain in n-ingenraith

                     Ferais écht ṅdochla ṅdobail
                     guin Fiachaig meic Conchobair.
                     Nípau chaíniu rocloth dó
                     guin Corpri[2] meic Fedelmtheó.   2400

                     Rígi nUlad ní chosnai
                     mac Lugdach meic Casrubai.
                     Iss ed dogní fri doíni
                     [3]a nad rubad cosaídi[3].

                     [4]Bid olc[4] la longais nUlad   2405
                     guin a meic nád lánulach.
                     Costud Ulad má dobí
                     adsuífet[5] in n-imirgi.

                     [6]Sirfid in noíndin hi fot
                     do Ultaib co nderasot[6].   2410

                     Bíait techta scélmara[7]
                     bíait rígnai dermara
                     bíait créchtai [8]fuidb bechtai[8]
                     bíait buidne airlechtai[9].

                     Biait collai fó chossaib   2415
                     biait brain for branḟossaib
                     beti[10] fáenscéith hi lergaib
                     bid[11] cumtach do díbergaib.

---

[1] *between cols.* U   [2] [Dairi Rec. III]   [3-3] anad ruband cotsuidi Y,
a nad rubai condsaidhe C   [4-4] Ní maith C [LL Rec. III]   [5] [consaífet
LL]   [6-6] Sirfid in noindin hi fot do Ultaib naconerasot Y, Sirfett a
náonden a fot do Ulltaibh co nderrissat (*added in blank space by late hand*) C,
[Scérdait far n-óendili (.i. far nindili *marg. gloss*) i fat re nUltaib acht co
n-éirset LL, Berthar for rigraidh a fad re hUltaibh acht go n-érsed Reç. III]
[7] scél mara U,   [8-8] *sic* U, fuidbecha Y, fuidbechtai C
[9] airslechta Y   [10] betit C [LL]   [11] bi U, bid Y C

Roínfid[1] fuil féne fo don
2420   la slúag inna ndunechon.
       Regaid ind longas hi fat
       do[2] Ultaib díanda[3] rísat.

       [4]Ní geib coistecht arubthá
       ber ass Dubthach nDóeltenga[4].
2425   ber .a.

Sréid Fergus Dubthach úad iar sin co n-arrasair di[a] ṡruib fri
budin anall.

       Co cloth ní Ailill co n-ebairt:
.r.[5]   'Ná fer báig, a Ḟergus, ar buaib sceó mnáib Ulad aithgén ara
2430 mbernaib beit mairt ili sund slig ceni silsiter acht i n-óenferaib
       ardeslig isind áth cach óenlathiu.'
       Co cloth ní Medb:
.r.[5]   'Comérig, a Ailill[6], co fíannaib fótrind[7] ar duth[8] buaib sceó genat
       m̅c̅ melchib athaib i ngrenchaib móraib i llinnib[9] dubaib forbrisfet
2435 comlund scéo Fergus dánae co loingis Ulad biaith and iartach i
       ndíaid in chatha memais cauma[10] co fil[eda]ib[11] Féne.'
       [12]Co cloth ní Fergus[12].
       'Banairle baetha nacha auchide nacha cluinte co teintib bláthaib
       sceó cholet muinter sceó chenel olca anapthai rosrí a chialla con-
2440 suidet na tádet.'
       Co cloth Gabrán file:
.r.[5]   'Ná briguid briathra sceó laidib rígnaib for bronnaib di thuathaib
       déni día messaib blassaib dia fáebra fichi cessóe cía bera na suí
       forellig na tulle miscais[13].'
82[a]   'Ná fémdit[14] far | céle.   Taít ara chend isin n-áth,' or Fergus.
       'Aúchaide Ailill,' or Medb.
       Co cloth ní Ailill:
.r.[15] 'Fergus rofitir morthúathaib for far muintir méilaith ní imthecht[16]
       ar far mbúaib acht cía far slig slattaib i mbúaib dithoing ceóbera di
2450 far mór di belgib brassaib.'

---

[1] Raghaid C   [2] di C   [3] diadon C   [4-4] om. Y [LL Rec. III]
[5] between cols. U   [6] sic Y C, Ailind U   [7] cotriunn Y, fottrind C
[8] do C   [9] sic U Y, llinndibh Dipl. Ed.. llindibh C   [10] coema C
[11] filib U C, fileadib Y   [12-12] misplaced U Y C between nacha and
cluinte   [13] na oirbire add. C   [14] femtit Y, feimditt C, read fémdid
[15] in marg. U   [16] imtheit Y

.r.² ¹Co cloth ní Fergus¹:

'Ná fer, a Medb, mórscoith dit loingis bairr brátha iar mbliadain
sceó cháthig mná massa iartaige nád imdat dit morchothaib³ día
thúathaib tisccet.'

⁴Imroll Belaig Eóin inso⁴   2455

Fíacha Fíaldána Dimraith dolluid do acallaim meic sethar a
máthar .i. Mane Andóe a ainm. Dolluid Dócha mac Mágach la
Mane nAndóe. Dolluid Dubthach Dóel Ulad la Fíachaich
Fíaldána Dimraith. Docorastár Dócha gaí for Fíachaig co lluid i
nDubthach. Focheird dano Dubthach gaí for Mane co lluid i ²⁴⁶⁰
nDócha.

Dí fieir immorro máthair Dubthaig ⁊ Dóche.

Is de atá Imrull Belaig Eúin.

Nó is de atá Imroll Belaig Eúin .i. tíagait na slóig do Beluch
Eúin. Anait ⁵a ndí dírim [i] suidiu⁵. Tic Díarmait mac Con- ²⁴⁶⁵
chobuir di Ultaib antúaid.

'Eirged marcach úaib,' or Díarmait, 'co tí Mane dom accallaim
dís ⁊ ragat-sa dís ara c[h]end.'

Condrecat⁶ íarom.

'Todeochad-sa,' or Díarmait, 'ó Chonchobar co n-erbora fri Medb ²⁴⁷⁰
⁊ Ailill co relcet na báe ass ⁊ slán uile a ndorónad and ⁊ tabár⁷ in
tarb aniar cosin tarb ille⁸ co comairset, ⁹úair ro báge Medb⁹.

'Ragat-sa,' or Mane, 'co n-apror friu.'

Ráti-side dano fri Meidb ⁊ Ailill.

'Ní hétar for Medb aní siu,' or Mane.   2475

'Dénam cóemchlód dá gaisced didiu,' or Díarmait, 'massu ferr
latt.'

'Maith lim,' or Mane.

Focherd cechtar de gaí for araile conid apthatar a ndís, ⁊ conid
Imroll Belaig Eóin ainm na maigni sin.   2480

Maitti a ndírim fo araill. Dofuittet trí fichit¹⁰ díb di cechtar dá
lína. Is de atá Ard¹¹ in Dírma.

---

¹⁻¹ *between cols.* U   ² *in marg.* U   ³ mor cathaib C   ⁴⁻⁴ *in marg.* U,
om. Y   ⁵⁻⁵ in di dirim a suidiu (a *added below line*) Y, a ndirim i suidhe C
⁶ an dí díss *add.* C   ⁷ *sic* U, = tabarr, tabair Y C   ⁸ anoir C
⁹⁻⁹ huair rombaigi Medb Y, in bar cetfuid C   ¹⁰ fer *inserted with caret
mark* C   ¹¹ Ár C

[1]Aided Tamuin Drúith inso[1]

FOruirmiset muinter Ailella a mind ríg for Tamun drúth. Ní
2485 lámair Ailill a beith fair fessin. Srédis Cú Chulaind cloich fair
oc Áth Tamuin co mmebaid a c[h]end de.
Is de atá Áth Tamuin ⁊ Tuga [2]im Thamun[2].

[3]Aided Óengussa meic Óenláma[3]

DOintaí íarom Óengus mac Óenláma Caíme[4], óclach dána di
2490 Ultaib, in slóg n-ule oc Modaib Loga—is inund ón dano ⁊
Lugmod—co tici Áth Da Ferta. Nís léic secha ⁊ dosmbidc
co llecaib. Ocus asberat ind eólaig im[mus]neblaid[a5] ríam remáin
co tíastais[6] fo chlaideb oc Emain Macha acht bid ar galaib óenfir[7]
conrístá friss. Brisit fír fer fair íarom ⁊ ra mbeótar i n-écomlond. |

82[b]   [8]Comrac Fergusa fri Coin Culaind[8]

[9]'TÁet nech úaib ar mo chend-sa,' ar Cú Chulaind, 'oc Áth Da
Ferta[9].'
'Nípa messe, nípá mé!' ol cách assa magin. 'Ní dlegar
cimbid dom cheniúl. Cía no dligthe, nípad mé dobertais tara
2500 chend i[10] cimbidecht.'
Is and gessa do Fergus mac Róich techt ara c[h]end-som. Opaid-
side dano dul ar cend a daltai .i. Con Culaind. Dobreth fín do ⁊ ro
mescad[11] co trén ⁊ ro guded im dula isin comrac. Téit ass íarom ó
ro bás [12]ocá etargude[12] co tromda.
2505 Asbert Cú Chulaind íarom:
'Is [13]co nglinni[13] dothéig ar mo chend-sa, [14]a popa Fergus[14],' ol
sé, 'cen claideb inna[15] intiuch.'
—Ar gatsai Ailill ass ut praediximus.
'Is cumma lim-sa etir,' or Fergus. 'Cia nobeth claideb and, ní
2510 imbértha fort-su. Teilg traigid dam, a C[h]ú Chulaind,' or Fergus.
'Teilgfe-so dano dam-sa arísi,' ar Cú Chulaind.

---

[a] .i. ro fost [M] (*misplaced, refers to* Nís léic secha); .i. ro fosta C (*similarly
misplaced*)

[1-1] *in marg.* U, *om.* Y   [2-2] in Tamuin Y C   [3-3] *in marg.* U, *om.*
Y, Oighidh Aonghusae meic Aonlaime Gaibhe C   [4] Gaibe Y C
[5] immusneblaid Y, imneablad C   [6] *sic* Y, tíastain U   [7] óenfer U
[8-8] *between cols.* U, *om.* Y C   [9-9] Toet nech uaib ar mo cendsai i mbuar-
ach oc Ath Da Fertai, ar Cu Chulind C   [10] *sic* Y C, im U   [11] mesca
U   [12-12] oc etarguidi fair Y, oca etarguidi . . . fair C   [13-13] *sic* Y C,
com glinni U   [14-14] a mo popae, a Fergus C   [15] it C

'Samlaid écin,' or Fergus.

Is and sin dolléci Cú Chulaind traigid for cúlu re Fergus co rrici
Grellig nDol[l]uid ara telced Fergus dó-som traigid i lló in c[h]atha.
Tairbling Cú Chulaind íarom hi nGrellaig Dolluid.   2515

'Ara chend dait, a Fergus!' or cách.

'Aicc,' ol Fergus. '¹Ní ord erossa. Is robeóda intí fil and.
Conom thí de chind chúarda ní reg¹.'

Tíagait secha íarom co ngabsat dúnad hi Crích Ross². Raclu-
nethar són dano Ferchú Loingsech buí for longais re nAilill. Dotháet- 2520
side ar cend Con Culaind. Trí fir déac dano ba hé a lín. Gontai
³Cú Chulaind³ oc Cingit Ferchon. Atát a trí líic déac and.

⁴Comrac Maind⁴

FOídis Medb ⁵Mand Muresci mac Dáiri do Domnandchaib do
c[h]omrac fri Coin Culaind. Derbráthair side ⁊ Damán athair 2525
Fir Diad. Ba fer borb brogda íarom im longud ⁊ im ligi in
Mand. Fer dothengt[h]ach dobeóil amal Dubthach Dóel Ulad. Ba
fer tailc trebur co sonairte ballraid amal Munremur mac Errcind⁶.
Trénfer tnút[h]ach amal Triscod⁷ trénfer tigi Conc[h]obair.

'Ragat-sa ⁊ mé anarma, ⁊ conmél eter mo lámaib hé, ar ní míad nó 2530
mas lem arm d'imbirt for siriti n-amulach amne.'

Luid íarom do saigid Con Culaind. Is and boí-side ⁊ a ara forsin
maig oc frecomét in tslúaig.

'Óenfer cucund sund,' or Láeg ⁸fri Coin Culaind.

'Cinnas fir?' ol Cú Chulaind⁸.   2535

'Fer dubdond tailc tarbda ⁊ sé anarma.'

'⁸Léic sechot,' ol Cú Chulaind⁸.

Tic cucu la sodain.

'Do c[h]ur chomlaind frit dodeochad-sa,' ol Mand.

Gabait íarom for imtrascrad fri ré cían ⁊ ⁹trascraid *Coin Culaind* 2540
fo thrí Mand⁹. Conid greis in t-ara.

'Díambad curadmír do chosnam i nEmain duit,' for sé, 'ropa-
datrén¹⁰ for ócaib Emna.'

Tic a ferg niad ⁊ atraig a bruth míled cor trascair Mand fón corthi
coro scor i mminágib.   2545

Conid de atá Mag Mandachta .i. Mand Échta .i. écht Maind and.¹¹

---

¹⁻¹ Condom raib di cend cuartai ni ragh ar ni hord irusa damsae. Is
robeoda inti fail and C   ² Rois Y C   ³⁻³ Fergus Y   ⁴⁻⁴ *between
cols. in ras.* H   ⁵ *from here to end of col. in ras. by* H   ⁶ Geirrcind C
⁷ Trioscattul C   ⁸⁻⁸ *om.* C   ⁹⁻⁹ trasccraiss Mand fo tri Cu Cul*aind* C
¹⁰ = ropadat trén   ¹¹ U *breaks off*

35ᵃ | Foídis Medb arna bárach naí[1] firu fichet ara c[h]eand i ngrellaich
Con Culaind. Fuiliarnn a ainm ina grellcha fri Áth Fir Dead de
siu. Sraitis[2] a naí ngaí fichet fair fo chétóir .i. Gaili Dána cona
2550 šecht maccaib fichet ꝗ mac a deirbšethar .i. Glas mac Delgna. In
tan íarom[3] rigset a[4] láma uili día claidmib, tic Fiacha mac Fir
Febe ina ndedhaid asin dúnad. Focheirdd bedg asa charput in
tan atcondairc a lláma uile i cind Con Culaind ꝗ benaid a naí rigthi
fichit díb.
2555 Is and asbert Cú Chulaind:
'Is cobair [5]i n-éimib[5] ém a ndorighnis.'
'A mbec sa,' ol Fiacha, 'is tar cotach dúindi ar[6] nUltaib. Día rí
neach díb a ndúnad, regma-ni ar tríchait[7] cét fo gin claidib.'
'Tongu et reliqua, in tan dorelced mo anál dam-sa,' or Cú Chulaind,
2560 'nícon ricfa fer díb-seom a mbeathaid.'
Gontais[8] Cú Chulaind [9]íar sin[9] an[10] noí fir[u] fichit ꝗ dá mac
Ficce[11] lais occo, dá ócláech dána di Ultaib dollotar do imbirt a
cumaiṅg forsin[12] slóg. Is é a ngním[13] insain forsin Táin[14] co llotar
don chath la Coin Culaind.
2565 Atá isin cloich i medón ind átha láthrach tele [15]a scéth[15] ꝗ a
ndornn[16] ꝗ a nglúine[17]. Ocus rolátha a naí coirthi fichit and sin.

Comrac Fir Diad ꝗ Con Culaind so

IS andsin ro himráided leó-som íarom cia fer bad túalaing dingbáil Con Culaind díb. Adbertsadar ꝗ ro nertsadar ꝗ ro ráidsetar
2570 ceithri cóiced hÉrend cia bad chóir do thabairt for áth i nn-agid
Con Culaind. Atrubartadar uili corb é in Conganchnesach a hIrrus
Domnand, in feidm nach fuilingther ꝗ in bairindlecc brátha, a derb-
chomalta dil díchra fodeisin. Ní baí ic Coin C[h]ulaind cles ná
beth aice acht mad cles[18] in gaí bulgai nammá, ꝗ cid[19] indar leó-som
2575 baí aici-seom a sechna ꝗ a imdegail fair, dáig cnes[20] coṅgnaidhi imbi,
noc[h]onisgébdis airm ná ilfáebair.
Dobretha Medb techta for cend Fir Diad. Nocho tánic Fer Diad
risna techtaib hísin. Dobretha Medb filid ꝗ áes dána ꝗ áes glámtha
grúaidi ara chend co nderntais a áerad ꝗ a aithised ꝗ a ainfíalad

---

[1] sic C, secht Y   [2] sic Y; read sréitius? or sréithit?   [3] ummorro C
[4] sic C, om. Y   [5-5] sic C, in | inn eimib Y   [6] inar C   [7] triochae C
[8] sic Y C   [9-9] iarom sin Y   [10] a C   [11] Uicci C   [12] sic C,
frisin Y   [13] gnim Y   [14] sluaigedh inda Tana C   [15-15] in sceth Y,
in sceith C   [16] dornn Y, dorn C   [17] gluine Y C   [18] sic C F, mo. Y
[19] read cid de? (gidheadh F)   [20] sic C F, om. Y

coná fagad[1] inad a chind for bith co tísad i pupall Medba ⁊ Aililla for ²⁵⁸⁰
Tána. Tánic Fer Diad leisna techtaib hísin ²ar úaman² a imderctha
dóib.

Tucad Findabair, ingen Medba ⁊ Ailella, fora leathláim. Is í ind
Findabair sin no gobad láim ar cach cúach ⁊ ar cach copán d'Fir
Diad; is í dobeired³ teóra póc fria cach copán díb-sin dó; is í no ²⁵⁸⁵
dáiled ubla fírchubra dar sedlach a léned fair. Is ed adberead-si ba
35ᵇ | hé a leandán ⁊ a toga tochmairc do feraib in tsáegail Fer Diad.

Inaim robo sáithech subach sofarbaílig Fer Diad, is and adbert
Medb:

'Maith aile, a Fir Diad, in fetair-seo cia fáth 'ma radgoired isin ²⁵⁹⁰
pupull sa?'

'Nád edar-sa ón óm,' ar Fer Diad, 'acht degmaithi fer nÉrind
and. Cid écóru mo beith-se and anás cach degláech?'

'Nád ed óm ám,' or Medb, 'acht da thobairt charpait trí secht
cumal dait ⁊ timthacht dá fer déac ⁊ cutruma Maigi Murthemne do ²⁵⁹⁵
mín Moigi Aíi, ⁊ bith a Crúachain do grés, ⁊ fín do dáil fort and;
saíri do chlaindi ⁊ do cheniúil do grés can cháin, cen chobach; mo
duileand-dealc óir-sea duit i failet deich fichit unga ⁊ deich fichit
leathunga ⁊ deich fichit crosach ⁊ deich fichit cethramthan; Findabair m'ingen-sa ⁊ ingen Aililla do óenmnaí dait ⁊ comaid dom ²⁶⁰⁰
sliasaid-sea. ⁴Dia rís a leas air sin anúas fogéba na dei ris.'

'Is móra na comada sin ⁊ na haisceda sin,' or cách⁴.

'Is fír ón,' or Fer Diad. 'Isat móra, ⁊ cidat móra chena, a Medb,
is acot-so fodeisin fáicfidther mad⁵ dula⁶ dam-sa i n-aigid mo
chomalta ⁷do chomrac⁷. ²⁶⁰⁵

'A firu trá', or sí or Medb, trí chóir n-indlaig ⁊ imc[h]osaídi, 'is
fír in bríathar asbert Cú Chulaind,' mar ná cloised Fer Diad itir.

'Cé guth éiside, a Medb?' or Fer Diad.

'Adrubairt, ⁸a m'anom⁸,' or sisi, 'nípad furáil leis do thuitim-siu
ina airigid gaiscid leis isin chóiced i rragad.' ²⁶¹⁰

'Nírbo c[h]óir dó-som a rád ón dáig ní hé mo t[h]ríamnass ná mo
midlochos ríam ⁹i lló nách i n-aidchi⁹ rofidir orm. Toingim-sa et
reliqua corob¹⁰ misi cétfer roficfa isin maitin imbárach co háth in
chomlaind.'

---

¹fagbad C   ²⁻²uaman Y, d'uaman C   ³*sic* C, nobeired Y   ⁴⁻⁴or
cách *comes after* na dei ris Y, dia ris a les ar sin anuas fogebiu dee fris sin
do com*all* (*said by Medb*) Tonccai ar cach isat mora na haiscedae C. As mor
na comhad sin ar cach (⁊) dia ccomhoillter iad. Dia re na comal uaimsi ol
Meadhbh F   ⁵*sic* C, ma Y   ⁶*read* dulta?   ⁷⁻⁷nocha reisiub C
⁸⁻⁸ám aamim C   ⁹⁻⁹a llo nach inn aichdi Y, *om.* C   ¹⁰coro *with* b
inserted later Y, conab C

2615 'Dotria búaid ⁊ bendachtain!' or Medb. 'Is ferr leam sin ná
tríamnas ⁊ midlochos do ḟagbáil occot[1], dáig condolb cách 'mo
daínib fodesin. Cid córo dó-som sochur Ulad do dénam ar apa a
máthar díb indás dait-siu sochar chóicid Connacht, dáig at mac ríg
Connacht adcáemnacair?'
2620 [2]Is amlaid ro bádar-som oc naidm a cor ⁊ a ndála ⁊ dorigniset laíd
and[2]:

> 'Rotfia lóg [3]mór mbuindi[3]
> co cuit maigi is cailli
> co saíre do chloindi
2625 > ó 'ndiu co tí bráth.
> A Ḟir Diad mic Damá[i]n
> Atted úas cach anáil
> [4]Is cóir dait[4] a gabáil
> aní gabus cách.'

2630 > [5]'Nocho géb[5] cen árach
> dáig ním láech cen lámach
> bid trom form-sa amárach
> [6]bid húas dam a ḟeidm[6].
> Cú dían comainm Culand
2635 > [7]ní hurisa a ḟulaṅg[7]
> is[8] amnas an urrand
> is[8] tairptheach in teidm.'

> 'Ca chan dait a fuireach?
> Naisc-siu corbat buideach
2640 > ar des ríg is ruirech
> doradsad[9] frit láim.
> Fil sund [10]nachad fuirfe[10]
> [11]rotfia cach ní chuingfe[11]
> dáig rofes co muirfi
2645 > in fer ticfa[12] id dáil.

---

[1] fort C [2-2] ⁊ is ann isbertt Medb na briathra sai and C [3-3] ocus
moinde C [4-4] cid doit cen C [5-5] Ni gebsa C [6-6] bud fortren
an feidm C [7-7] Ní hulaṅg ni hurisa a ḟulang Y [8] budh C
[9] doragat C [10-10] noc[at t]uilbthe C [11-11] sic C, om. Y
[12] tic C

36ᵃ | 'Ní géb cen sé curu
             níba ní bus lugu
             siu[1] donear mo mudu
                 [2]i fiadhnaisi in tslúaig[2].
             [3]Dánamtora[3] m'ardarc   2650
             [4]cencop céin co comnart[4]
             rachad isin chomrac
                 co[5] Coin Culaind cruaid.

             'A Medb co méd búafaid
             nít cerb[6] caíme núachair   2655
             [11]dearb leam[7] is tú is búachail
                 ar Crúachain na clad.
             Art glór is art gairgnert
             [8]domroiched sról santbrecc[8]
             tuc dam th 'ór is t'airced   2660
             [9]méd rofairced[9] dam.

             '[10]Geb brugaid, geib oirgni
             ocus óes na bairdne[10]
             rodfia-so cen[11] acht.
             Fonaisc lat ar Morand   2665
             mad áil dait a chomall
             geib Cairbri Nia Manand
             is naisc [12]ar dá[12] mac

             '[13]Gébad-sa na rátha
             do thobairt frim láma   2670
             ocus gébad écnairc
                 ó Choin Culaind chrúaid.[13]

             'Is[14] tusu in cor codnach
             dá tibér delc drolmach[15]
             [16]rotfia úaim fa domnach[16]   2675
                 níba dál bu[s] sía.
             A laích blatnig bladmair
             cech sét cáem ar talmain
             dobérthar daid amlaid
                 is uili rodfía.   2680

---

[1] sul C   [2-2] innd bail i mbiat sluaig C   [3-3] Danam toirsed C
[4-4] cindfet cincob comnart C   [5] fri C   [6] credb C   [7-7] is derb C
[8-8] om. Y, sic C   [9-9] between o and f, t added later hand Y, oro fairced C
[10-10] Cidh Domnall na Cairpre | na niadh is na n-aircene C   [11] cidh C
[12-12] for a C   [13-13] om. C   [14] nach C   [15] sic C, dromlach Y
[16-16] o' niu co ti Domhnach C

'Findabair na ferga
rígan íarthair Elga
ar ndíth Con na Cerda,
  a Fir Diad, rotfía.'

2685
                                    R.

[1]Ro baí láech amra do Ultaib hi fiadhnaisi na coraidechta sin, ⁊
rob éiside Fergus mac Róig. Táinic Fergus coa pupall.

'Trúag lim-sa in gním dogníther isin maidin sea imbárach,' or
Fergus.

2690   'Cia gním and sin?' for lucht na pupla.

'Mo degdaltán Cú Chulaind do marbad.'

'Maith aile, cia nadmaídenn ón?'

'Ní anse. A chomalta dil díchra fodeisin .i. Fer Diadh mac
Damáin.[1] Cid ná berid mo bendachtain,' ar Fergus, '⁊ táet nech
2695 úaib co robud ⁊ co n-airchisecht do Choin Chulaind dús in fácbad
in n-áth isin maitin imbárach?'

'Dar ar cubus,' for siat, 'cid tusu fén no beith for áth in chomlaind,
nocho ricfamis dot insaigid conici[1].'

'Maith a gilla,' for Fergus, 'geib dún ar n-eocha ⁊ indill in carpat.'

2700   Atracht in gilla ⁊ [2]ro gab na heocho ⁊ ro indill in carpat[2].

Tángadar rempo co háth in c[h]omlaind, áit i mbaí Cú Chulaind.

'Óencharpat[3] chucaind sunn, a C[h]úcacán,[4]' or Lóeg. Dáig is
amlaid baí in gilla ⁊ a druim fria thigerna. —[5]Dobered leth
brandaigechta ⁊ fi[d]chillachta fora thigerna[5]; [6]fer foraire ⁊ for-
2705 cométa[6] for cheithri airdib hÉrind ó sin amach.

'Cindus carpa[i]d ann sin ale?' or Cú Chulaind.

'Carpat imbar rígráith romóir cona chuingib dronórdaib, cona
t[h]arbc[h]lár umaide, cona feirtsib crédumaib, cona c[h]reit cróestana cróestirim cleasaird colcda clocatcain curata, for díb echaib
2710 duba dénmecha [7]suntig séitrig[7] sogabáltaich sodaim ma[8] grindib
állib a fén. Óenóclach rígda rosclethan ba chumsclaig in charpait.
Ulcha dúalach dégablánach fair co soiched dar máethíchtar a
36[b] máethimlenn sís | sel sechtair co nn-aingébad cóeca lóech i lló
doinindi ⁊ dertain bith[9] fo thromfoithin a ulchu inn óclaich. Crom-
2715 scíath gelscabal brec fair co trí radhaib[10] rodénma co taillfed osair-
chosair ceth[e]óra ndroṅg ṅdeichenbair fa thairrlethar in scéith

---

[1-1] *om.* C   [2-2] dorigne samlaidh C   [3] oenchairp- Y   [4] Chugáin C
[5-5] *om.* C   [6-6] dognith forairi et forcomet C   [7-7] *sic* C, suntrigsigh
Y (*corrupt*)   [8] fo C   [9] *om.* C   [10] *sic* Y (*mark of aspir. later*),
randaib C, rothaibh F

fil foro thairrsceo thaullethan inn óclaich. Claideb fota fáebur-
chrúaid derglethan hi trúaill fichthi[1] fíthe findarcait úas chróeba*ib*
a chnis chathchalma. Sleg thrén thredruimnech co féthan[aib] ⁊
co fonascaib arcaid báin óengil [2]ace tarsin carpat[2].   2720

'Ní duilig [a] aithni,' for Cú Chulaind. 'Mo poba Fergus dotháet
and co rrobad ⁊ co n-airchisecht dam-sa re ceithri cóicedaib Érend
uile.'

Doríacht Fergus ⁊ tarblaing asa charpat, ⁊ ferais Cú Chulaind
fáilti fris.   2725

'Fo chen do thíachtain, a mo popa, a Ḟergais!' bar Cú Chulaind.

'Is tairisi lind inn ḟáilti,' for Fergus.

'Is tairisi daid-se ón,' or Cú Chulaind. 'Dia toichle[3] [4]liath
léna[4] in mag, rodbía-so cadan[5] co leith; araile [6]dia toichle íasg i
n-inberaib[6], rodbía éo co leith; araile glac biroir ⁊ glac ḟochlachta ⁊   2730
glac ḟema[i]r ⁊ deog usci ḟuair gainmidi ina deghaid.'

'Is inḟoglaga in chuid sin,' ar Fergus.

'Is fír ón. Is cuid foglada acum-sa,' for Cú Chulaind, 'dáig
atú-sa[7] ón lúan iar samain cosin tan sa [⁊] ní dechad-sa aidchi n-aidi-
dechta acht[8] ic trénḟastud fer nÉrend ar Táin Bó Cúailgne don chur   2735
sa.'

'Dámad dó sin tísmais,' ar Fergus, 'robad fer[r]di linn a ḟagbáil,
⁊ ní dó tángamar.'

'Cid ní chena 'mo tángabar?' or Cú Chulaind.

'Dia indisin dait-siu láech dotháed do c[h]omrocc ⁊ do c[h]omlond   2740
ar do chend-so isin maitin sa imbárach,' for Fergus.

'Findam ⁊ cluineam úait dono,' for Cú Chulaind.

'Do chomalta fadéin .i. Fear Diad mac Damáin.'

'Dar ar mbréithir ám [9]nochon ina dáil[9] is dech lend no ragmais,'
ar Cú Chulaind, '⁊ nochon ara omun [10]c[h]ena acht ar mét a gráda   2745
lind[10].'

'Is cóir ecla de,' or Fergus, 'dáig cnes congnai imbi oc comroc
fri fer. Nochon nosgabaid airm ná fáebair.'

[11]'Ná ráid-siu itir ón,' or Cú Chulaind,[11] [12]dáig luigim luigi luigis
mo thúath[12] [13]coro[b] boigithir fri boigsibind[13] for lár aba cach n-alt   2750
⁊ cach n-áigi de fo déis mo chloidib-sa diana taiselbai óenḟecht dam-
sa for áth.'

---

[1] om. C   [2-2] ina certsesam isin carpat C   [3] taichela C   [4-4] id.
F, elta en C; read elta én or iall én?   [5] caduth C   [6-6] om. C, iasg i
ninberaib add. in marg. Y   [7] om. C   [8] sic C, om. Y   [9] sic C,
nochon an andail Y   [10-10] sic Y F, om. C.   [11-11] uaitsi on eitir C
(corrupt)   [12-12] Toingimsi do Dia toinges mo thoath C   [13-13] combo
boicithir boinnsibin C, nach ba luaithe boigṡibhen F

Is amlaid ro bátar igá rád sin ⁊ dorigénsed in laíd and:

'A Chú Chulaind, comal ṅglé,
adchíu is mithig duid érge.
Dofuil sund chucad re feirc
Fer Diad mac Damá[i]n drechdeirg.'

2755

'Atú-sa sunn, ní seól seṅg,
ag trénḟasdod fer nÉrend.
Ní berim ar teiched troig
ar aba comlainn éinḟir.

2760

'[1]Ní do t[h]obairt triamnaid leat
a Chú Chulaind cloth míadach[1]:
cneas coṅgnai im Ḟer nDiad na ndroṅg
risná geb cath ná comlond.'

2765

37ᵃ | '[2]Dá comraicem forsinn áth[2]
misi is Fer Diad gaiscedgnáth[3],
[4]nochon é in scarad cen sceó[4]
bid fergach ar fáebargleó.'

'[5]Is calma a lám dia lái feirg
a llos a c[h]laidib c[h]rúaiddeirg[5]
nert cét 'na c[h]urp, calma in modh,
ní gon rind, ní thesc fáebar.

2770

'Bí 'tast, ná tacair do scél,
a Ḟergais na n-arm n-imthrén.
Tar cach feronn, tar cach fond
dam-sa [6]ní ba hanborrlond[6].'

2775

'Ro bad ferr leam iná lúag,
a Chú Chulaind claidebrúad,
co mbad tú doberad sair
coscar Ḟir Diadh dímosaigh.'

2780

[1-1] Amnas in fer da lae feirg | a los a claidib crodeirg C   [2-2] Mad die comrisam ar ath C   [3] aon na trath C   [4-4] ni ba hi in scartein cen scleo C   [5-5] Amnas in fer fichtib gal | nocha nurusa a troethad C   [6-6] = ní ba hanforlann, nocha n-ecomlond C

'¹Dober mo c[h]obais cen cháin
acht ni[m] maith-se d'imarbáig¹
²co mba mé búaideóchas de
ar mac Damáin meic Dáire².'   2785

'Mé tharclaim na slúaig sea soir,
lúach mo sáraichthi d'Ultaib;
leam tángatar ó tírib
na curaid, na cathmílig.

'Manbad Conchobar 'na c[h]es   2790
robad c[h]rúaid ³ar comaithches³
ní thánic Medb Maigi in Scáil
turus ríam bad móa congáir.

⁴Itá fedm is mó ad láim⁴: 2795
gleó re Fer nDiad mac nDamáin.
Airm chruaid chadaid cardid roind
bid acot, a C[h]ú Chulaind.'
                    A Culaind.

Asa haithli sin:
'⁵Cid immo tánacais, a mo popa, a Fergais?' or Cú Chulaind.   2800
'Isí sin mo thoisc,' or Fergus.
'Maith sén ⁊ solad,' for Cú Chulaind, 'nach nech aile do feraib
hÉrenn tánic frisin toisc, acht mani dáildis ceit[h]ri cóiced hÉrenn
uile i nn-óenfecht, nephní lem robad re n-énláech dam⁵.'
Tánic Fergus remi iar tain dá pupull⁶.   2805
Ocus imthúsa Con Culind:
'Cid ní dogéna-so inocht?' or Lóeg.
'Cid ón itir? 'or Cú Chulaind.
'Is amlaid doraga Fer Diad dot indsaigid-so fo núamaisi figi ⁊
ber[r]tha ⁊ foilc[th]i ⁊ fothraicthi, ⁊ ceithre cóicid hÉrenn lais do
fégad in chomlaind. Rob áil dam-sa do dula-su co háit a fuig-   2810
bigthea in córugud⁷ cétna fort co tici fail⁸ hi fil Emer Foltchaín, co
Cairthenn Clúana Da Dam hi Slíab Fúait.'
Tánic Cú Chulaind inn ai[d]chi sin didiu conici sin, ⁊ ro faí ré
banchéle fodeisin.

1-1 Atiursa brethir co mbaidh | cen cob maitsi ac imarbaig C   2-2 curab
me buadaigfes de | do mac Damain meic Dáiri C   3-3 ar comaigthes C,
ab (altered from ar) + ar in margin comeas Y   4-4 Ro fil gnimh is mo
reit laim C   5-5 this passage before the verses in C (correct place)   6 imus
with ara under line Y (abortive attempt at ocus imthusa of next sentence?)
7 suidigud C   8 baile C

2815   A imthúsa ó sin amach nochon iad chestnaighther [1]sund colléicc[1],
acht imt[h]úsa Fir Diad.

Tánic[-side][2] coa pupull.   Ro bo cendgrugánach[3] mertnech lucht
pupaill Fir Diad in aidchi sin.   Demin leó baili i comrecdais dá
úait[h]ne chomlaind in tsáegail co mbad comthoitim dóib, nó didiu
2820 inní ro bíad de oc mbad hé a tigerna fén dofáethsad ann.   Dáig
nocho[4] soréid comrac fri Coin Culaind for Tánaid[5].

Bátar imsníma móra for menmain Fir Diad in aidchi sin coná
reilcset cotlud dó.   Ba dia imshnímaib móra in[a] tairces do sétaib
dó ⁊ ind ingen do légud úad ar apa comruicc fri hoénfer; mani dernad
37[b] comrac frisin n-óenfer sin didiu, comrac frisna sé curadaib | arna
bárach.   Imsním robo móo aici-som andás sin, dá nataiselbad
óenfecht for áth do Choin Culaind, demin lais ná bíad commus a
chind nach a anma aici bodéin asa hait[h]li.

Ocus atracht[6] Fer Diad mochthráth arnabárach.
2830   'Maith a gilla,' for éisim, 'geib dún ar n-eocho ⁊ indill in carpat.'

'Dar ar mbréithir ém,' for in gilla, 'ní lía molas dúnd techt in
turussa so andás a nemdula.'

Ro baí-som ic acallaim ind arad ⁊ dorigni in laíd [7]mbicc and ac
gresacht an arad[7]:

2835   'Tíagam isan dáil-sea
          [8]do chosnom[8] ind fir-sea
          co rísim in n-áth-sa[9]
          áth forscara[10] in badb,
          hi comdáil Con Culaind
2840   dá guin tre cherd[11] cumaing
          [12]co rruca[12] trít urraind
          corob de bus marb.

          'Robad ferr dúnd[13] anad
          ní ba réid bar mbagar[14]
2845   biaid neach dámba galar
          far scarad bid snéid.
          Techt in ndáil n-alt nUlad
          is dál dá mbía pudar
          is fada bus cumain
2850   mairg ragas in réim!

---

[1] o sunna amach C   [2] Tanicsidhe C   [3] cendgrugach C   [4] ni ba C
[5] tanaich Y, tanai C   [6] aatracht Y   [7-7] *om.* C   [8-8] *sic* LL, cor
cosnom Y C   [9] intathsa Y, ind ath sa C   [10] friscera C, fors ṅgéra LL
[11] chreitt LL   [12-12] cor ruca Y, cu rug(a) C   [13] linn C, dúib LL
[14] b *added above line* Y, maghar C, magar LL

'Écóir anní ráidhi
ní hobair níad náire
nocho dluig[1] áli
    ní anfam fa[t] dáig.
Bí 'tast dínd, a gilli,   2855
bid calma ar síst sinne
ferr tendi ná timi
    tíagam isin dáil.'

                              Tíagam isin dáil.

Ro gob in gilla na heocho ⁊ ro indill in carpat, ⁊ táncadar rempo 2860
asin longport imach.

'A gilla,' for Fer Diad, 'ní cóir i ndénmait, dula cen celebrad do
feraib hÉrenn.   Impó dúnd agaid [2]na n-ech[2] ⁊ in charpait for feraib
hÉrind.'

Ro impó in gilla aiged na n-ech ⁊ in charpait fo t[h]ri fri feraib 2865
hÉrenn[3].   Is and dorala Medb ic sriblad a fúail for urlár in pupaill.

'In cotlad do Ailill innosa?' or Medb.

'Nad ed ámh,' ar Ailill.

'In cluine[4] do c[h]liamain núa ac celebrad duit?'

'An ed dogní-som ón?' ar Ailill.   2870

'Is ed écin,' for Medb.   'Acht luigim-sa a luigend mo t[h]úath ná
tic arna cosaib cétna chucaib-si in fer dogní in celebrad út.'

'Ar aba ina tairtemar[5] dá deigc[h]leamnas didiu,' or Ailill, 'acht
co táethsad Cú Chulaind lais, fó linn cémad chomthuitim dóib[6].   Ane
robad ferrdi lind Fer Diad [7]do thérnom[7].'   2875

Tánic Fer Diad remi co háth in chomlaind.

'Féga lat, a gilla,' or Fer Diad, 'in fil Cú Chulaind forsinn áth.'

'Nád fil ám,' or in gilla.

'Féga lat co maith dún,' or Fer Diad.

'Ní broth bec a falach [8]Cú Chulaind[8] áit i mbíad,' for in gillai. 2880

'Is fír, a gilla.   Nocho cúalaid Cú Chulaind deglóech nó deigfer
do thiachtain ina agaid cos inndiu for Táin Bó Cúailnge, ⁊ in tráth[9]
adchúalaid, forácaib in áth.'

'Mór in líach Cú Chulaind do écnach ina fégmais, dáig in cumain
lat-su in tan tucsabair in cath do Germán Garbglas úas eochairimlib 2885
38[a] Mara Toirrían?   Ro fácbais-[s]eo | do c[h]laideb oc na slúagaib
corob[10] é Cú Chulaind ro marb cét lóech icá rochtain ⁊ tucastair dait
hé.   Ocus in cumain lat [11]cá rabamar[11] an aidchi sin?' or in gilla.

'Nád fetar,' or Fer Diad.

²⁸⁹⁰ '¹Do thig¹ rechtairi Scáthaigi,' or in gilla, '⁊ dochódais-[s]iu co soindim sogenda remond isin teach ar tús. Dobert in t-aithech béim dond n-áel trebennach dait hi midbach do droma co tarlaic irchor dít darin dorus imach. Tánic Cú Chulaind isteach ⁊ dobert béim dá c[h]laidiub dond n-aithech co nderna dá n-ordain de. ²⁸⁹⁵ Misi robo rechtaire² dáib eret robabair³ isin baili. Dá mbad in lá sin, ní epertha co mbadad ferr do lóech anná Cú Chulaind.'

'Écóir i ndernais, a gilla,' for Fer Diad, 'dáig ní ticfaind ar amus in chomlaind dá mbad ar tús adbertha frim. Cid nách srengai feirtsi in charpait fom thaíb ⁊ mo fogaimen fom chind coro codlaind ²⁹⁰⁰ colléic ?'

'Monúar !' for in gilla. 'Is cotlad troch sin ar cind aigi ⁊ cúanart sund.'

'Ced ón, a gilla, nách túalaing tusu forairi ⁊ forcomét dam ?'

'Isam túalaing,' or in gilla, 'acht mina thíastar ⁴a néllaib nó ²⁹⁰⁵ asan áer⁴ dot indsaigid, ná ticfaider anair ná 'niar dot indsaigid cen rabad cen rathugud.'

Ro srengtha fertsi a charpait fó thóeb ⁊ a fogaimen fó chenn, ⁊ cid ed níro chotail a becc.

Dála Con Culaind doberar ar aird.

²⁹¹⁰ 'Maith a mo popa, a Laíg, geib na heocho ⁊ indill in carbat. Má tá Fer Diad acar n-irrnaidi, is fada lais.'

Atracht in gilla ⁊ ro gab na hecho ⁊ ro indill in carpat. Cindis Cú Chulaind ina charpat ⁊ tángadar rempo do indsaighid an átha.

Imthúsa gilla Fír Diad, nírbo chian dó oc forairi co cúala chucu ²⁹¹⁵ culgairi in charpait. Ro baí ic dúscud a thigernai ⁊ dorigni in laíd :

'Rocluiniur cul carpait
dar druing⁵ n-álaind n-argaid
is fúath fir co farpairt
²⁹²⁰   úas dreich charpait c[h]rúaid
dar Broinfeirtsib Broine
dochengait in tsligi
re táeb Baili in Bili
is búadach in búaid.

---

¹⁻¹ A tig C   ² fer tigis C   ³ d *added later above first* a = robadbair Y ⁴⁻⁴ an ellaib (*space due to defect in vellum*) no aanaer Y *read* i néllaib nó i n-áer ?, a ninaib ⁊ aieraib C   ⁵ cuing C LL, *sic leg.*

'Is cú airctech eigis[1]   2925
is cairptech glan gabus
is seabac saer soighes[2]
a eocho bo deas
[3]demin lim [4]da rua[4]
[5]eich charpait in c[h]ua[5]   2930
dobéra dúnd tres.

'[6]Dorairngert ón uraid[6]
mairc bías isin tulaig
ar cind in c[h]on c[h]ubaid
ticfa[7] cebed chuin   2935
Cú na hEmna Macha
Cú co ndelb cach datha
Cú chreichi, Cú c[h]atha
adcluinim, rocluin[8].'

                                   Rocl.   2940

[9]Túarascbáil charpait Con Culaind annso, in tres prímcharpat na
scélaigeachta for Tánaich Bú Cúalnge.
'Cindus adchí Coin Culaind?' ar sé ar Fer Diad fria araid.

38^b   'Atchíu,' ar sé, 'in carpat | forḟairsing féta findglaine, co [10]cuing
dronórda[10] co tarbc[h]láraib umaidib, co fertsib[11] crédumaib, co 2945
lungetaib findruine, cona c[h]reit cróestana cróestirim cleasaird
clocatchain curita ara taillḟitis secht n-airm n-inḟlatha[12]. Cain
sosad a ḟlatha contacmaing in carpat sin [.i.] carpat Con Culaind co
lúas faindle nó cliabaigi allaid tar cend machairi maigślébe, is é
tricius ┐ áithius[13] imoroget dáig is chucaind imthigit. Dafil didiu in 2950
carpat sin for díb echaib cendbeca cruindbeca coirrbega birig
bascind[14] bruindideirg sesta súaithinte sogabálta sodain fo grindib
áillib a [ḟ]én. Andara hech díb-sidi ocus sé lugaid lúathlémnech
tresmar traigmar fótmar fochairsid. In t-ech aile ┐ sé casmoṅgach
caschóel cois[s]eṅg cáelṡeiredach[15] airgdech[16]. Dá droch[17] duba 2955
dorchaidi. Sitbe créda crúanatai dathálaind. [18]Dá n-all[18] n-órda
n-indtlaisi. Fil fer findchas foltlebar [19]i n-airinach[19] in charpait

---

¹ aigis C, aiges LL   ² slaidess LL   ³ *line omitted here* Y; is crodatta
in cua C LL   ⁴⁻⁴ dinruaa C, donrua LL   ⁵⁻⁵ is derb niba thuaa C,
rafess níba tua LL   ⁶⁻⁶ *this line comes third* C LL   ⁷ ticfad C LL
⁸ rarcluin LL   ⁹ *this long descriptive passage om.* C   ¹⁰⁻¹⁰ tuing
ndorordaib Y (*corrupt*)   ¹¹ fersib Y   ¹² nilatha no ninfiatha Y
¹³ attius Y   ¹⁴ *sic*   ¹⁵ seiredach cael Y   ¹⁶ c *inserted overhead
later to give* cairgdech *for alliteration* Y   ¹⁷ dreich Y   ¹⁸⁻¹⁸ daill
with na *added overhead later* Y   ¹⁹⁻¹⁹ inairinenech Y

sin. Fil didiu imbi-sidi brat gorm crúanchorcra. Laigen .i. gaí
co n-eitib, ⁊ sé derg daigerdai ina durnn ar derglasad. Faircsi trí
2960 folt fair .i. folt dond fri toind a chind, folt cróderg iar n-airmedón,
mind n-óir dotuiget[h]ar in tres folt. Caín cocorus¹ ind [f]uilt sin
co cuirend teóra imsrotha 'ma formna síar sell sechtair. Samalta
leam fri hórsnáth iar ndénam a datha dar or n-indeóna nó re buidi
mbech² frisa taitnend grían i llaithi samrata taitnem cach óenfinda
2965 don [f]ult sin. Secht meóir for cach cois dó ⁊ secht me[ó]ir ar cach
láim. Ruithnigud³ tened rómóiri ima⁴ rusc. Cém comfossaid⁵ i
crúithib a ech. Cróib⁶. ⁷Glac⁸ laích ina lámaib⁷.

Ara carpait a diṅgbála ina fiadnaisi. Folt cass círdub fair.
Berrad lethan ar fud a chind. Cochall eitech imbe ⁹co fúaslucud da
2970 duilend⁹. ¹⁰Echlasc urchaín órda in[a] láim¹⁰ ⁊ brat findglas imbi, ⁊
brot findaircit ina láim ic ¹¹indsaidi brot¹¹ forsin n-echraid cech
conair imatéit in mílig mórglonnach dafil isin c[h]arput. ¹²A
chaicle atacomnaic¹². Is bec leis ¹³in neiriu¹³. Ocus [asbert] fria
gilla:

2975 'Eirig, a gilla,' ar sé for Fer Diad, '⁊ romór molai-siu sin itir, ⁊
indill na harmu isinn áth ara chind.'

'Dá n-impóind m'aigid i lleth atá mo chúl, dar lim no ragdais
fersde in¹⁴ charpait triam chúlmuinél.'

'A gilla,' for sé, 'romór molaid-siu¹⁵ Coin Culaind úair ní lúag
2980 molta darad duit.'

Ocus is amlaid ro baí ic tobairt a t[h]úariscbála ⁊ atbert:

39ᵃ

| 'Is mithig in c[h]obair
dáig ní gním ar codail
bí 'tast is ná blodaich
dáig ní brāth tar brúach.
2985
Má 'tchí curaid Chúailgni
¹⁶co n-adabraib¹⁶ úailli
¹⁷fritháilfither úaindi¹⁷
dáig is dar cenn lúaigi
2990 leitérthar co lúath.'

---

¹ cocortus Y   ² cech oenfinda *add.* Y   ³ ruithnigid Y   ⁴ *read*
ina?   ⁵ co fosaib Y   ⁶ *gloss on* crúithib, *incorporated in text*   ⁷⁻⁷ *sentence
to come after* secht meóir ar cach láim *or possibly a gloss on that phrase*
⁸ *originally* glic, *attempt to alter to* glec; *read* glac   ⁹⁻⁹ *sic* Y; *corruption
of* co n-urslocud fora díb n-uillendaib   ¹⁰⁻¹⁰ *misplaced here; a variant of* brot
findaircit ina láim   ¹¹⁻¹¹ *sic* Y, *read* indsaige broit   ¹²⁻¹² *a gloss
incorporated in text?*   ¹³⁻¹³ *sic* Y   ¹⁴ *sic* Y (*om.* TBC²)   ¹⁵ = molai-siu
¹⁶⁻¹⁶ *sic* LL, co nadadbur Y, cona urradh C   ¹⁷⁻¹⁷ *om.* LL (*line is
superfluous*)

'Má 'dchíu curaid Chúailgne
co n-adamraib úailli
ní ar teiched téit úaindi
acht is cucaind tic.
Gid rogáeth ní rogand 2995
is ar maith romolam
reithid is ní romall
imar thorand tricc.'

'Bec nár chonair chonais
ara mét romolais 3000
cia fáth ara thogais
[1]ó tháinic ó thaig?[1]
Is anoissi fúacraid[2]
is atáit 'gá fóbairt[3]
nach tánic dia fúapairt 3005
acht mad [4]aigith meith[4].'

Is mithig.

Ní cían iar tain coro comraicedar ar lár ann átha ⁊ adubairt Fer
Diad ri Coin Culaind:
'Can tici-siu, a Chúa[5]?' ar sé. 3010

Dáig cúa ainm na claíne isin tsengaidilc, ⁊ secht meic imleasan
bátar i rígrosc Con Culaind, dá mac imleasan díb-sidi ⁊ siat cláena,
⁊ nocho mó a domaisi dó iná [a] maisi dó-som, ⁊ dá mbeith ainib bad
mó for Choin Culaind, is ed rothuibébad fris.

Ocus ro baí 'cá thabairt úas aird, ⁊ dorindi laíd, ⁊ im[f]recair Cú 3015
Chulaind co tarrnaic:

'Can tici-seo, a Chúa,
do t[h]roit re nert núa?
Bid cróderg do chúa
úas análaib t'ech. 3020
Bid atód fri hairis
mairg tánic do thurus
ricfa a leas do leigis
mad dá rís do t[h]ech.'

[1-1] ó thánac ó[t]tig LL, o tangais od tigh C   [2] thocbait LL C   [3] fuacairt
LL, fogairt C   [4-4] athig mith LL, atha*i*dh mbicc C   [5] Chu Y

'Dodechad[1] ré n-ócaib
im t[h]orc toraig trétaig
ré cathaib ré cétaib
     dot chur-su 'mon lind
d'ḟeirg[2] rit is dot ḟromad
i comruc cét conur
corob dait bas fogal
     do chosnum do chind.'

'Cair cindus condricfaim?
In far collaib cnetfem?
[3]Cia linn ara ficfam[3]
     do[4] chomruc for áth?
In for rendaib rúada
nó for claidmib crúada
dat shlaidi ret tslúaga
     má thánic do[5] thráth?'

'Rê fuiniud ré n-aidche
madat éicen airthe
comruc duid re Boirche
     [6]níba bán in gleó[6]
Ulaid acot gairm-seo
[7]rot gabsad ar t'ḟaill-seo[7]
bid olc dáib in taidbsiu
     ragthar tairrsi[8] is treó.'

'Dotrala i mbeirn báegail
[9]tánic cend do ṡáegail[9]
imbérthar fort fáebair
     níba fóill in fáth
Bid mórglonnach bías
[9]condricfa cach días[9]
níba toísech triair[10]
     ó 'niu co tí in bráth.'

---

[1] *sic* LL C, dodechaid Y   [2] *sic* LL C, eirc Y   [3-3] *sic* C, *om.* Y,
gid leind rarrficfam LL   [4] daig do Y   [5] a LL C   [6-6] *sic* LL C,
niba ba banna gleo Y   [7-7] ra ṅgabastar aillsiu LL C   [8] = tairrsiu
     [9-9] *sic* LL C, *om.* Y   [10] trías LL

'Dá mbámar ic Scáthaich
a llos gaiscidh gnáthaig
is amaráen[1] imríaghmais
   imtíagmais cach fích.   3060
Tú mo choicli cridi
tú m'acme tú m'fine
ní fúar[2] ríam ba dile
   ba dirsan do díth.'

'[3]Bí 'tast dím do robud[3]   3065
is tú is braisi ar domun
nítfía lúag ná logad
   [4]dáig ní[4] dos úas dus.

39[b]

| As misi rofitir
it gilla co ngicil   3070
a chridi inn eóin eitig
   cen gaisced cen gus.'

'Romór faidi[5] th 'enech
coná dernum deibech
siu gaireas in cailech   3075
   biaid do chend ar bir.
A C[h]ú C[h]ulaind Cúalinge
rotgab baile is búaidre
rotfía cach n-olc úaindi
   dáig is dait[6] a c[h]in.'   3080
              Can.

[7]Asbert Cú Chulaind íarom fria araid ara ngresad an tan ba ráen
fair et ara molad in tan ba ráen riam og comracc [8]fri Fer Diad[8].
Is íarom aspert a ara[9] fris;
'Tét an fer tarat amail téti bott tar catt[10].   Nodnigh an fer amail   3085
neghar coipp i llundai.   Notcúra an fer amail cúruss ben boídh a
mac.'
Is íarom lotar do chluichiu[11] an átha connigset[12] ind ro múin
Scáthach dóib díb línaibh   Cloisid Fer Diad ⁊ Cú Chulaind clesa
ingantai.   3090

---

[1] aróen LL *sic leg.*   [2] fuar LL, fuair Y C   [3-3] Beir ass dín do
robud LL C, *sic leg.*   [4-4] nidat LL C,   [5] fácbai LL C   [6] tait Y
[7] *Here a different hand begins* Y   [8-8] fria fer Y, fri fer C   [9] araid Y
[10] not tregda in fer amal tregdas rodb omna. Not timcella amal timcellas
feith fid *add.* C   [11] cluithi Y   [12] = co ngníset ?

Luid Cú Chulaind íarom co rro leblaing ina scíath Fir Diad. Focerd[1] Fer Diad húath isind áth co fo thrí. Co nangresed[2] in t-ara arithisi. [3]Ra lín at[3] ꝩ infisi amail anáil i llés[4]. Forbrid a méd co mba móam oltás Fer Diad.

3095 'Fomna an gaí mbulga!' ol in t-ara.

Dolléci[5] ndó lasan sruth. Gaibt[h]i Cú cona ladair ꝩ imambeir do Fir Diad[6] a timt[h]iracht a chuirp. Tochomlai amail óenga co mba cetheóra randa fichet. Tairindi Fer Diad sís in scíath[7] ar sodin.

Atnúara Cú Chulaind cusann gaí ósin scíath curro bris a cléith 3100 n-asnai conlá triana c[h]ride Fir Diad.

Trén uindes as do des
maidid asnae foidb
mo chride is crú.
Mad ro ferus báig
3105   dorochar, a Chúa.

Dursan a eó óir
a Fir Diad, a áin
a bailcbémnig chaín
ba búadach do lám.

3110   Ar comaltus cóem
a airer na súl
do scíath co mbil óir
do c[h]loidem ba cóem.

T'ornasc arcait báin
3115   immo do láim soír
t'fit[h]chell ba fiu móir
do grúadh c[h]orcra choín.

Do barr buidechas
ba bras ba caín sét
3120   do c[h]ris duillech máeth
no bíth imod thóeb.

---

[1] focerde Y   [2] Condo greisid C, *after this* C *breakd off, loss of leaf*
[3-3] riatiad Y (corrupt)   [4] llesss Y (*line end*)   [5] (Tolleci TBC[2])
[6] Diadd Y (*line end*)   [7] sis *repeated* Y

Do thoitim fria Cú
ba dirsan, a lóeg
nír anacht do scíath
no bíd lat fria feidm.   3125

Ar comracc ¹in tor-¹
ar mairce as ar ndeilm
ba caín in scál mór
no bristi ar cach slúag
no curthea fo thraig   3130
dursan a eó óir.
A Fir Diad.

                        et idem

Cluithe cách, caíne cách
co Fer Diad isind áth   3135
dursan úaitne óir
forfuirmedh for áth.

Cluichi cách, caíne cách
co Fer Diad isind áth   3140
indar limsa Fer dil Diad
is am diaid no biad co bráth.

40ᵃ | ²In tan trá bátar in tslóig oc techt ó Áth Fir Diad sades, boí Cú
Chulainn ina otharligiu andside conatatánicc³ ria cách Senoll
hÚathach co mbaí-side ⁊ dá mac Fice [and].   Dolotatar la Coin 3145
Chulaind for ⁴cúlaib ailli⁴ do ícc ⁊ búalad a c[h]récht do uscib Conailli.

It hé a n-anmanna-side⁵: Sás, Búan, Bithslán, Finnglas, Gleóir,
Bedc, Tadcc, Talaméd, Rindd, Bir, Brenide, Cumang, Cellend,
Gaenemain, Dichu, Muach, Miliucc, Den, Delt, Dubglaise.

Céine doluid Cú Chulaind íarom dia búalad asna huscib sin, lotar
an slúaig secha fodes co ngabsatt dúnad a nImorach Smiromrach. 3150
Dolluid⁶ Mac Roth ón tslóg fodes⁷ do frecomét ar hUltaib co mbaí i
Sléibh Fóit dúss ind faicfed nech ina ndiaid.   Isbert-side friu ná⁸
faca acht óen-charpat².

1-1 in *or* ni tor- Y (*read* ní cóir Windisch).   2-2 *whole section in later*
hand   ³ conata | tanicc Y, *read* condid tánicc?   4-4 *corrupt? Read* for
cúlu [do uscib Con]ailli *and omit last* 3 *words of sentence?*   ⁵ nanmandasid
Y   ⁶ (dolluidi TBC²)   ⁷ *sic* Y, *read* fothuaid   ⁸ nan Y

41^a | Dinda na Tána so sís

³¹⁵⁵ .i. CAladgleó Cethirn meic Findtain, Fiacalgleó Fintain,
Rúadruca Mind, Bángleó Rochada, Mellgleó Iliach,
Airicar nArad, Aisling nAimirgin, Sírrabad Súaltaim,
Tochestal nUlad, Aislingi Dubthaich, Aislingthi [Cormaic] Con
Longes, Toichim na mBuiden, Gleóud¹ in Chatha, Damgal na Tarb,
³¹⁶⁰ ²a Us² in Duib C[h]úalngni for Táin.

Caladgleó Cethirn ³inso afec[h]tsa³

'ATchíu-sa carpat tarsin mag atúaid⁴ indiu,' or Mac Roth, ⁊
fer findlíath cen gaisced⁵ acht óendelc n-argaid ina láim.
Indar lat is denn céttamun fil forsin carpat. Is cumma
³¹⁶⁵ congoin in [n]-araid ⁊ inna heocho. Is ed hed⁶ lais nícon tair in
slóg i mbethaid. Mílchú alath ríam.'
'Cia sin, a Fergais?' bar Ailill. 'In dóig bad é Conchobar ⁷nó
Celtchair⁷?'
'Nách dóich,' ol Fergus. 'Dóig lim immorro rombad hé Cethern
³¹⁷⁰ mac fial fóebuirderg Fintain.'
Ocus ba fír són didiu.
Fosnóbair-side íarom tresin dúnad ⁊ gontai-seom sochaidi, ⁊
gontar-som co mór co lluid cona inathar ima chosa dochum Con
Chulaind triasin cath. Arceisi de a guin.
³¹⁷⁵ 'Cuinnig liaig dam-sa,' ol Cethern fri Coin Chulaind.
Dogníthi cosair úrlóchra dó ⁊ frithadart fris. Is and foídis Cú
Chulaind Lóeg úad isin duibdúnad⁸ co Fiacha mac Fir Febe do
chuindchid legi ⁊ asbert nosmairfed-som uile cid fo thalmain no
betis isin dúnad mani ríastais chucai-som do c[h]omchisin Cethirn.
³¹⁸⁰ Nírbo réid lasna leigi anní sin ar ní baí isin dúnad náchidrubad-som.
Tégit⁹ as trá na leigi dia indsaigid. Danéici íarom in cétna liaig
donánic.
'Nícon bía a mbethaid,' or seiside.
'Nícon bía-so didiu it bethaid,' ol Cethern. Beantai dia durn co
³¹⁸⁵ tuilid¹⁰ a inchind fora chlúasaib. Marbaid cóecait leigi díib fón indus
sin, nó marbaid cóic firu déac díb amin. In fer déidenach níndránic
acht ind mbéimme conid corastair i mmúaidhi¹¹. Anachtai-side la
Co[i]n Culaind íarom.

---

¹ gleo C   ²⁻² (Aus TBC²), Us C   ³⁻³ cetus C   ⁴ sic C, antuaid Y
⁵ ann add. C   ⁶ sic Y, illegible C, read mod   ⁷⁻⁷ om. C   ⁸ dunad C
⁹ Tegit Y, Tecait C   ¹⁰ sic Y, illegible C, read tuiled or tuilend?   ¹¹ itir
na legha eile add. C

Tíagar úaidib co Fíngin fáithliaig .i. liaig Conchobuir, co tísad do choimchisin Con Culaind ⁊ Cethirn. **3190**

'Ní maith dait,' or Cú Chulaind fri Cethern, 'na leigi da marbad. Ní fuigébthar for[r]o tuidecht cucut itir[1].'

'Ní maith dóib-som didiu epert ind uilc frim-sa.'

Air is ed adbered cach liaig díb adoféchad ná bad beó ⁊ ná bad indlego itir, conid iar sin nambenad-som[2] cona durn. **3195**

Conacadar-som in carpat Fíngin a ndochum, air adcúas dó trummi do Choin Chulaind ⁊ do Chethern.

Téiti Cú Chulaind ara c[h]end.

'Foimte dún Cethern,' or Cú Chulaind, '⁊ ba di chén ar ro marb cóic leigi déac ocu.' **3200**

Téit Fíngin cuici.   Danéici di chéin.

41[b]   'Cotumaici-si,' | ol Cethern.   'Is tend[3] lim in forgom sa cetadomránic[4].'

'Bangal báethúallach insin,' or[5] Fíngin.

'Is dóig bid fír,' ol Cethern.   'Dománic ben[6] máethainech bánai- **3205** nech lecanfata chaínmar[7].   Mong find fuirri[8], ⁊ dá én óir fora gúalaind, ⁊ brat tlachtgorm corcarrda [9]hi cennfait impe[9].   Cóicdornn fuillechta di ór ara druim[10].   Craísech[11] foráith fáebrach étrom ina léim.   Claideb benndornach[12] iarna imdae [13]osé amulach[13].   Is mór a delb.   Is é[14] rombí ⁊ cetadomthánic.' **3210**

'Aill amae!' or Cú Chulaind.   'Meadb Crúachan sin.'

'Fingal étrom induthrachtach inso.   Nítbérat,' ol in liaig.

'Is fír,' ol Cethernn.   'Dománic ócláech.   Cromscíath co fáebar condúala fair.   Sleg c[h]uarrind ina láim.   Calc dét [15]iarna imda[15].   [14]Trí tuith[16] fair.   Brat donn i filliud imbi, delg n-argait n-and. **3215** Ruc fuil mbic húaim-sea.'

'Rofetar-sa,' or Cú Chulaind.   'Illand mac Fergusa meic Róig sin.'

'Galach dá féindid andso,' ol in liaig.

'Is fír,' or Cethern.   'Damánic dias.   Dá fotalscíath leó, dá fiamchalad arcaid for cechtar de, búaile argait im chechtar n-aí. **3220** Dí sleig cúicrindi leu, féthan arggait imppu.   Tuidmaíle foraib. Muinchorach n-argaid im chec[h]tar n-aí.'

'Rosfetar-sa,' ol Cú Chulaind.   'Oll ⁊ Oichne, dá dalta Ailella ⁊ Medba, insin.   Nícon[17] tíagait a noíndin itir nach erdalta gona duine bís leó-som[18].   It é[19] nodgonad.' **3225**

---

[1] afrithisi C   [2] nambennadsom Y   [3] tinn C   [4] citedomranic Y, cetadom[ranic] C   [5] orsin Y, ar C   [6] laech C   [7] caoinmar C, *read* chaín már?   [8] fair C   [9-9] i cendaitt uimbi C   [10] durn C [11] gai C   [12] bendornach Y, bendach C   [13-13] *sic* Y C, *omitt.*   [14] *sic* Y C, *read* í   [15-15] iarnimda Y, *illeg.* C   [16-16] *sic* Y, *illeg.* C *Read* Tuidmaíle (*as in* LL), trí *omitt.*   [17] *sic* C, Nico Y n-*stroke omitted*   [18] *sic* C, leoso Y m-*stroke omitted*   [19] iet C

'Dománcadar dá lóech aili didiu,' ol Cethern. 'Coṅgraim n-án n-éicside foraib oté ferrnaidi.'

'Rusfetar-sa,' ol Cú Chulaind. 'Bun ⁊ Mecon insin di ṡain-muintir ind ríg.'

3230 '¹Duba ind ḟuil se¹,' ol in liaig. 'Dochótar triat chridi forr-tharrsnu co ndernsat crois de indut. Ní argenus² a nn-ícc,' ol sé, 'Fil lim immorro di ḟeib eolais co náchatbertais³.'

'Dergrúathar dá mac⁴ ríg Chailli inso,' ol in liaig.

'Is fír,' ol Cethern. 'Dommánic dias óicḟénded oté findliatha
3235 ⁊ fidc[h]úach ⁵cechtar de is mó⁵. Fír,' ol Cethern, 'dochóid a mbiur-sa tresind ala n-aí.'

'Rusfetar-sa,' ol Cú Chulaind. 'Dagóic do mórthelig Meadba insin. Bróen ⁊ Láiréne, dá mac teóra soillse, dá mac ríg C[h]ailli.'

'Congal trí níath anísiu,' ol Fíngin⁶ .i. in liaig.
3240 'Fír,' or sé. 'Dománic triar cutrumai. Rond créduma eturra rocrechta fo eill ⁊ luin.'

'Trí trúaill Banba insin di muintir⁷ C[h]on Raí meic Dáiri.'

'Búrach trí féindetha⁸ annísiu,' or Fíngin.

'Fír,' or sé. 'Dománic triar ócḟénde[d]. Congraim⁹ féindidi
3245 foraib. Muntorc¹⁰ argaid ¹¹ima mbráigit¹¹ cach áe ⁊ dorn lán do
42ᵃ c[h]ruíseachaib la cach n-áe. Adcomaing cach fer | díb biur n-indam-sa. Adcomchus-[s]a a ṁbiur sa tria cechtar de didiu¹².

Triar¹³ di ḟéindedaib na hIrúaithi insin,' ol Cú Chulainn.

'Doreclasa¹⁴ ara n-amainsi dot guin. Imruidbiset ém,' ol in
3250 liaig, 'féithi do chridi indit co n-imreith do chridi indit amail ceirtli a fásbolg. ¹⁵Ní ricaim¹⁵,' ol Fíngin.

'Imathc[h]osán¹⁶ trí feólc[h]ar inso,' or Fíngin.

'Is fír,' ol Cethern. 'Dománic triar remar mór ro bádar oc mo muídim ria siu domístais. Trí broine liatha foraib.'
3255 'Trí rechtaire Medba ⁊ Aililla sin,' or Cú Chulaind. 'Scenb ⁊ Rand ⁊ Fodail.'

'Trí bémend maitine inso,' or Fíngin.

---

¹⁻¹ Dub in fuil si C   ² sic Y C = argénus? read argén-sa?   ³ a muchai add. C (i mmucha LL)   ⁴ om. Y C   ⁵⁻⁵ sic Y (corrupt), for muin cech ai C, sic leg.   ⁶ Fengine Y   ⁷ muinter Y   ⁸ sic Y, feinnedh C   ⁹ sic C, congarman Y   ¹⁰ sic C, triar muntorc Y (triar misplaced, prob. marginal in exemplar)   ¹¹⁻¹¹ im bragaitt C, sic leg.   ¹² sic Y, cechtarde dibseom C   ¹³ Triar dano C, om. Y (prob. triar supra l. 3244)   ¹⁴ (doreclamsa TBC² but I read as unintentional overhead stroke, not m), do[r]ecclasai C   ¹⁵⁻¹⁵ (nir caim TBC²) (second i faint Y), ni ricai(m) C   ¹⁶ (mathcosan TBC²) Mathchosan C

'Fír,' ol Cethern. 'Dománic triar ócíénde[d]. Putrall máile duibe for cach n-áe. Cochléne brec lígda im gach n-aé ⁊ trí lorga iairn ina lámaib.'   3260

'Trí Fruích Baíscne sin, trí fuis méisi Medba,' or Cú Chulaind.

'Attach dá derbráthar inso,' ol Fíngin.

'Is fír,' or Cethern. 'Damánic dias cétríglach[1]. Dá brat dub-glasa impu. Dá chromscíath co fáebar c[h]ondúala foraib. Manaís lethanglas for crunn midsing[2] i lláim cechtar de.'   3265

'Rofetar,' or Cú Chulaind. 'Cormac Colomon ind ríg ⁊ Cormac Maíle Ogath,'

'It imfoicsi[3] ém inn ÿuil ro fersat fort,' ol in liaig. 'It c[h]róes dochótar [4]a ndís[4]. Immosrocréchtatar[5] a ngái indut[6].'

'Cungus dá derbráithre inso,' ol in liaigh.   3270

'Dóig,' ol Cethern. 'Domáinic dias ócláech. Folt cass buide forsin dara n-aí, folt cas dond fora chéli. Dá gelscíath leu co túagmílaib óir. [7]Claideb dorngel[7] [8]iarna n-imdaib[8]. [9]Léini c[h]ul-patach[9] co nndergindliud impu.'

'Rusfetar,' or Cú Chulaind. 'Mane Aithremail ⁊ Maine Máith-   3275 remail andsin.'

'Imrubad meic ⁊ athar inso,' or in liaig.

'Is fír,' ol Cethern. 'Damráncadar dá ÿer dermóra caindeldercai co mbendaib óir fora cennaib. Claideb órduirn foa choim cech ÿir. Ferbolc impu co tici a ndí aithircc. Ardarcc óir bric im chechtar de.'   3280

'Rosfetar,' or Cú Chulaind.' "Ailill sin ⁊ a mac .i. Mane Condus-geb Uile.'

'Ceist cindas atomchíi-sea, a poba a Ÿíngin?' ol Cethern.

'Ní gó ém,' ol Fíngin, 'nítad tabartha buí duit ar dartaib indosa.[10] Céin ba deisib ⁊ tririb, ba herusa do chomchisi' or Fíngin. 'In tan   3285 as slicht slúaig[11], ar [12] atbéla do anim cip cruth.'

Imsoí[13] Fíngin in carpat úad la sodain.

'Romsechis-[s]e amail do chéiliu.'

Is and tucaib[14] dornd dó co mbaí dar dí ÿert in charpait condreised[15] in carpat huile.   3290

Is andsin asbert Cú Chulaind:

[1] sic C, cetrilach with letter elided after i, no righlach gloss added later in margin Y   [2] midhsing aspiration mark added later, no e added above i of -sing Y, miseng C   [3] imoicsi with f added later Y, imfaicsi C   [4–4] read after ro fersat?   [5] immosrocechatar with c and t added later after -ch- Y, imosroechetar C   [6] duit Y, indutt C   [7–7] claidib dorngelae C   [8–8] sic C, iarna imda (a added later after n) Y   [9–9] leinti culpaidhechai C   [10] ar cia dobertha ni tú féin nodus meala add. C   [11] nit rocar ic motpera forsna sluagadh (sic) add. C = ní trócairech 'motbéra forsna slúagaib?   [12] omitt.?   [13] sic C, amsai Y   [14] sic Y C   [15] conid geis C

'Is dúaig in lúae sengrantae se lat[1].'

Is de atá [2]Óchtur Lúi[2] hi Crích Rois beós[3].

'Ba córu bid for náimdib immabertha[4],' or Cú Chulaind, 'oldás[5]
3295 for legi[6].

42[b] Is andsin íarom erpais in léig togu dó, im bad buith fora | huthar
co cend mbliadna ⁊ beathu dó íarom fa nert trí lá ⁊ trí n-aidchi fo
chétóir do imbirt fora náimdib. Is ed ón íarom [7]do thog-sam[7].

Is íarom condiacht Cú Chulaind smiur don léig dia frepaid[8]. Do-
3300 rigne[9] smirchomairt[10] di chnámaib ina cethra frisi comairnig. Is de
atá Smirombair a Crích Rois.

Co ro chotail lá co n-aidche iar n-ól in smero[11].

'Nímthat asnai,' or Cethern. 'Tabair asnai creti in charpait
indium,' or sé.

3305 'Rotbía,' or Cú Chulaind.

'Mad mo gaisced fén [12]do beith[12] no beth agum-sa,' or sé, 'robad
airisiu co bráth a ndogénainn.'

'Inmain samail frisnid[13] cosmail a n-adchíu-sa,' or Cú Chulaind.

'Cid atchí-si?' ol Cethern.

3310 'Cosmail lim bid hé carpat [14]Finde Becce ingine Echdach[14] do[15]
mná-so dotáesad cucund.'

Conacatar ní: in mnaí[16] cosin ṅgaisced isin charput.

Gaibid Cethern[17] a gaisced ⁊ fosnópair in slóg íarom ⁊ a chreit a
c[h]arpait [18]i nn-imnaidm fria thairr[18] ar mba treisi di.

3315 Berid robud remi isin dúnud in liaig marb[19] hí thall adrolla
úadh-som remi ro baí itir collaib na legi n-aile.

Is íarom ara omun-som foruirmed mind nAilella[20] forsin coirthi.
Fóbair-som didiu in coirthi ⁊ benaidh in claideb trít co luid a dornn
trít i ndeadaid[21] in c[h]laidib. Is de atá Liaa Toll i Crích Rois.

3320 'Is brég anísa trá,' or sé. 'Nícon aniub-sa díb ém,' for sé, 'conid-
nacor for duine in mind se Ailella.'

Is íarom conmelt foroib [22]laithe co n-aidchi[22] [23]coro gab[23] Mane
fora chend in mind ⁊ fosfóbair ina charpat remi. Focherd didiu
a scíath ina diaid conid ro rand cona araid ⁊ co lluid triasna[24]
3325 heocho hi talmain.

---

[1] beos add. Y C (misplaced)   [2-2] Uachtar Lua C   [3] taken from end of
preceding sentence   [4] imbertha C, read immotbertha?   [5] sic C, ol Y
(scribal error) and attempt to add some letter after 1)   [6] leghaib C   [7-7] ro
toghsomh C   [8] frebaid Y, freptai C   [9] Dorigne Cu Chulaind C   [10] smir
don liaigh C   [11] ⁊ ierna fotracadh and add. C   [12-12] sic Y, om. C, omitt.
[13] frisnad (sic) C   [14-14] Findbéice iṅgine Echach C   [15] da Y   [16] mai
(n- stroke omitted) Y   [17] ass add. C   [18-18] imbi C   [19] sic C, in marg. Y
[20] nAileillo Y   [21] = ṅdegaid, ndeadh C   [22-22] laithiu conaithiu Y, la
co n-aidchi C   [23-23] cor gaib | ib Y, coro gaib C   [24] trina C

Ro iadh in slóg imbi-som íarom.   Conmelt-som didiu foraib co
torchair eturru amlaid[1].

[2]Fiacalgleó Findtain so sís[2]

IS íarum dolluid Findtan do dígail a meic doraib.   Trí cóecait
fer n-imrind dó.   Dá gáe for cach crunn leu, ⁊ fochroisse impu. 3330
Dober-sidi secht cathu dóib conná térno nech dia muintir[3] acht
héseom fesin ⁊ a mac.   Is íarom etarscarthar-side fris-[s]om [4]fon
amdabaid scíath[4], ⁊ anachta la hAilill ara omun-som ⁊ ar nách
n-imbred foraib co tísad la Conc[h]obar don chath.
Dobert-som cairdi friu-som íarom ar telcod a meic dó.   3335

[5]Rúadrucca Mind annso sís[5]

DOlluid Mend mac Salchada chucu íarom, trícha fer n-imrind
dó.   Docer la Meidb[6] íarom dá fer déac díib-som ⁊ dá fer
déc dia muintir-som[7] didiu, ⁊ goíta-som fesin calad ⁊ ba
forrderg a muinter.   Is de atá Rúadrucca Mind.   3340
Doléicsed dúnad iar sin do Miunn ⁊ ní gegain-side didiu nech
43ª díb-som acht insin namá. | [8]Asbreth fris ní bboí cin no mbeith
dóib[8].   Ní adalsad a mendot for Bóaind hi Correndaib.   Is and
baí-side ⁊ ní po sár dó telcudh dúnaid dó co taísed don chath la
Conc[h]obar.   3345

Bángleó Rochada annso

IS íarom dosnáinic Rochad Rigderg mac Faithemain di Ultaib,
trícha fer n-imrin[n] dó, ⁊ gabais telaich ina farrad ⁊ arfócarthar
isin dúnad.   Asbert Findabair íarom ba hé a cétṡerc.
'Má rodcarais didiu,' or Ailill ⁊ Medb, 'guid ossad dó co tí la 3350
Conc[h]obar don chath, ⁊ foí lais ambárach d'adaig.'
Dogníth uile [9]cen corbo réith a breith fair[9].   Focres a phupall
do ṡuidiu a Findabair ⁊ faíd laisin n-ingin.
Adfiadar són dona secht rígaib di Muma.   Asbert rí díb-side.
'Dobrethai dam-sa an ingen sin,' ol sé, 'for cóic aitirib déac [10]ar 3355
tuideacht in tslúaigid sea[10].'

---

[1] ar in calad sin unde Caladgleo Cethirn C   [2-2] *om.* C   [3] muinter Y
[4-4] *read after* la hAilill, *misplaced*   [5-5] *om.* C   [6] idb *on erasure* Y,
read Mend   [7] muintersom Y   [8-8] ismbred fris ni mbai cin ima *mbet*
doibh C; *read* ní boí cin 'no (= 'na) mbeith dóib?   [9-9] ⁊ nibo reith firsim
(*sic*) a breith fair C   [10-10] *om.* C

Atamatar a móirṡeiser dambreth[1] [2]da cách[2] úadib in cor sin.
Tíagait dia dígail íarom for maccu Ailella i nGlenn Domain.   Bátar
oc foraire ón tslóg.

[3360] Faráith Medb ón íarom.   Faráith in trícha cét na nGailian
Faráith Ailill.   Faráith Fergus.   Docertar[3] and secht cét i n-Im-
ṡligi Glindi Domain.

Is hé Bángleó Rochada insin ⁊ [4]Imṡligi Gleanndomnach[4].

Rochúalai Findabair annísin .i. apthain na secht cét triana
[3365] fochann[5].   Atbail ar ḟéili [6]and sin[6].   Is de atá Findabair Slébe.

Meillgleó nIliach so

DOlluid chucu íarom hIlech senathair Lóegairi Búadaig[7] for
Áth Feidli.   Lóegaire Búadach mac Connaich Buidi meic
hIliach.   Buí [8]icá gairi[8] la húa hi Ráith Impail.   Dofóccair
[3370] [9]dochom in tslúaig[9] co tóetsad a [n]dígail lais.

Is amlaid [10]dolluid ina charput c[h]retach n-imbi[10] cen fogaimen
cen fortgai.   Dí ṡengabair buidi fón c[h]arput crín.   Ocus línais a
charpat n-imbi di c[h]lochaib co mbu lán co tici a ḟocharpat[11].

Asorggad cách dothéiged dia déchsain ossé tarrnocht lebarpentol
[3375] ⁊ in clapar triasin creit sís.   Rathaigis íarom in slóg indas [12]in
toichime[12] dombert, contibset in fear tarnocht.   Is and [13]ro choisc[13]
Dóchae mac Mágach in dáescorslóg ocon chuidmead, ⁊ asbert-som
fri sudiu tara héisi is é no bered a c[h]laideb ⁊ no bíad a chend de
deuth laí [14]acht imrobreth-som[14] a chumaṅg forsi[n] slóg.

[3380] La sodain raithigestair[15] in smirc[h]omairt.   Adfes dó ba do
chnámaib bó nUlad dogníth.   Is íarom dogní-som in smirc[h]-
omairt n-aile ina farrad co fil in dí smirumair immaille [16]di chnámaib
43[b] | fer Ól nÉcmacht[16].

Gatais Dócha a chend de-som íarom d'adaich [17]⁊ bertai[17] dia
[3385] húa.   Dogéni cairdes fri suidiu ⁊ baí a c[h]laideb lais.

Mellgleó Iliach sin [18]uair condidnatib in slóg[18].

---

[1] ⁊ dam breth Y, dobretha C   [2-2] do cach aen C   [3] docearatar C
[4-4] Imsligi Glinne Domain C   [5] bithin C   [6-6] sin Y *and space before*
word, indsein C   [7] buagaich Y   [8-8] *om.* C   [9-9] doṅ tsluag C
[10-10] boi in carpat cretach n-imbiu C   [11] fogaimen C   [12-12] na
toichme C   [13-13] consechae .i. ro coisc C   [14-14] acht ro imbridsom C
[15] *sic* Y, *rathaigsim* C, *read* rathaigestair   [16-16] *sic* Y C, *misplaced from after*
n-aile   [17-17] ⁊ bertai ⁊ bentai Y, et *bentais* C   [18-18] uain condidnatib
in slóg Y, ba huime conatib (*read* cotnatib)in sluagh C

Airecor nArad ann so

DOllotar dochum Thaillten íarum in slóig.   Ataroirthet[ar]
araid Ulad, trí chóeca a llín.   Dofuitet a[1] trí comlín leó
⁊ dofuitet-som feisine.

3390

Roí[2] Arad is hed a ainm ind luic i torchratar[3] [4]cona feadain ar
Tánaig Bó Cúailṅgi[4].

Aislinge nAimirgin annso

AIslingi nAimirgin trá iar sin hi tír Thailten.   Dosmbidc[5] asa
aislingi coná hétad [6]dune a ainech do[6] i Tailtin.

3395

Is and táinic Cú Raí mac Dáire cusin slóg do chomruc fri
Coin Culaind.   Adchúas dó ro gab a óenur trí mísa gaimrid fri feraib
hÉrend.   Ní ba fearrda la Coin Ruí mac Dáiri[7] teacht íarom ara
cheand ind fir tregdaithi créchtaigthi, ar ro bíth Cú Chulaind co
ndec[h]aid a áltaib[8] dó.   Is íarom dobidc Cú Raí díbrucud[9] ar ceann 3400
araile fri hAmargine co 'mmafrecraidis na clocha isinn áer.   Is íarom
gáid Cú Raí inní Amargine im légud ina tána dar Tailtin.   Léicsis
íarom Amargin.   Nír bo machtad immorro bith ar égin nombertha.

Ocus doringelt Cú Ruí dó-som nád bíad i coímthecht in tslóig ón
húair sin.   Dogníth didiu.   Luith Cú Raí [10]ón tslóg[10] fo chétóir. 3405

In tan íarum adidchondairc Amairgin dosoíset clár clé fri
Tailtin ⁊ fri Ráith nAirthir, feccais forro aithirrach.

Is ed tres[11] ṅdiríme na Tána arro marb díb-sin.   Ocus a mac
Conall Cernach[12] anais lais oco thimthirecht di c[h]lochaib ⁊ gaib.

Sírrabad Súaldaim annso

3410

CÉini dongníthea trá ina hí-siu adchuadamar[13] rocluinethar
Súaltaim[14] ó Ráith Súaltaim i mMaig Muirrthemne búadrugud
a meic Con Culaind fri dá mac déc Gaile Dána ⁊ mac a ṡethar.
Is and asbert Súaltaim:

'In nem maides fa muir thar chrícha fa thalam conscara fa gáir 3415
mo maic se,' ol sé, 're n-éccomlonn?'

[1-1] *sic* C, an Y   [2-2] Ré C   [3-3] torchar ar Y, torcratar C   [4-4] *om.* C,
Conid Airecor nArad innsin on airegar dobertsat for na trensluagaib *add.* C
   [5] dosbiudc Y, dosmbedcc C   [6-6] *sic* Y, *read* dune no lamad a ainech do
thaisbénad (*or* thócbáil) dó *or the like,* duine dorucath ainech C   [7] frisin
slóg *add.* Y C (*misplaced gloss on* fri feraib hÉrend)   [8] altaib Y, haltoib C
   [9] dib dibrucud Y   [10-10] *original reading of* Y, a ndiaid *added later above,*
on tsl*u*ag C   [11] tris Y   [12] chernach Y   [13] adchuidimar Y,
atcuadamar C   [14] suallaith Y

Dothét íarom dochum a meic.　Ba holc la suide[1] tuidhecht dó chuccai.　Cia nongonta ní mbiad-som nert dia dígail.

'Erg co hUltu,' ol Cú Chulaind, '⁊ taibret cath fo chétóir donaib
3420 óccaib.　Mani thibreat, [2]nícon díastar foraib[2] co bráth.'

Ammanaca[3] a athair íarom nícon robai [4]ina chorp áit[4] | [5]forsa　　**44ª**
roised[5] rind simni nád bad[6] tregdaithi.　A lám c[h]lé namá doet in
scíath, coíca fuile is ed ro baí inti.　Farruma do Emain, congair do
Ultaib:

3425 'Fir gontair, mná brattar, baí agthar!'

A chétna gairm a táeb ind lis, [7]anní n-aill[7] di thaibled[8] in
dúne, an tres gairm íarom for Duma na nGiall i nEmain.

Ní frecart nech.　Ba airmert di Ulltaib ní labrad nech díb acht[9]
fri Conc[h]obar, ní labrad Conc[h]obar acht[10] [11]ressna tríb druídib[11].
3430 'Cista brata, cisda gata, cisda ben?' ol in draí.

'Nos mben,' ol Súaltaim, 'nos gata, no mbrata Ailill mac Máta la
heolus Fergusa meic Róig.　Ro indertha far muinter co tici Dún
Sobairc[h]e.　Ructha a mbaí ⁊ a mná ⁊ a n-éti.　[12]Nís leíci[12] Cú
Chulaind a Maig Murthemne ⁊ a Crích Rois trí mísa gaimrid.　Túaga
3435 trá congabait a brat fair.　Suip šesca fail ina áltaib[13].　Ro gáet co
ndechaid a áltaib[14] dó.

'Ba huise[15],' ol in draí, 'a bás ind fír ro gresi ind ríg.'

'Is deithbir dó,'[16] ol Conc[h]obar.

'Is dedbir dó,' ol Ulaid[16].

3440 'Is fír a canas Sualda[i]m,' ol Conc[h]obar, 'Ón lúan aidche
samnai co ricci lúan aidchi imbuilc ocor n-indred.'

Focherd Súaltaim bedc imach la sodain.　Nír lór lais [17]a n-aithesc[17]
rodbaí.　Ocus dofuit fora scíath co mbí fáebar conndúala in scéith
a chenn de.　Dobeir [18]i nEmain[18] aitherroch a chend forsin scíath
3445 [19]isa teach[19] ⁊ asbeir an cend an focol cétna.　—[20]Cia asberat[20]
alaili[21] is inna c[h]otlud [22]ro boí-som[22] forsind liaic, ⁊ is de dorochair
fora scíath oc diuchtrad.

'Ba romór a núall sa trá,' ol Conchobar.　'Muir ara cendaib, in
nem húasa mbennaib, talum foa cosaib, dobér-sa cech mboin ina
3450 hindis díb ⁊ cach mben ⁊ cech mac dia tig iar mbúaid chatha.'

---

[1] sic C, suthe Y　　[2-2] sic Y, ni bia tocbail cind doib C　　[3] f added later
above aca Y, imfaca C　　[4-4] ina charpat (sic) Y, ina corp C (áit omitted)
[5-5] forsa roi sed Y space before s (forsaroi acht TBC²), forsa rosith C　　[6] ba C
[7-7] anni | naill Y, a n-aill C　　[8] taib- led Y, taiblib C　　[9] in marg. Y
[10] added later under line Y　　[11-11] fri nech dinaib trib druithib C　　[12-12] Nis
reilic C　　[13] aaltaib Y　　[14] altaib Y, haltaib C　　[15] hisa Y, hussa C
[16-16] ol in ri ocus ol Ulaid C　　[17-17] in t-aitesc C　　[18-18] indemain Y C
[19-19] sic Y, isin tech C, read in t-ech after dobeir?　　[20-20] ciasi berad Y,
cias atberat C　　[21] sic C, alailiu Y　　[22-22] ro boi so Y C

Forrumai Conchobar íarom láim fora mac, for Findchad Fer
mBend. —Is aire asberar do ṡuidiu fo bíth no mbítis benna
argaid fair.

Tochestol Ulad inso

'ATroí, a Ḟindchaid! Not foídiu co Dedad[1] có inber, co [3455]
Leamain, co Fallach, co hIllann mac Fergossa, co Gabar, co
Dorlunsa, co hImc[h]láriu, co Derg Inderuc, co Feidlimid
[2]co Cilar Cétach[2], co Fáeladán, co Rochaid mac Faithemain co
Rigdond, co Lugaid, co Lugda, co Cathbuith[3] có inber, co trí Coir-
briu co hAelai, [4]co Lae[g] | coa thachur,[4] [5]coa Glend[5], oc Senoll [3460]
hUathach, co Débul Ardda, co Cethirn mac Findtain [co] Carlaig,
[6]co Cethern co Eillne[6], co Aurothor[7], co Mulaig coa dún, cosin rígfilid
co hAmirgin, [8]cosin nŪathadaich Fodoblaid,[8] [9]cosin Mórrignai[9] co
Dún Sobairche co hIeth, co Roth, co Fiachna có ḟert, co Dam
Dremed, co Andiaraid co Mane mac mBraitharge, co Dam Derg, co [3465]
Mod, co Maithes, co hIrmaithis, co Corp Gliath, [10]co Gabar Leigi
Line[10], co hEchtaich[11] Sainmech[12], co Saimne, [13]co hEchdaich Lathach[13] co Latharnu, [14]co hUma mac Remarbisi[41], co Fethain[15],
co Muinremur mac Gerrgind, co Senlobair co Canaind nGall, co
Follamain, co Lugaid rí Fer mBolc, [16]co Laigi Line[16], co Búaidgalach, [3470]
[17]co Ambúach[17], co Fergna, co Barrene, co hÁine, [18]co hAirigi
nEchbél coa bri[18], co Celtchar mac Cuithechair co Lethglais, co
Lóegairi Milbél có breó, co trí macaib [19]Dromscailṫ meic Dregamm[19],
co Drenda, co Drendas, co Cimb, co Cimling, co Cimmene, [20]co Fána
Caba[20] co Fachtna mac Senchath, [21]coa ráith[21], co Senchaid, co [3475]
Senchairthe, co Briccir, co Bricirne, co Breic, co Búan, co Bairech[22],
co hÓengus mac Leti, co Fergus mac Leiti, co hÓengus Fer m[B]olg
co Bruachar[23] co hAlaniach in fénnich[24] co Slánge, co trí macu
Fiachna[25] co Cúailṅge, co Conall Cernach co Midlúachair, co Connad

---

[1] co Ardo co Moen add. C   [2-2] oc hIlar cetaig C, Chilair chetaig LL
[3] Cathbad C, Cathbath LL   [4-4] co Laeg coa thōchur LL, sic leg.   [5-5] co
Geimen coa Glend LL, sic leg.   [6-6] om. LL, omitt.   [7] Torothor C,
Tarothor LL   [8-8] cosin Uathaig Fodoblaid C, cosin nUathaig mBodba LL
[9-9] cosin Morrigain C LL, sic leg.   [10-10] co Gabarlaig i lLine LL   [11] om.
C, Eocho LL, hEochaidh St   [12] saimnech TBC[2], om. C, semnech LL
[13-13] co hEochaid Latach C, co hEochaidh Laithrech St   [14-14] co hUma
mac Rémorbsi C, co hUma mac Remarfessig LL   [15] Fedain Cualṅge LL
[16-16] co Laeg di Line C, co Lugdaig Line LL   [17-17] co Búach C, co
hAbach LL   [18-18] . . . co habra Y, co hAirigi Echbel co Bri C, co hErrgi
Echbél co Bri Errgí LL   [19-19] Trosgail LL, Trioscatail St   [20-20] co
Fán na Coba LL   [21-21] co haraid Y, coa ráith LL   [22] Boairne C,
Barach LL   [23] Bruchur Y, Bruachur C LL   [24] feindid C   [25] co
Ross co Daire co Imchaid add. LL

3480 mac Morna co Felunt[1], co Coin Culaind mac Súaltaim co Muirthemne, co hAimirgin co hEas Rúaid, co Lóeg, co Leiri, [2]co mac
Sálc[h]olca[2] co Coirenda, co [3]Coin Rí[3] mac Amargin [4]coa ráith[4], co
hÓengus Fer mBenn Umai, co hOgma nGrianainech, co Brecc, co
hEo mac nOircne[5], co Toillc[h]end, co Saithi, co Mogoll Echbél [6]co
3485 Magnai[6], co Conla Sáeb co hÚarba, co Láegairi mBuagach co
hImpail, [7]co hAilile nAmargine[7] co Tailtin, co Furbaidi Fer Benn
[8]co Seil co Manes[8] [9]co Cúscraid Mend, co Maich[9], co Fíngin co
45ᵃ Findgabra, co Cremath | co Blae Fichit, co Blae Brugaich, co
Fesair, co hEógan mac Durthacht co Fer[n]mag, [10]co hOrd[10],
3490 [11]co Seirid co Serthe[11], co hOblán, co Cuilén, co Cuirther[12] co Liana,
co hEithbenne, co Fernél, co Findc[h]ath Slébe Betha, co Talgobain[13]
co Bearnas, [14]co Mend mac Fer Calca[14], co Maigi Dulo, co hÍroll co
Blárígi, [15]co Tibraidi mac nAilcotha[15] [16]co hIala Ingraimme[16] [17]co
Maigi Doblo co Ros mac nAilchatha[17] [18]co Mane mac Cruinn[18], [19]co
3495 Nindich mac Cruind[19] [20]co Dipsemilid[20], [21]co Mál mac Rochraidi[21],
[22]co Muindi mac Munremair[22], [23]co Fiatach Fer nDoirre mac Dubthaich[23], [24]co Muirne Mend[24].

[25]Nírbo andsa thrá do Findchath a techtaireacht [26]ar ro bátar[26]
cóiceth Conchobair huile, cach tigerna díb, oc irnaidi Conchobair.
3500 Nach óen trá baí fri hEmain anair ⁊ antúaid ⁊ aníar[27] dolotar uile co
mbádar oc Emain Macha. In tan [28]bátar and[28] adcúaladar
comérge do Chonc[h]obar i nnEmain. Lotar-som sech Eamain
fodeas i ndiaid in tslóig.

A cétna tochumluth íarom ó Emain co hIrard Cuilleand.
3505 'Cid fris n-anaid sund?' ol Conchobar.

---

[1] sic Y, Felann C, Callaind LL   [2-2] sic Y, co Menn mac Salcolco C, co
Mend mac Salcholcan LL   [3-3] Conri Y, Coin Righ C, Condraid LL
[4-4] co haraithi Y, co haraith C, coa ráith LL   [5] Oircni C, Forne LL
[6-6] co Maigne C   [7-7] co hAmergin Iergiun C, co hAmargin Iarngiun-
naig LL   [8-8] co Síl co Mag nInis LL, sic leg.   [9-9] co Cumscruidh
Mend Macha C, co Causcraid Mend Macha mac Conchobuir co Macha LL
[10] sic C LL, co Dord Y   [11-11] co Seirid C, co Serthig (th added over
line) LL   [12] Cuirechair C, Curethar LL   [13] Salgabann C, Talgo-
baind LL   [14-14] co Mend mac Fir Chúaland LL   [15-15] co Tipritte
mac nIlchada C, om. LL   [16-16] co nIla ngraimine C, co hÍalla nIlgremma
LL   [17-17] co Maigi co Blai co Rus mac Ailchada C, co Ros mac nIlchroth-
aig co Mag Nobla LL   [18-18] co Mane mac Crunn Y, co Mane mac
Cruinn C, om. LL   [19-19] co Nindid mac Cruinn C (placed last in list), om.
LL   [20-20] co Dinbsid Milid C, om. LL   [21-21] om. LL   [22-22] co
Muinne, co Munremar C, co Bunni mac Munremair LL   [23-23] co Fiachna
Fer nDaire mac Dubtaig C, Fidach mac Doraire LL   [24-24] om. C LL
[25] Aisling Cormaic Con Longes so added before this section Y (misplaced)
[26-26] at added above later Y, ro boi C   [27] in tan batar and add. Y (mis-
placed) om. C   [28-28] om. C

'Oc irnaidi do mac-su,' or in slóg.   'Dochótar co tríchaid cét[1] leó
[2]do Theamraig[2] do chuindchid Eirc meic Cairpri Níad Fer ⁊ Fedelme
Nóichridi.   Condontísat a ndá tríchaid cét sin ní ragam don maigin
sea.'

'Ní aniub chétus,' ol Conchobar, 'co fesadar fir hÉrend mo   3510
diuchtrad-sa asin ches a raba.'

Luid Conc[h]obar ⁊ Cealtchair tríb cóictib carp*at*[3] co tubartadar[4]
ocht fichti cend díb ó Áth Airthir Midi.   Is de atá Áth Féne.   Bádar
and oc frecomét in tslóig ⁊ ocht fichid ban, [5]ba sí a n-ernail din
brait[5].   Dobretha a cenda and ⁊ dofaídi Conc[h]obar ⁊ Celtchair   3515
dochum an dúnaid.

Is and sin asbert Celtchair fri Conc[h]obar:

'Táibli lethderga la ríg n-ága samlaithiu[6] co fodbaib fethe dees
miomain im chét cróeb di thailc traigead trícha cetharriad cét
crúaid neach damela cét im cét druad diar tuus na esbiad fer feraind   3520
im druimne Conc[h]obair fochleamar cath clichit a féine rogenetar
cath for Gáirich ⁊ Irgáirich,' ol sé.

—Nó comad hé Cúscraid Mend Macha mac Conc[h]oba[i]r ro
chanad in laíg sea in adaig riasin cath for slicht na laídi ro chan
45[b]   Lóegaire | Búadach .i. 'Afraigid, rig Macha.   Aurclichid et reliqua,'   3525
⁊ comad isin dúnad tair ro canta.

Ba isin n-aidchi[7] sin adchondairc Dubthach Dóel Ulad in aislingi
a mbádar ind tslóig for Gáirich ⁊ Irgáirich.   Is and asbert triana
chotlud:

Aislingi Dubthaich so   3530

'Amra maitne amra mithisi mescfaither slóig, sóithfidir[8] ríg,
memsite muineóil, ruidfes grian, dommema for trí slúagu slicht
slúaig Ulad im Chonchobar, imconsénat a mná, doséset a n-éti isin
maitin manairther, arsilsither laích, diroirpiter coin, ardidsiter eich
i llenith loth ibther sinis cluipetach di dálaib mórt[h]úath.'   3535

Dofochtradar tria chotlud la sin.

Cotmesca [9]ind Némain[9] forsin slóg.   Adbail cét fer díb.   [10]In tan
tóeter didiu íarom[10] co cúaladar dorís[11] Cormac Con Longes, [12]nó
comad hé Ailill mac Mátae isin dúnad tíar no chanad so[12].

[13]Búadris Aililla[13].   3540

---

[1] *sic* C, *om.* Y   [2-2] *om.* C   [3] cair[pt]- iuch C, *read* cairptech   [4] tucatar C
[5-5] ba sed ind ernail braitti boi occu C   [6-6] domsamlatha C (*some letters
erased before* samlaithiu Y)   [7] naichdi Y   [8] soithfidir Y   [9-9] ind
emain Y, in demhain C   [10-10] it (*with overhead stroke*) tóeter didiu iarom Y,
ettorra. Toethar iaromh aitherrach C   [11] *om.* C   [12-12] (nó) Ailill. Aislingti
Corpmaic Conloinges nó Ailella C   [13-13] huair | Aililla Y (*corrupt*), *om.* C

'Mór a ossad, osad Cuilleand. ¹Móra cocuir, cocuir Delend¹.
Móra ²echgracha, echracha Alais nó Asail². Móra tedmand, tedmand ³Tuath Breissi³.'

Toichim na mBuiden annso

3545 CÉin trá ro gníthea ina físi seo ro airlesatar Connachta a
comairle Ailella ⁊ Medba ⁊ Fergusa techtaireda úaidib do
décsin Ulad dús in torpart[at]ar an mag.

Is and sin íarom asbert Ailill:

'Eirc, a Meic Roth, trá,' or Ailill, '⁊ décca dúnd ⁴indat ole⁴ inna
3550 fir isin mag sa Midi ⁵i tám⁵. Tucas-[s]a a mbrait ⁊ a mbú. Do-
bérad cath dam-sa mad⁶ tacar dóib. ⁷Mani torpartadar didiu⁷
nísnidnus sund ní bus síriu.'

Luid Mac Roth íarom do décsain ⁊ do frecomét in maigi. ⁸Da
athrala⁸ aithirrech co hAilill ⁊ Medb ⁊ Fergus. In cétna fecht
3555 íarom doréccacha Mac Roth húad do accmac Slébe Fúaid, co n-acca
jar sin dorrala ina huili fiadmíla asin fidbaid co rabadar isin maig
huile.

'In fecht n-aili didiu,' or Mac Roth, 'doréccacha úaim in mag co
n-acca in tromchiaich ro lín na glendu ⁊ na fántu co nderna na
3560 tilcha⁹ eturru amail indsi i llochaib. Dommárfas iar sin ina
oíble tened asin mórc[h]iaich sin. Iar suidiu domárfas ilbrechtrad
cach illdatha isin bith. Atchondarc¹⁰ íar sin ¹¹in saignénraith¹¹ ⁊ in
mbreisimnich ⁊ in tornich ⁊ in gaíth móir—bec nád rucc mo folt dom
46ᵃ chind ⁊ nácharam trascair dar m'aiss | ⁊ ní bu mór gáeth in loí chena.'
3565 'Ced sucat, a Ferguis?' or Ailill. 'Samalta lat.'

'Ní andsa dam-sa a samail ón,' or Fergus. 'Ulaidh indsin ar
tíachtain asa ces. It é torpartatar a fid. Imdrong íarom ⁊ mét
⁊ imforráin na láth ngaile, is ed forrochraid in fid, is rempu ro
thechadar na fiadmíla isin mag. An tromcheó atchonnarcais ro
3570 lín na fántu, anála na trénfer sein ro lín na glenntu co nderna na
tulcha amail indsi i llochaib eturru. ¹²In tsaignénrath¹² ⁊ ¹³ind
aíblech¹³ tened ⁊ in t-ilbrechtrad ¹⁴adchondarcais-siu¹⁴, a Meic Roth,'
or Fergus, 'it é súile na caurad assa cennaib sin doraitniset frit amail
oíble tened. In toirnech immorro ⁊ in breisimnech¹⁵ ⁊ in tormgal¹⁶

1-1 om. here C   2-2 écgracha écgracha asail C   3-3 ted Y, tuath
[Bressi] C LL   4-4 sic Y, indad foilid C   5-5 om. C   6 ma Y   7-7 before
Tucas-sa etc. YC   8-8 Do athrala C   9 (tulcha TBC²)   10 Atchondairc
Y, Atconarc C   11-11 in saighnenrath Y (aspiration marks late)
12-12 intsaignenath Y (int saignenach TBC²), in tsaignenrad C   13-13 ind
naiblech Y   14-14 adchondaircsiu with i added later between c and s Y,
atconaircaissi C   15 sic C, breisbennech Y   16 tromgal Y, tromnelgal C

rochúalu-su, fetgaire na claideb ⁊ na calg ṅdét insin, breisimneach na **3575**
n-arm, caulgairi na carpat, basgaire na n-each, nert ina n-errad,
búrach ina féndeda, fúaim na mmíled, mórbruth ⁊ ferg ⁊ borrfod ina
láth ṅgaile oc dechrad dochum in chatha. La mméit inna feirgi ⁊
ind lúthbasa inddar leó ní tairset itir,' or Fergus.

'Artanesamar,' or Ailill. 'Itát óic lind dóib.' **3580**

'Ricfa-su a lleas ón,' or Fergus, 'fo bíth ní foigébthar i nnÉrind
uili nach a n-iarthar domain, óthá Greciae ⁊ Sceithiae síar co hIndsi
Orcc ⁊ co Colomna Hercoil ⁊ co Tor mBreogain ⁊ co hIndsi Gaid,
nech foló Ultu foa mbruth ⁊ foa ferg,' or Fergus.

Is iarsin íarom luid Mac Roth aridise do décsain toichme fer **3585**
nUlad co mboí inna ndúnadh oc Sleamain Midi. Luid íarom
aridisi co hAilill ⁊ Medb ⁊ Fergos, ⁊ adfét scéla derba dóib ¹co n-ebert¹
Mac Roth acá n-aisnéis:

'Táinic buiden mór bruthmar brígadach borrfadach isin telaich oc
Sleamain Midi,' for Mac Roth. 'Dóig lim immorro ²is árim² tríchat³ **3590**
cét inti. Rostellsad⁴ a n-étaigi díib fo c[h]étóir ⁊ ro cechladar fert
fótmaig⁵ fo suidiu⁶ a taísich. Lóech cáem seta fota ard óemind,
caínem do rígaib a delb, i n-airinach na buidne. Folt findbuidi fair
ossé cas deas tóbach druimneach co rrici áth a dá gúaland. Fúan
cas corcra imbi hi forcipul. Bretnais derscai[g]thech dergóir ina **3595**
brut fora brundib. Rosc roglas rochaín ina chind. Coinsiu
c[h]orcarda lais ossí fochóel forleathan. Ulcha dégablánach⁷
erchas órbuidi occa. Léne gel c[h]ulpatach co ndeirgindliud i
custol⁸ imbi. | Claideb órduirn iarna imdae. Gelscíath co túagmíl-
aib óir fair. Manaís lethanglas fora chrund midenn⁹ ina láim. **3600**
Áilleam di ḟlaithib domain a thochim¹⁰ itir slúag ⁊ bruth ⁊ chruth ⁊
errad, eter écosc ⁊ erúad¹¹ ⁊ báig ⁊ choscor, itir greit ⁊ gráin ⁊ ordan.

'Tánic buiden aile and didiu,' or Mac Roth, 'is tánasti dia séitche
itir lín ⁊ costud ⁊ errad ⁊ erúad ⁊ gráin. Óclaech caín caurata inna
hairinach na buidne sin. Brat húainide imbi hi forcibul. Eó óir **3605**
húasa dóit. Folt casbuidi fair. Calc dét¹² co n-imdurn diad¹³ foa
chlíu. Léne co n-echlaim i custul cota glún¹⁴. Scíath béimnech co
fáebar condúala fair. Caindel rígthaigi ina láim, féthan aircit imbe
⁊ imrith iar craund co sleig sair¹⁵, in céin n-aile dorreith co ticci a
dorn. Ocus dofessid in buidin sin for láim chlí thoísich na **3610**

46ᵇ *(marginal, left)*

---

¹⁻¹ co n-epert C, co ṅeber Y   ²⁻² is ar Y, is ar *with faint bar over* is *and*
m-*stroke over* ar C (*read as* is arm *Ed.* C)   ³ trichaid Y, trichatt C   ⁴ Ro
lasat C   ⁵ fotbaig C   ⁶ suigiu *with* no d *added later over* g Y, suidi C
⁷ eicside gablanach C   ⁸ costol *with* no u *added later over first* o Y, custal C
⁹ midseng C   ¹⁰ thothim Y   ¹¹ erad *with* fu *added beneath* Y   ¹² om.
C, *omitt,*   ¹³ diat C (= dét)   ¹⁴ ṅglun Y   ¹⁵ siar C

cétbuidne, ⁊ is amlaid doesetar ⁊ a ṅglúne fri talmain ⁊ imbel a
scíath fria smecha. Ocus domḟárfas atá forminde for erlabra ind
óclaích móir borrfadaich as toísech don buidin sin.

'Tánic buiden aile and didiu,' or Mac Roth. 'Is aidbliu[1] trícha
4615 cét a forcsi. Fer cróda annsam[2] [3]caín cendlethan[3] inna hairinach.
Folt dondchas fair. Ulcha fota indchóel[4] dégablach lais. Brat
dubglas [5]fo *los*[5] hi forcipul imbi. Delg nduillech d'ḟindruine húasa
bruindib. Léne gel c[h]ulpatach co glún. Scíath erradach co
túagmílib fair. Máeldorn[6] findargait foa choim. Sleg c[h]óicrind
3620 ina láim. Dofesid ar bélaib toísich na cétbuidne.'

'Cia sin, a Ḟergais?' or Ailill.

'Roḟetar-sa ém,' or Fergus, 'ina buidni sin .i. Conchobar rí cóicid
Érind, is hé deisid forsin fert fótmaig; Sencha mac Aililla, erlabraid
Ulad, is é deisid ara bélaib; Cúscraid Mend Macha mac Conchobair,
3625 is hé deisidh for láim a athar. Is bés don gaí fil 'na láim ind abairt
ucut ria coscor. [7]Ní *imrind*[7] ríam ná híarom. Is dagáes n-imgona
fri fúabairt cach nítha tánic sin[8],' or Fergus.

'Fogébad a n-acallaim sund,' or Medb.

'Tongu do día toinges mo thúath ém,' or Fergus, 'ní rogénair i
3630 nÉrind co se slúag argara Ulad do grés.'

47ᵃ 'Tánic buiden aile and didiu,' or Mac [Roth]. 'Is | uilliu tríchait
cét a llín. Lóech mór calma co ṅgráin[9] ⁊ erúath ossé gormda
grísainech ina hairinach. Folt dond temnidi fair ossé slimthana
fora étan. Cromscíath co fáebar condúala fair. Sleg c[h]óicrind
3635 ina láim, foga forgabalach[10] ina farrad. Claideb cróda iarna
c[h]inddruim. Brat corcra hi forcibul imbi, eó óir fora dóit. Léne
gel c[h]ulpatach [11]cota glún[11].'

'Cia sin, a Ḟergais?' or Ailill.

'Is cor láma ar debaid ém,' or Fergus, 'is cathmílid for[12] níth, is
3640 bráth for[13] bidbadu dodánic ann .i. Eógan mac Durrthacht rí
Fernmaigi sin,' ar Fergus.

'Tánic buiden már borrfadach aile isin telaich oc Sleamain Midi,'
or Mac Roth. 'Ro lásat a n-étaigi tara n-ais. Aṅgó didiu is tailc
dondechadar[14] isin telaich. Tromda in t-erfúath ⁊ is mór in gráin
3645 [15]donucsad forru[15]. Húathmar in t-airmgrith ro lásad ocon toichim[16].
Fer cennremar calma caurata inna hairinach ossé cichorda gráinne[17].

---

[1] aidblium Y, uaisle (*for* uilliu ?) C   [2] *sic* Y, annso C, *read* ossé?
[3]–[3] chain chendlethan Y   [4] finncoel C   [5]–[5] folus C (fol*us* TBC[2])
[6] mael ṅdorn Y, moeldorn C   [7]–[7] *sic* Y (= ní imrith ?) (nī imre*th*id TBC[2]),
nimrid C   [8] annsin C   [9] ṅgain Y   [10] *sic* Y, forgablach C   [11]–[11] cota
nglun Y, coa glun C   [12] fri Y (bar LL fri St)   [13] fri Y (bar LL, for St)
[14] dond | dechadar Y   [15]–[15] (= rabertatar leo LL)   [16] toithim Y
[17] grainne Y (*sic for* gránda ?)

Folt étrom grelíath fair. Súili buidi móra ina chind. Brat buidi co n-echlaim gil i faithi imbi. Scíath bémnech co fóebar condúalach fair dianechtair. Gaí slindleathan slegfota co mbróen fola iarna c[h]runn ⁊ gaí a thánaisi co crú bidbud ¹iarna gin ina láim¹. ³⁶⁵⁰ Claideb bémnech már iarna formnu.'

    'Cia sin, a Fergais?' or Ailill.

    ²'Ní imgeb² comroc ná comlond ná comrom in láech dodánic .i. Lóegaire Búadach mac Connaig meic Ilech ó Impuil³ antúaid,' or Fergus.   ³⁶⁵⁵

    'Tánic buiden mór aili and didiu i Slemain Midi isin telaich,' or Mac Roth. 'Lóech munremar collach caín i nn-airinach na buidne sin. Folt dubchas fair ossé corcra gormainech. Rosc nglas lainderda inna chind. Brat odarda fochlaidi⁴ imbi, bretnas bánairgit and. Dubscíath co mbúailid humae fair. Gaí súilech co ³⁶⁶⁰ foscadaib ina láim. Léne trebraid co ndeircindliud imbi. Claideb co n-imdornn diad tara étach anechtair.'

    'Cia sin, a Fergais?' or Ailill.

    'Is cor láma⁵ ar ugra dodánic. Is tond romara⁶ báides min-glaisi. Is fer trí ngretha. Is bráth mbúabthana bidbad dodánic,' ³⁶⁶⁵ or Fergus, .i. Muinremur mac Gerrcind ó Moduirn atúaid.'

    'Tánic buiden mór aili ann didiu isin telaig i Sleamain Midi,' or Mac Roth. 'Buiden rochaín roálaind itir lín ⁊ costud ⁊ timthaigi⁷. Is borrfadach dofarfobrit⁸ in tulaig. Forrochroth in slóg an armgrith rolásad oc teacht ind réimme. Lóech cáem gráta i ³⁶⁷⁰ nn-airinach na buidne. Áilldem⁹ do daínib | a delb itir folt ⁊ rosc ⁊ húamain, itir errud ⁊ chruth ⁊ guth ⁊ gili, itir míad ⁊ méit ⁊ maisi, ⁊ itir arm ⁊ ergnas ⁊ cumtach, itir dechelt ⁊ gaisced ⁊ córi, itir feib ⁊ gaís ⁊ cenél.'

    'Is é a epert¹⁰,' ar Fergos. 'Is luchair dego in fer álaind Feidlimid ³⁶⁷⁵ dadánic ann. Is borrfadach caurad. Is tond anbthine bádis Is gus nád fulangthar co coscraib a aile-c[h]ríchaib iar foirtbiu¹¹ a námad .i. Feidlimid Cilair Cétaig ann.'

    'Tánic buiden aili and didiu isin telaich i Sleamain Midi,' ar Mac Roth, 'ná[t] húaiti trícha cét.¹² Lóech mór calma odarda cóir ³⁶⁸⁰ comendaisc inna hairinach. Folt dubchas fair. Cromrosc [n-]odarda n-adard ina chind. Fer tarbga tailc garb. Brat glas imbi co ndelc argaid ara dóit. Léne gel c[h]ulpatach i custul imbi.

---

¹⁻¹ iarnaginalaim Y   ²⁻² nimgeb Y   ³ *changed to* Impiul Y (Immail LL)
⁴ *sic* Y, (bachuaslae LL,) *read* fo chaslói   ⁵ *om.* Y, (lám LL)   ⁶ (romra LL)   ⁷ timthaidi Y   ⁸ (forrópartatar LL)   ⁹ Aillde Y (m-*stroke omitted*)
¹⁰ (epert chomadas LL)   ¹¹ foirtib Y   ¹² ergal an riam *add.* Y

47ᵇ

Claideb iarna śliasaid. Dercscíath co mbúaili chaladargait fair.
3685 [Gaí] tresemnech slindlethan ina láim:
'Cia sin, a Fergais?' or Ailill.
'Is lonnbruth barand, is laimnid cach catha, is búaid cech ergaile
dadánic ann: Connad mac Mornai ó Challaind and sain,' or Fergus.
'Tánic buiden aili ann didiu isin telaig oc Slemin Midi,' or Mac
3690 Roth. 'Is toichim slúaig ar méit. Toíseach fíl i n-airinach na
buidne sin ní coimdig láech bad chaíme itir delb ⁊ timthach ⁊
dec[h]elt. Folt tóbach dergbuidi fair. Gnúis chóir c[h]orcra
chutromae. Aged focháel forlethan. Beóil derga thanaidi. Dét
níamda némonnda. Guth glan gleórda. ¹Cuinsiu chaín c[h]or-
3695 carda chumdachtach¹. Áilldem do delbaib doíne. Brat corcra hi
forcibul imbi. Bretnais foa llánecor de ór húasa bánbruindib.
Cúarscíath co túagmílib ildathacha co cobroth aircid húasa clíu.
Gaí fota fáebarglas la foga féig fobartach ina láim. Claideb órduirn
óir fora muin. Léne c[h]ulpatach co ndergindled imbi i custul.'
3700 'Cia sin, a Fergais?' or Ailill.
'Rofetamar immorro,' or Fergus. 'Is leth gliad ém,' or sé,
'dadánic² and. Is cláriud comlaind. Is lonnbruth árchon. Rochaid mac Faithemain ó Brig Dumae, far cliamain, insin, rofoí la
far n-ingin-si .i. la Findabair.'
3705 'Tánic buiden aile and didiu isin telaich i Sleamain Midi,' or Mac
Roth. 'Lóech oircnech remarśliastach mór i nn-airinach na buidne
sin. Bec nach remithir fer cach mball de. Angó is fer co talmain,'
48ª ol sé. | 'Folt dub fair. Gnúis chnedach c[h]orcarda lais. Rosc
mbrecht n-erard ina chind. Fer án athlom samlaid co ngráin ⁊
3710 erúath ³co nn-ocaib dafil congraim³ adamra itir étach ⁊ arm ⁊
écosc ⁊ áni ⁊ erred, conócaib co comrom níad, co n-anglonnaib
samnae⁴, co mmiad imtholton, ⁵co saidig⁵ tar comlond do brisiud⁶
for forlond, co mbaraind for bidbadu, co n-imthecht for ilchrícha
ecraidi ⁷cen choméirge⁷. Ní gó is tailc ⁸doroacht a rréim⁸ hi
3715 Sleamo[i]n Midi.'
'Baíthi do gail ⁊ gaisced óm,' ol Fergus, 'baíthi di drúis ⁊ tairp-
thigi, baíthi di nert ⁊ miadamlai. Tatha didiu di ślúagaib ⁊ airbrib.
Mo chomalta fén Fergus mac Leiti rí Líne, rind n-ága túaiscirt
hÉrind.'
3720 'Tánic buiden mór borrfadach aili and didiu isin telaig a Sleamain
Midi,' or Mac Roth⁹. "Errada ingantai foraib. Lóech cóem
álainn ina hairinach. Búaid crotha huile itir folt ⁊ rosc ⁊ gili, itir

---

¹⁻¹ sic Y, omitt.?   ² dandanic Y   ³⁻³ sic Y   ⁴ sic Y, read lasamnae?
⁵⁻⁵ sic Y, read co saigid?   ⁶ briusiud Y   ⁷⁻⁷ read cen chomairge? (can
chommairge LL)   ₋⁸⁻⁸ (doroachtar rēim TBC²)   ⁹ ergal an riam add. Y

méit ⁊ costud ⁊ córi. Cúicroth óir fair. Brat húaine hi forcibal
imbi. Bretnas[1] óir isin brot húasa dóit. Léne gel c[h]ulpatach i
custol imbi. Tuiri rígthaigi ina láim. Claideb órduirn iarna ³⁷²⁵
formna.'

'Is bruthmar a bara in chaurad chomramaich dadánig and ém,'
or Fergus. 'Amorgene mac Eccetsalaig[2] Goband ó Búais atúaid[3]
ann sin.'

'Tánic buiden aile and didiu isin telaig a Sleamuin Midi,' ar Mac ³⁷³⁰
Roth. 'Is bádud ar méit. Is tine ar áine. Is leó áithigi. Is cath
ar lín. [4]Is all ar mét. Is oll ar nert[4]. Is bráth ara bláiriud. Is
torand ara tharpt[h]igi. Lóech garbainech[5] húathmar i n-airinach
na buidne sin ossé brúach bélmar. Folt garb grendliath fair, ossé
srónmar ballderg. Brat riabain imbi, cúailli iaraind fora brut. ³⁷³⁵
Cromsciath co fáebur conndúala fair. Garbléne trebraid i custol
imbi. Liathgaéi már ina láim, tricha semand aire[6]. Claideb secht
ṁbrotha iarna formnai. Atracht in slóg uile ara chind ⁊ ro lá
dírmae din chath imbi oc teacht isin telaig.'

'Is cend erbága dadánic,' or Fergus. 'Is leth catha. Is greit ³⁷⁴⁰
ar gail. Is tond ainbt[h]ine bádas. Is muir dar crícha .i. Celtchair
mac Cuitheochair ó Dún Lethglaisi atúaid.'

'Tánic buiden aile ann didiu isin telaig a Sleamain Midi,' or Mac
Roth. 'Lóech óngel ina hairinach. Find huile itir folt ⁊ abrotchor
⁊ ulchai ⁊ dec[h]elt. Scíath co mbúailid[7] | óir fair ⁊ claideb co ³⁷⁴⁵
n-imdorn diad ⁊ manaís bréifnech ina láim. Adláechda donárlaid
a tochim.'

'Inmain ém in bethir bailcbéimnech dodánic,' ol Fergus, 'in
mathgamain mórglonnach fri hécraidi conboing[8] firu: Feradach
Find Fechtnach ó Nemiud Slébe Fuait atúaid ann sin.'   ³⁷⁵⁰

'Tánic buiden aili and didiu isin telaich a Slemain Midi,' or Mac
Roth. 'Láech úathmar inna hairinach essé brúach bélmar. Méit
a béil beólu eich. Folt dondchas fair, ossé lethglóir cadissin
lethanchend lámḟota. Brat dublúascach[9] imbi, roth créda and
húasa [10]dóit. Bocóit[10] líath[11] huasa c[h]líu. Manaís muincech ina ³⁷⁵⁵
deis. Claideb fota [12]iarna formnu[12].'

'Is leó lámderg londandsclech dadánic,' or Fergus. 'Is [13]art
glonnach[13] ágmar amnas. Is bruth ar thír nád fulangthar: Eirrgi
Echbél ó Bri Eirgi atúaid,' ol Fergus.

---

1 bratnas Y   2 Eiccitsach Y   3 antuaid Y (n-*stroke added later*)
4–4 (is ald ar nirt LL, St)   5 garbaineiuch Y   6 *sic* Y (trina cró LL,
tria cro St)   7 mbuailich Y   8 conloing Y   9 lu *erased* Y (dublúascach
LL)   10 (dondbocōit TBC²)   11 liaeth Y   12–12 iar formnu Y
13–13 ard glonnach Y (ardglonnach TBC²) (is é in t-art amnas ágsidi LL, St)

3760 'Tánic buiden aile ann didiu isin telaig i Slemain Midi,' or Mac
Roth. 'Dá óclóech cáema cosmaili díb línaib ina hairinach. Fuilt
buidi foraib. Dá gelscíath co túagmílaib argait [foraib]. Atá
immáes eturru. Immalle doaurcbat[1] dóib[2] a cossa ⁊ fosruimet;
nocon alt dóib taurcbáil a coss do neachtar de seach araile,'
3765   [3]'Cia sin, a Ḟergais?' or Ailill[3].

'Dá ánrad, dá anloise, dá rind ága, dá chaur, dá [4]chleth bága[4],
dá drec, dá thene, dá c[h]athmilid, dá chathchuimnid ergaile, dá
deil, dá dána, dá t[h]reitill Ulad imma ríg: Fiachna ⁊ Fiacha, dá
mac Conc[h]obair meic Neasa, dá c[h]ridiscél thúaiscirt Érenn,' or
3770 Fergus.

'Tánic buiden ele and didiu isin telaig a Slemain Midi,' or Mac
Roth. 'Trí hóclaích grísta gráta gormanig ina hairinach. Trí
bearrtha blaibuidi foraib. Trí broit óendatha impu hi forcibul,
trí delgi óir húasa ndóitib. Teóra léne monasacha co ndergindtliud
3775 i custul impu. Trí scéith cosmaili foraib. Trí claidib órduirn
iarna fórmnu. Teora slega lethanglasa inna ndeaslámaib. Atá
imáes eturru.'

'Trí[5] anchinnid Choba[6]. Trí mórglonnaich Midlúachra. Trí ruirig
Roth. Trí harsidi Airthir Fúata,' or Fergus. 'Trí meic Fiachna
3780 ind sain i ndegaid[7] in tairb .i. Rus ⁊ Dáiri ⁊ Imchath,' or Fergus.

'Tánic buiden aile and didiu isin telaig i Slemain Midi,' or Mac
Roth. 'Fer bresta bruthmar ina hairinach. Súile rúaderga
curata[8] ina chind. Brat brec imbi, roth aircid and. Scíath glas fora
chlíu. [Claideb][9] co n-imdorn argaid fó ṡliasait. Gaí derscai[g]thi
49ª   [10]co nagam[10] amainse ina [11]deis díglaig[11]. Léne geal | c[h]ulpatach
i custul cota glún. Buiden ḟorderg co fuilib imbi ossé fuileach
créchtach cadesin.'

'Is é sin,' or Fergus, 'in dána díchondarcil[12]. Is é in lamnid
leatarthach[13]. Is é in rob rigthi[14] ergaili. Is é in tarb dásachtach.
3790 Is é in búadach Baili. Is é in t-anglondach Bernais. Is é in
cathchuindich[15] Colpt[h]ai. Comla cóicthi[16] thuaiscirt hÉrenn .i.
Menn mac Sálchada ó Chorannaib. Do dígail a crécht foraib[17]
tánic in fer sin,' or Fergus.

'Tánic buiden aile ann didiu isin telaig a Slemain Midi,' or Mac
3795 Roth, '⁊ siat adlóechda[18] imt[h]oltonach[19]. Ócláech odarda mór

---

[1] (doaurcbad TBC[2])   [2] doib *taken from next sentence, omitt.*   [3–3] *In*
MS. *this sentence comes after* ... imma ríg l. 3768   [4–4] clt bagid Y   [5] tria Y
[6] th *added under* b Y (Copha Stowe)   [7] ndegaich Y   [8] curita Y
[9] om. Y   [10] conag am Y. *read* co n-agaib?   [11–11] diglaig deis Y
[12] dichonnarcell Y   [13] leathathach Y   [14] rigi Y   [15] *read* cathchuingid
[16] coicthi Y, *read* catha?   [17] foraib *comes after* sin Y   [18] adloeochda Y
[19] immm | toltonach Y

lecanḟota ina hairinach. Folt donn cráebach fair. Brat derg fo
loí c[h]aín imbi. Léne dergscoi[g]thi. Dealc n-óir húasa dóit[1]
ina brot. Claideb dercscoi[g]thi co n-imdurnn findarcaid fora
c[h]líu. Scíath derg fair. Manaís leathanglas for dúal altchaín
uindsenn ina láim.'   3800
    'Fer trí mbailcbémend dadánic,' or Fergus. 'Fer trí raiti. [2]Fer
trí ruti[2]. Fer trí ramada. Fer trí mbúada. Fer trí ngretha conboing nitha for náimdiu i n-alailiu crích. Fergnae mac Findchoíme
a Coronn sin.'
    'Tánic buiden aile and didiu isin telaich i Slemain Midi,' or Mac 3805
Roth. 'Is aidbliu trícha cét a faircsi. Láech uchtgel rochóem ina
hairinach, cosmail fri hAilill ucut itir mét ⁊ maisi ⁊ dec[h]elt ⁊
errad. Mind óir húasa mullach. Brat drgscoi[g]thi imbi hi
forcibal. Bretnas óir isin brot fora bruindib. Léne co ndergind-
liud i custul imbi. Scíath bémnech co n-imlib óir fair. Tuiri 3810
rigthaigi ina láim. Claideb óirduirn iarna ḟormna.'
    'Is muir tar glasa dodánic ann ém,' or Fergus. 'Is londbruth loga.
Is díḟulaing a bara fri hécraidi. Furbaidi Fer Benn inn sin,' or
Fergus.
    'Tánic buiden aile and didiu isin telaig i Sleamain Midi,' or Mac 3815
Roth. 'Adláechda díáirme,' ol Mac Roth. 'Errada inganta
écsamla impu seach na buidne olcheana. Is bladach dodechadar
didiu itir arm ⁊ étach ⁊ errodh. Slóg mór borrfadach isin buidin.
Mac brecderg ina hairinach. Áildem do delbaib doíne a delb.
[3]Ergal án riam[3]. Scíath taulgel ina láim co cobrud óir fair ⁊ bil 3820
óir imbi. Gaí áith étrom co foscod ina láim. Brat corcra cor-
tharach i forcibul imbi, delc n-arcuid isin brot ara bruindib. Léne
gel c[h]ulpatach co ndergind[liud] imbi. Claideb | órduirn tara
étach aneachtair.'
    Contúaissi Fergus la sodain.   3825
    'Ní fetar-sa ém,' or Fergus, 'indas in meic sin la hUltu, acht óen
bad dóig lim beidis hé fir Themra immon mac cóir n-amra n-oir[d]-
nidi im Erc mac Coirpre Niad Fer ⁊ ingine Conc[h]obair. Ní
'mmuscarat tairrid. Dichmairc a athar dodeachaid in fer sin do
chobair a ṡenathar. Is [4]triana ág[4] in meic sin,' or Fergus, 'brisfi[t]- 3830
hir[5] in cath foraib. Nícon aithigi[6] in mac sin húath ná homun oc
far ṡaigid etorro a medón fa[r] catha. Bad ferrda bhúrigfite láithi
gailli fer nUlad oc teasarcain luíg[7] a cridi [8]oc sligi in chatha remib[8].

49ᵇ (margin)

---

[1] doidib Y   [2-2] added later in margin Y   [3-3] sic, omitt. ? (marginal
note?)   [4-4] trianag with a added under last a Y   [5] t faint, as if erased
    [6] read aiccigi   [7] luig and o written over u= loíg   [8-8] oc sligid in
chatha Y

Dos-icfe uile ell condolba oc aicsin in meic isind níth már sin[1].
3835 Rocechlastar rucht claidib Conc[h]obair amail gloim n-árchon ic
tesorcain in meic. Focicher Cú Chulaind trí múru doíne immon
cath oc saigid in meic bic. Bith condalb donuapérat láith gaili fer
nUlad in díairmi,' or Fergus.

'Is fota leam trá,' or Mac Roth, 'bith fri haisnéis ineich adcondarc
3840 uili, acht dodechad[2] etarport co fis scél dúib-se.'

'Dofucais,' ar Fergus.

'Ní thánic didiu Conall Cernach cona mórbuidin,' or Mac Roth.
'Ní thángadar trí meic Conc[h]oba[i]r cona trí cóectaib[3] cét. Ní
thánic trá Cú Chulaind and iarna chréchtunugud i nn-écomlund.
3845 Acht mása err óenc[h]arpait,' or Mac Roth, 'nammá is dóig bad n-é
inso thánic ann.

'Dá each dronchara fona c[h]arpat ité scúablebra baslethna
forlethna fosseṅga ardchenda túagmair gobc[h]óela bolcṡróna. Dá
ndroch ṅduba tairchisi. Fonnaid réidi ruirthecha. Cret urard
3850 dresachtach. Pupull [4]uainidi huaitne[4] intnaise[5]. Óclách isin
charpat sin, cetherlethan corcaineach. Súasmáel cas círdub fair
co ticci áth a dá ghualand. Cethochruss nó ceatharfochrus bruit
deirg imbi. Ceithri claidbíni[6] clis hi cechtar a dó dhóit. Claideb
órduirn fora chlíu. Sciath ⁊ sleg lais. Ceit[h]ri cneslénti[7] fichit
3855 imbi fo thétaib ⁊ refedaib. Ara ara bélaib. Dá chúlaid ind arad[8]
frisna heocho. Na éisi ina ladair riam sair. Fithchell for scarad
eturra. Leth a fairne di ór buidi, anaill ba de ḟindruine. Búanbach
foa díb slíastaib. Naí cles do chor dó a n-ardai.'

'Cia sin, a Ḟergais?' or Ailill.
3860 'Ní anse,' or Fergus. 'Cú Chulaind mac Soaltaim a sídaib ⁊
Lóeg mac Riangabra a ara Con Culaind insain,' or Fergus.

'Mór do chétaib trá ⁊ mílib,' or Mac Roth, 'doroacht in dúnad[9] sa
50ᵃ Ulad. | Mór do churadaib ⁊ do thrénḟeraib ⁊ láthaib gaile roachtadar
grafaind isinn áonach. Mór do buidnib didiu,' or Mac Roth, 'ro
3865 bátar [10]oc torachtain[10] ín dúnaid c[h]étna do neoch ná toracht ⁊
ná tánic an dúnad [11]an [tan] dodechad-sa[11]. Acht namá,' or Mac
Roth, 'nocho tarneastair mo rosc for tulaich ná din[d]gna do neoch
rosiacht mo ṡúil óthá Áth Ḟir Diad co rici Sleama[i]n Midi acht for
ech ⁊ dune.'
3870 'Fer[12] muinter adchondaircais ém,' or Fergus.

---

[1] oc sligi in catha remib *add.* Y (*repetition*).   [2] dodoechaid Y   [3] *sic*
Y, *read* tríchtaib   [4-4] *read* úainide *or* úaine?   [5] *sic* Y, *read* intlaise?
[6] *tricht* binni Y (*corrupt*)   [7] *sic leg.*, cleithini Y, *or read* léinti?
[8] araid Y   [9] dunaid Y   [10] oca torachtar Y   [11-11] an dode-
chadsa Y   [12] *sic* Y

Luid Conc[h]obar trá cona slógaib co ngab dúnad hi comochraib dia c[h]élib. Guitir[1] dál ó C[h]onc[h]obar do[2] Ailill co turcbáil ngréne arabárach, ⁊ basisestar Ailill ar feraib hÉrend ⁊ ar in longess, ⁊ basisestar Conc[h]obar ar Ultaib, ⁊ focertar pupaill Conc[h]obair[3] íarom. [4]Is heth moth[4] ba fornocht talam eturru ⁊ [5]daneccab hUla*id*[5] re fuined ngréne. 3875

Is ann sin asbert in Mórrígan isin dorbles itir in dá dúnad: 'Crenaid brain bráigde fer. Bruinded[6] fuil. Feochair cath. Coinmid luind. Mesctuich tuind taib im thuill im níthgalaib iar luimnich luud fianna fetal ferda fir Crúachan cotascrith imm ard- 3880 bith [7]cuirither cath ar cosa alailiu[7] cén mair hUltaib, mairc Iarnaib, mairc d'Ultaib immorro, cén mair Iarnaib. [8]Is ed dobreth hi clu[a]saib Iairn[8], mairc hUltaib ol niscainedar a ngle.'

Ro baí Cú Chulaind trá oc Fedain Chollna ina n-arrad. Dobreth biad dó óna bri[u]gadaib in n-aidchi sin ⁊ dothéigdis dia acallaim 3885 fri dé. Ní rubai neach díib clíu do Áth Fir Diad.

'Huinse albani asin dúnad aniar 'sin dúnad sair,' ol in t-ara fri Coin Culaind. 'Huindse ceithern gilla ara cend.'

'Conricfet in gilla sin,' or Cú Chulaind. 'Regaid in t-albani tarsin mag. Intí nád géba acorthi[9] regaid do chobair na ngilla.' 2890

Dogníth són íarom amail asindubairt Cú Chulaind.

'Cindus nondfechad gilla Ulad in cath?'

'Is fearrda,' ol in t-ara.

'Ba bág dóib-som a[10] toitim oc tesorcain a n-éiti,' ol Cú Chulaind. 'Ocus anosa?' 3895

'Na óclacha amulc[h]acha nodfechad indosa,' ol in t-ara.

'In tánic néll solus forsin ngréin beós?' for Cú Chulaind.

'Nathó ém,' ol in t-ara.

'Apraind nachimbaí-si nert do theacht cucu,' ol Cú Chulaind.

'Consinter chena indiu,' ol in t-ara, im thráth turcbála gréne. 3900 'Aes úallach fiches in cath indossa,' ol in t-ara, 'acht nád fil rígu and air is cotlud beós dóib.'

Is and asbert Fachtnai in tan donórcaib grían: —Nó is hé Conc[h]-obar ro chan trena chodlad:

'Comérgid, ríg[11] Macha morglonnaich. Muinter fial. Meilid 3905 fáebra. Fichith cath. Claidig búrach. Bendaich scíathu. Scítha láma. Labra a n-éiti. Écórai cosnadae. [12]Concherd cách cath[13] ar cosa araile[12]. Laith tigernach dodaircéba. Liblait a rrém. | Bid

50ᵃ

---

[1] Guithir Y   [2] da Y   [3] *read* fer nÉrend?   [4] = Is ed mod   [5-5] *sic* Y, *read* dúnad nUla*d*?   [6] (brunnid LL)   [7-7] (Cuirther cath ba chossaib araile LL)   [8-8] (iss ed dobert i clúais nÉrand LL)   [9] (a corti TBC²)   [10] an Y   [11] ri (*letter deleted after* -i) Y   [12-12] (Curther cath ba chossaib araile LL)   [13] cach Y

ferrda fid forsa saig ⁊ forsa leasad. ¹Ibaib dagda doirp a fuile¹.
3910 Línfaid cauma chridi a rígna tuidicfaid. Eblaid a samgubae
commed fuileach férach fót forsa lestais forsa sestais. Comérgid,
ríg Macha.'

'Cia ro chachain so ?' or cách.

'Conc[h]obar mac Nesa,' or sét. —Nó 'Fachtna ro chachain,'
3915 ol sét.

'Cotlaid, cotlaid acht far cathais!'

Co cloth² Lóegairi Búadach:

'Afraigid, ríg Macha. Aurc[h]laidig³ far mbú. Tesorcid far
mbroit. Inneossartar Connachta di aird hUisnich diupart taib
3920 imdid loissither feithi selais domun clár Gáirigi.'

'Cia ro chachain so ?' or cách.

'Láegairi Búadach mac Connaid Buidi meic Ilech. Cotlaid,
cotlaid,' ⁴for siat⁴, '[acht] far cathais.'

'Anaid fris beós,' ol Conc[h]obar 'co taurcba⁵ grían co mmaith hi
3925 nglennaib ⁊ hi tuaigebra*ch*aib⁶ na hÉrend⁷.'

An tan adchondairc Cú Chulaind na ríga anair oc gabáil a mind
fora cennai ⁊ oc tesorcain⁸ na mbuiden, asbert Cú Chulaind fria
araid ⁹ara ndiuscad⁹ Ultu. Ocus asbert in t-ara:—Nó is é Amargind mac Eicit in fili asbert:

3930   'Comérgid, ríg Macha mórglondaich. Muintir fial. Miandaigther
Bodb bú Imbial¹⁰. Insernd crú cridi. Inreith níth niaba nertaid gal
cridi crú for telaib nó for tinn teched .i. for toind teiced tercbaid
nó teilcfid isnis nithu. Ní fríth fri Coin Culaind cosmail Con Culaind conben mian Macha mochtrád más ar búaib Cúail[n]gi. Comér-
3935 gid.'

Com.

'Dosruisces,' ol in t-ara. 'Samlaid dodeochadar 'sin chath
tornocht acht a n-armo namá. In tí dia tá¹¹ dorus a pupaill sair is
trít síar dodeochaid.'

3940   'Is degc[h]obair éigne¹²,' ol Cú Chulaind.

Imthúsa Ulad trá ní de leantar sund calléic.

Imthús immorro fer nÉrind, cotagart Badb ⁊ Bé Néit ⁊ Némain
forru ind aidchi sin for Gáirig ⁊ Irgáirich conidapad cét lóech díb ar
úathbás. Nírbo hísin adaig ba sámam¹³ dóib.

1-1 (ibait deoga duirbbi fola LL)   ² concloith Y   ³ aurclaid*m*ig *with*
m-*stroke added later* Y   4-4 for sin Y   ⁵ taurcbail (*sic*) Y   ⁶ tuaigebraib
with later stroke over r   ⁷ hairend Y (h *added above line*)   ⁸ terorcain Y
⁹-⁹ arnandiuscad (n-*stroke later*) Y   ¹⁰ *sic for* Imbail (Immail LL)
¹¹ da Y   ¹² (ēigme TBC²)   ¹³ samu Y

Tochos[t]ul Fear nÉrend andso

R O chachain Ailill mac Mátae in n-aidchi sin riasin cath co
n-epert:

'Atraí, a Thriagt[h]réin. Nodfoídiu co trí Conaire Slébe Mis,
trí Lesfind[1] Lúachra, trí Meid Corpthe Loste, trí Buidir Búaisi, trí
Boidb Búaidnigi, trí Búaideltaich Berba[2], trí Muredaich Marga, trí 3950
Lóegairi Leici Dergi, trí Suibne S[i]úire, trí Échtaig Áne, tirí Doíl
Eirrig, trí [3]Damaich Dergderce[3], trí Bratrúaid Lacha Rí, trí Miel-
leth[4] Lacha Érni, trí Bresail Bodgna, trí hAmalgaid Aíi, trí Fiach-
raid [5]Feda Némain[5], trí Nechtain Maigi Murisci, trí Meic Amra
Esa Rúaid, trí Ruirig Aigle, trí Bruchair Glais Febrad, trí Conaill 3955
51[a]   Collamrach, | trí Féic[6] Findabrach, trí Coirpre Cliach, trí Mane
Milscoth, trí [7]Descostaig Droma[7], trí Fintain Femin, trí Rathaich[8]
Raigne, trí Et[er]scéle Etarbáine, trí Gúaire Gaible, trí Áeda Aidne,
trí Mongaich Mitaine, trí Dúadaid Áine, trí [9]Gairb Glunnraidi[9],
trí [10]Discirt hÚaga[10], trí Leathluind Linti, trí Coinchind Shile, trí 3960
Dauich Leamna, trí Cellchair hUmuill, trí Coscraich Clothra, trí
Bairrchais Eilli, trí Dáiri Tibrat Find, trí hAirt [11]Arda Ladlarn[11],
trí Muredaich Maigi Femin, trí Congbaidi Cliach, trí Mordai Mosoth,
trí Roir Rois Buiti, trí Ánraid Turbi, trí hEitirscél Temrach, trí
Galgaidi Goain, trí Feradaid Foltc[h]ais, trí Feidmnig Rotail, 3965
trí Scáil Soobail, trí hAilill hUaiti, trí Gortaich Granaisc, trí Mea-
saich Maethla, trí hUilleith Arda Airthir, trí Coirp Cláiri, trí hAirt
Arda, trí Foimdig hIrruis, trí hIllai[n]d hÉrend, trí Sochaidi Sinna,
trí Brónaig Bethra, trí Mongaid Muccruma, trí Mochmaidne Maigi
Aíi, trí Tigernmais Túath Ambrais, trí hÉchtaich Findabrach, trí 3970
Cormaic hUiscrend, trí hUidir Buaile, trí Ruis Ruscae, trí Fearad
Find, trí hAthchuirp Tulcha, trí Túathail Tanni, trí Maccáech
Femrag, trí Lóegairi Berramnach, trí Fidaig Saigthi, trí Cormaic
Cauanach, trí Coirbri Luingi, trí hUidir Conc[h]obair, trí Glais meic
Cathbath, trí Duib Drúad, trí hAirich Cluichiur, trí Laiten Luiged, 3975
trí Conc[h]obair Collsen, trí Elair Deiuais, trí Fiadail Duinergin,
trí hAirich Insi hUan, trí Níth Átha Croíbe, trí hÓengusa Uisce, trí
Fiach Fernna nImbais, trí Duirn, trí Bailcbruindi, [12]trí Moín Maigi[12],
trí Cais Cuile, trí Triúin[13] Maigi Éle, trí Sruthmair Maigi Ochtair,

---

[1] (Lussin LL, Les Find TBC[2])   [2] (Breg LL)   [3-3] Damaich Derg . . .
rc Y (Dámaltaig Dercderce LL)   [4] (Nnelleth TBC[2], Malleith LL)
[5-5] fedñmain Y (Feda Némain LL)   [6] (Find LL)   [7-7] (Descertaig
Dromma Fornochta LL)   [8] (Rótanaig LL)   [9-9] (Gairbglunnraidi TBC[2])
[10-10] (Discir Thuaga TBC[2])   [11-11] perhaps gen. of Ard Ladrann   [12-12] sic
Y, read Moenmaigi with preceding names and omit trí   [13] truin Y

3980 trí Glonnmair Maigi Leathain, trí Dornmair Maigi hUisce, trí
Glaisderg Tethba, trí Tigirn Taince trí[1] Tibraidi Talindi,'
Ferc[h]uidred Fer nÉreand inso, cach triar cenmot[h]á an robí
Cú Chulaind díib riam.

Imthúsa Con Culaind immorro is ed indister sund coléic:
3985 'Fég dúind, a mo popa a Loíg, cindus fechtha Ulaid in cath
indosa.'

'Is ferda,' ol in t-ara. 'Cia conualaind-se mo charpat ⁊ Óen ara
Conaill C[h]ernaich didiu ina charput[⁊]co tíasmais ón eite[2] di araile
[3]iarsind indiu[3], ní regad crua ná fonnad[4] trít.'

3990 'Is damna mórgliad sin.' ol Cú Chulaind. 'Ní derntar isin cath,'
or Cú Chulaind fria araid, 'ní nád fesur úaid.'

51[b] 'Bid fír ón do neoch connisor-sa de,' ol in t-ara | 'Airm i tát
ind láith gaile indosa aníar,' ol in t-ara, 'berait toilc isin chath sair.
A commiét cétna anair beraid tolc isin chath siar.'

3995 'Abrand ná badim slán-sa,' ol Cú Chulaind. 'Ropad réill mo
tholc-sa and a cuma cháich.'

Is and sin táncadar ina ferchuitreda[5] ind athslógaid[6]. [7]I n-inam[7]
trá hi tuladar fianna íarom don chath for Gáirich ⁊ Irgáirich [8]is
ann sin didiu[8] thánic ind noí carpait [9]di féindidib inna Irúaithi.
4000 Triar remib di thraig. Nírbo mailli dolotar olmbátar in charpait.
Nistailcc Medb isin chath [acht] ar srengail nAililla[10] asin chath mád
fair no maidset nó ar guin Conchobair mád fair bad lén.

Is íarom ro indis a ara do Choin Culaind bith do Ailill ⁊ do Meidb
og guidhi Fergusa im thecht isin cath ⁊ asbertadar fris nárbo chol dó
4005 ar doradsad mór do maith dó fora lonnges.

'Má no bith ém mo c[h]laideb acom-sa,' ol Fergus, 'beitis lir
leam-sa cendae fer [11]for óeib scíath[11] andáte bommann ega hi ngrellig
donnicc echrad ríg ó ro roietar[12] [13]i tír[13].'

Is and sin dorad Fergus in lugu sa:
4010 'Tongu et reliqua mebsaitis lim-sa glaini fer dia mbráigde, bráigde
fear la ṅdóite, dóite[14] fer la n-uille[15], uille[16] fer la[17] rigthe, rigthe[18]
fer la ndorndaib, dornna fer la[17] méra, méra fer la n-ingne, ingne[18]
fer la forcléthi, forcléthi fer la medón, medón[19] fer la slíasta, slíasta
fer la nglúne, glúne fer la colp[th]a, colpthai fer la traigthe, traigthi

---

[1] omitt.　　[2] oiti with no e over o Y
LL = iar n-indaib) read merely indiu?　　[4] fonnaid Y　　[5] -a added under
-d Y, omit ina and read ferchuitred? (ferchuitredaig LL)　　[6] (áth slōgaid
TBC[2])　　[7-7] in | inam Y (Inmain TBC[2])　　[8-8] Is ann didiu sin Y
[9] (ccairptig St)　　[10] nAileollo Y　　[11-11] sic LL, St, uae (altered
to liae) sceith- Y,　　[12] read roithetar?　　[13-13] itir with d under first i Y
(ditir TBC[2])　　[14] rigthi Y　　[15] nuaille Y　　[16] uile Y　　[17] lan Y
[18] om. Y　　[19] modon Y

fer la méra, méra fer la n-i[n]gne. [1]Doruchtfaid a méderad[1] na [4015]
háeru feib dodrimsired[2] beach i lló áinle.'

Is and sin asbert Ailill re araid:

'Domiced[3] in claideb cuilleis[4] toind. Tongu do dia toingeas mo
thúath mád meso a bláth lat indiu olldás a llaithi dondmbiurt-sa
duit isin letir[5] i crích nUlad, cia no beidis fír hÉrind ocot anocol [4020]
airim-sa, nítansitis.'

Is íarom dobreth a c[h]laideb do Fergus, ⁊ asbert Ailill:

'Geib do c[h]laideb. Ci assor-seo hÉriu húand, ferfaid for Gáirig
dia macaib mórlóech. Mád la fír n-einech nád bad fornn n-imbrae
do barann borrfad barainn fiad nUlad errathaib. La díuscud [4025]
Gáirigi for fótaib fesar la maten forderg.'

'Fo chen colad miel macrad, caladc[h]olc claideb Leidi lasinta
huath óenhúair bodba beisemil macrad nai ar doirsib ata re tánic a
ndígail diu. Pa feithi fairtbe a cend consuidfea na cotaigfe coimdiu
in claidiub sa cordib combaig aithscélaib. Ní firba foraib galnas [4030]
mo chlaidiub. Atan rí úallach | ria feraib hÉrend.'

'Is liach do thoitim i roí remur,' or Fergos fri hAilill.

Cotogart Badb ⁊ Bé Néit ⁊ Néamain forro in aidchi sin for Gáirich
⁊ Irgáirich, [6]conid apad[6] cét lóech díb ara úathbás. Nírbo sí sin
adaich ba sáimiu[7] dóib.   [4035]

Gaibid Fergus [8]a suidiu[8] a gaisced ⁊ imasaí isin chath ⁊ glanais
berna cét isin chath cona c[h]laideb ina díb lámuib. Gabais Medb
íarom [a] gaisced [9]⁊ forfóbair[9] isin chath ⁊ maidter rempi[10] fo thrí
conad ed rosoí in cúal gaí fora cúlu.

'Ní fetar,' ol Conc[h]obar fria muintir bátar imme, 'cia resa maid [4040]
in cath frind atúaid. Geibid-si sunn in cath didiu co ndechar-sa
fora chind.'

'Gébma-ne[11] íarom i mbale i tám,' ar na hóca, 'acht mani maidi in
talam found nó an nem anúas [12]foraind, nícon memsam-ne[12] de sund.'

Farrumae íarom Conc[h]obar ar cind Fergusa. Tócbaid in [4045]
scíath fris .i. ind Óchaín, scíath Conc[h]obair. Cetheóra benna óir
fair, ceithre sethnecha[13] óir thairrse. Benaid Fergus trí bémind fair
nád comairnic cid bil a scéith dó-som fora cend.

'Cia di Ultaib argab in scíath?' ol Fergus.

1-1 (do-rucht faid am ederad TBC²)   2 *read* dodrimthired ?
3 domiceb Y   4 = coilles (choilles LL)   5 liter Y   6-6 conidbad Y
7 *sic* Y = sámam   8-8 *read* ar suidiu (iar s.) ?   9-9 fer (*with stroke
over* f) ⁊ foebar Y (*or read* furri ⁊ fóbair)   10 (rempo LL)   11 gemane Y
12-12 foraindiconmemsamne Y   13 *sic* Y = sethnacha (sethrachaib LL,
sethnachaib St)

[4050] 'Fer as[1] ferr ⁊ . . . [2]' ol Conchobar, '⁊ rodatuc for longes i nn-adba con alltai ⁊ sindach ⁊ dotningéba anndiu ar gail gaiscid[3] fiad feraib hÉrend.'

Inmidir Fergus la sodain bém ndígla dá díb lámaib for Conc[h]obar co comránic [1]gráinni in chloidib[4] fri talmain iarna chúl. Focherd [4055] Cormac Con Longes láma for suidiu ⁊ íadaid a dí láma 'ma rigid.

'[5]Ainbchellach ainbchellach[5], a mo popa a Fergais!' ol Cormac. '[6]Foichleach n-airfoichlech[6] insin, a popa Fergais. Náimtidi in chairdine, huise for náimde. Ro called for cairde. Olcai bémend benai, a popa a Fergais,' ol Cormac.

[4060] 'Ceist, cóich bíu?' ol Fergus.

'Ben a trí telcha tarsiu[7]. Toí do láim. Slig immud do cach leith ⁊ nísnairle. Imráid[8] ainech nUlad nádcon fárcbad. Nícon fáicébthar muna[9] fácabtha triut-sa indiu.'

'Airg-siu 'na leath n-aill, a Chonchobair,' ol Cormac fria athair. [4065] 'Nícon méla in fer sa a baraind for Ultu ní bus móo sund.'

Imsoí as Fergus. Arsligi cét lóech di Ultaib lasin cétna comroc cosin claideb co comairnic fri Conall Cernach.

'[10]Ba ramór[10] in bríg sin,' ar Conall Cernach, 'for túaith ⁊ cenél ar thóin mná drúithi.'

[4070] 'Ceist, cid dogén, a fírlaích?' or sé.

'Slig[11] na tulchu tairrsiu ⁊ na dusu impu,' or Conall Cernach.

Sligis Fergus na tulchai íarom coro ben a teóra máela Midi dá thrí béimennaib. Rocluinethar Cú Chulaind la sodain ina builli dobert Fergus forsna tulcha nó for scíath Conc[h]obair fodeisin.

[4075] 'Cóich benas na bailcbémenda[12] móra imc[h]iana sa?' or Cú
52ᵇ Chulaind. 'Iadais crú chridi. Conscar bara bith. Dos | cara trait túaga.'

Frisgart Lóeg co n-epert:

'Bentus forgu fear Fergus mac Róich rodána. Fuile formach [4080] n-áir[13], an fer Fergus mac Róeich. Ro cleth claideb carpait [14]hi sithbiu[14] [15]coná roacht[15] eochraidi mo popa Conc[h]obair mórc[h]ath.'

Is and asbert Cú Chulaind:

'Fúasailc[16] thrait túaga. Tuigthir fuil firu. Firfidir cleas claideb. [4085] Caithfidir dé daíne.'

---

[1] some letters deleted after as Y   [2] MS. partly illeg. iss oo ol ilatoi (tentative reading) corrupt for ⁊ as ó oldaí?   [3] caisc- Y   [4-4] grinni in claideb Y   [5-5] read Ainbchellach nád ainbchellach?   [6-6] read Foichlech nád n-airfoichlech?   [7] iarsiu Y (dar cendaib na slúag LL)   [8] (imrap TBC²)   [9] na Y (I make out a faint mu overhead)   [10-10] (bara mór TBC²)   [11] Clig Y   [12] bailcbemendasa Y   [13] nane (sic) Y (n-áir LL)   [14-14] (a ssídib LL)   [15-15] (rasiacht LL)   [16] fuaisailc Y (oslaicc LL)

Scendit la sodain a ṡuip ṡesca as a n-ardai eiret téiti uiseóc [1]i
n-áer[1] ⁊ scendit a thúaga de co mbádar i Maig Thúag la Condachta.
Rethaid immorro anaill [2]ille as[2]. Gabaid a ḟuile ergraim [de][3].
Ocus benaid cend ceachtair de in dá inailte fri araile combo líath
ceachtar de de inchind a séitche. —Dolotar do ḟásguba fair-seom 4090
ó Meidb conroimsitis a ḟuile fair ⁊ do ebert madma for hUlltu ⁊
toitim Fergusa hi frecor in chatha, ar adroas[4] a thedacht-som isin
chath. —Riasdardha imbi ⁊ dobretha dó secht cneslénti fichit no
bídis imbi fo thétaib ⁊ refedaib oc teacht hi cath, ⁊ gabaid a charpat
fria ais cona chreit ⁊ a díb fonnodaib ⁊ dofóbair dochom Fergusa 4095
timchell in chatha.

'Toí ille, a popa Fergais,' ol Cú Chulaind.

Ocus ní frecart co fa thrí.

'Tongu do dia toingthe hUlaid,' ol sé, 'notninus amail negar forcor
hi lunggu. Rega thorut amail téti bot tar catt. Atotiurr amail 4100
asoirc ben baíd a mac.'

'Cia do ḟeraib hÉrend asber frim-sa so?' or Fergus.

'Cú Chulaind mac Soaltaim ⁊ mac sethar Conchobair,' ol Cú
Chulaind, '⁊ immomimgaib-sea,' or sé.

'Ro gellas-[s]a cid ed ón,' ol Fergus. 4105

'[5]Dó duit[5] didiu,' ol Cú Chulaind.

'Maith,' ol Fergus. 'Romimgabais-[s]iu in tan basat[6] tretholl-sa.'

Luid Fergus as íarom in tan sin cona thríchtaib[7] cét. Lotar didiu
in Gaileóin ⁊ na Muimnich, ⁊ fácbaid noí tríchaid cét Medba ⁊ Ailella
⁊ a secht mac isin chath. Meadón laí is and dolluidh Cú Chulain 4110
isin chath. Amail doluid grian hi folt ḟeda is and ro memaid lais
forsin mbuidin ndéidenaich, [8]conná tuairthet[8] don charput acht dorn
dona hasnaib imon creit ⁊ dorn dona fer[t]sib imon droch.

Tarraid Cú Chulaind íarom Meidb oc teacht isin[9] cath.

'Nomanaig!' ol Meadb. 4115

'Cid guin nodgonam[11] ba deithbir dam,' or Cú Chulaind.

Rosnanacht íarom húair nád gonad mná. Adnaig idnacol forru
síar co lotar for Áth Lúain [⁊] tairis didiu. Beanaid trí bémend[10]
cona c[h]laidiub forsin licc i nn-Áth Lúain. Máelana Átha Lúain a
n-ainm. 4120

An tan trá ro memaid in cath, is and asbert Meadb fri Fergus:

'Correcad lochta ⁊ fulachta sund indiu, a Ḟergais,' ar sí.

[1-1] īna . . . line end, unfinished Y (immorro TBC[2]) (i cléthib aeóir ⁊ firmiminti
LL)   [2-2] (illeas TBC[2])   [3] sic LL, om. Y   [4] adragas with o written
overhead between r and a Y (deletion of -ag- overlooked?)   [5-5] do thuit Y
    [6] asat with small faint b added above first a Y   [7] sic Y, read thríchait
    [8-8] connatathrith with one or two letters erased at end Y (connat aithrith
TBC[2])   [9] = asin   [10] bemaend Y   [11] sic Y, read nodgonainn?

'Is bésad,' ol Fergus, 'do cach graig remitét láir, rotgata, rotbrata, rotfeither [1]a moín[1] hi tóin mná misrairleastair.'

4125 Fochesath trá in tarb isin maitin sin in chatha co comarnic fri 53ᵃ Findbeannach hi Tarbga hi Muig Aíi | .i. tarbguba nó tarbgleó. Roí Dedond a chétainm in c[h]nuic sin. Nach áen trá adroindi isin[2] chath ní feith ní acht déicsin in dá tarb oc comruc.

Baí Bricriu Nem[h]enga thíar ina thor[3] iar mbrisiud a chind do 4130 Fergus cusna feraib fithchilli. Doluid la cách dá ndéicsin [.i. do déicsin] in c[h]omraic na tarb. Lotar in dá tharb tar Bricrind ocon imforráin combo marb de. Is é aigid[4] Bricrinn sin.

Focairt [a] chos in Duind Chúailngi ar adairc a chéle. Láa co n-aidchi ná tuc a c[h]ois fris conidgres Fergus ⁊ co n-imbert slait 4135 [5]iarna sethnaig[5].

'Níp sén,' or Fergus, 'in sengamain troitech sa tucad sunn do fágbáil a enach[6] claindi ⁊ ceiniúil ⁊ imo fárgaibthea [7]mairb ili[7].

La sodain dosrenga a chois fris co mebaid a ḟergaire ⁊ co sescain[8] [9]a adarc[9] dia chéle co mbaí asain tsléib ina ḟarrad. Sléb nAdarca 4140 són íarom dono.

Bertius[10] riam íarom uide lá co n-aidche condocorostor asin[11] loch fil i táeb Crúachan co tulaid dó ass co lúan ⁊ leithiu ⁊ trom-chridiu a chéli[12] for[a] díb n-adarcaib. Dolodar iar sin ina slóig dia guin. Ní léig Fergus acht a t[h]echt leth bud mellach lais. Is 4145 iar sin doascain dochum a thíri. Ibid dig i Findleithiu ic tuidecht. Is and fácaib leithi a chéli[12]. Findleithiu[13] didiu íarom ainm in tíri. Ibis dig n-aile i nn-Áth Lúain. Fácaib lúan a chéli[12] and. Is de itá Áth Lúain. Atnaig a gém n-ass for Iraird Chuillind. Roclos fón cóiced n-uile. Ibis dig i Tromuib. Is and docher tromchride a 4150 chéli[12] dia díb n-adarcaib. Is de itá Troma. Dolluid do Étan Tairb. Dobert a étan frisin tealaig oc Áth Da Ḟerta. Is de itá Étan Tairb i Muig Muirrthemni. Luid íarom for slighidh Midh-lúachra i Cuib—is and no bíth la sescach Dáiri—⁊ dogní búrach ann. Is de atá Gort mBúraig. Luid íarom combo marb itir Ulto ⁊ hUa 4155 Echach ic Druim Thairb. Druim Tairb dano ainm in puirt sin.

Dogéni Ailill ⁊ Medb córae fri Ultu ⁊ fri Coin Culaind. Secht mblíadna iar sin ní roibi guin duine eturru i nn-Érind. Anaid Findabair la Coin Culaind ⁊ tíagaid Con[n]achta dia tír ⁊ tíagaid Ulaid do Emain Macha cona mórc[h]oscar.

Finit. Amen.

[1-1] only iṁ *at line end legible* Y (*immoin* TBC[2])   [2] = asin   [3] *gloss* .i. tuirse *overhead* Y   [4] = aided   [5-5] arna sednaig Y   [6] = enech (aenach TBC[2])   [7-7] ilib Y (mairbi lib TBC[2])   [8] scescain Y [9-9] aidarc Y   [10] *sic* Y   [11] = isin   [12] cheliu Y   [13] *sic* Y, *read* Findleithe

TRANSLATION

Táin Bó Cúailnge

A great army was mustered by the Connachtmen, that is, by Ailill and Medb, and word went from them to the three other provinces. And Ailill sent messengers to the seven sons of Mágu: Ailill, Anlúan, Moccorb, Cet, Én, Bascall and Dóche, each with his fighting force of three thousand, and also to Cormac Conn Longas the son of Conchobor, who was billeted with his three hundred men in Connacht. They all came on then until they reached Crúachain Aí.

Now Cormac's men were in three companies as they marched to Crúachain.

The first band wore vari-coloured cloaks wrapped around them. Their hair was shorn. They had tunics falling to the knee. They carried long shields, and each man bore in his hand a broad, bright spear on a slender shaft.

The second band wore dark-grey cloaks and red-embroidered tunics reaching down to their calves. Their long hair hung down behind. They carried white shields, and in their hands they bore five-pronged spears.

'It is not Cormac as yet,' said Medb.

Then came the third band. They wore purple cloaks and hooded red-embroidered tunics reaching to their feet. Their trimmed hair fell down to their shoulders. They bore curved shields with scalloped rims, and each man carried a spear as great as the pillar of a palace in his hand.

'This is Cormac now,' said Medb.

So then the four provinces of Ireland were gathered together in Crúachain Aí. Their prophets and druids did not permit them to go thence, but kept them for a fortnight awaiting an auspicious omen.

Then, on the day that they set forth, Medb said to her charioteer:

'All those who part here today from comrade and friend will curse me for it is I who have mustered this hosting.'

'Wait then,' said the charioteer, 'until the chariot has turned right-handwise to strengthen the good omen so that we may come back again.'

When the charioteer turned back the chariot and they were about to descend, they saw in front of them a grown maiden. She had yellow hair. She wore a vari-coloured cloak with a golden pin in it and a hooded tunic with red embroidery. She had shoes with golden fastenings. Her face was oval, narrow below, broad above. Her eyebrows were dark and black. Her beautiful black eyelashes cast a shadow on to the middle of her cheeks. Her lips seemed to be made of *partaing*. Her teeth were like a shower of pearls between her lips. She had three plaits of hair: two plaits wound around her head, the third hanging down her back, touching her calves behind. In her hand she carried a weaver's beam of white bronze, with golden inlay. There were three pupils in each of her eyes. The maiden was armed and her chariot was drawn by two black horses.

'What is your name,' asked Medb of the maiden.

'I am Feidelm, the poetess of Connacht,' said the maiden.

'Whence do you come?' asked Medb.

'From Albion after learning the art of divination,' answered the maiden.

'Have you the power of prophecy called *imbas forosna*?'

'I have indeed,' said the maiden.

'Look for me then and tell me how it will fare with my hosting.'

Then the maiden looked and Medb said:

'O Feidelm Prophetess, how do you see the fate of the army?'

Feidelm answered and said: 'I see it bloody, I see it red.'

'That is not so,' said Medb, 'for Conchobor lies in his debility in Emain together with the Ulstermen and all the mightiest of their warriors, and my messengers have come and brought me tidings of them. O Feidelm Prophetess, how do you see our host?' asked Medb again.

'I see it blood-stained, I see it red,' said the maiden.

'That is not so,' said Medb, 'for Celtchar mac Uthidir is in Dún Lethglaise together with a third of the men of Ulster, and Fergus mac Roeich meic Echdach is here in exile with us with three thousand men. O Feidelm Prophetess, how do you see our host?'

'I see it blood-stained, I see it red,' answered the maiden.

'That matters not indeed,' said Medb, 'for in every muster and in every army assembled in a great encampment there are quarrels and

strife and bloody woundings.   So look once more for us, and tell us
the truth.   O Feidelm Prophetess, how do you see our host?'
'I see it blood-stained, I see it red,' said Feidelm and she spoke as
follows:

'I see a fair man who will perform weapon-feats, with many a
wound in his flesh.   A hero's light is on his brow.   His forehead
is the meeting-place of many virtues.

'In each of his eyes are the seven jewel-bright pupils of a hero.
His spearpoints (?) are unsheathed.   He wears a red mantle
with clasps.

'His face is beautiful.   He amazes women-folk.   This lad of
handsome countenance looks in the battle like a dragon.

'Like is his prowess to that of Cú Chulainn of Murthemne.
I know not who is this Cú Chulainn of fairest fame, but this
I do know, that by him the army will be bloodily wounded.

'I see a tall man in the plain who gives battle to the host.
In each hand he holds four small swords with which to perform
great deeds.

'He attacks with his *gáe bolga* and also with his ivory-hilted
sword and his spear.   He can ply them on the host.   Each
weapon as he casts it has its own special use.

'This man wrapped in a red mantle sets his foot on every
battle-field.   Across the left wheel-rim of his chariot he attacks
them.   The distorted one kills them.   I see that he has changed
from the form in which hitherto he has appeared to me.

'He has moved forward to the battle.   Unless heed be taken,
there will be destruction.   I think that it is Cú Chulainn mac
Súaldaim who now comes to you.

'He will lay low your entire army.   He will slaughter you in
dense crowds.   Ye will leave with him a thousand severed
heads.   The prophetess Feidelm does not conceal your fate.

'Blood will flow from heroes' bodies. Much harm will be wrought by the hand of this hero. He will kill warriors; the men of Clanna Dedad meic Sin will flee. Men's bodies will be hacked and women will weep because of the Hound of the Smith whom I now see.'

On the Monday after the autumn festival of Samain they set out. They travelled south-east from Crúachain Aí, past Mucc Cruinb, past Terloch Teóra Crích, past Túaim Móna, past Cúil Silinne*a*, past Fid, past Bolga, past Coltain, past Glúne Gabair, past Mag Trego, past northern Tethba*b*, past southern Tethba, past Tíarthechta, past Ord, southwards past Slais, past Indeóind, past Carn, past Ochtrach, past Mide, past Findglassa Assail, past Delt, past Delind, past Sailig, past Slaibre, past Slechta (where they hewed down the trees), past Cúil Sibrinne, southwards past Ochuinn, northwards past Úata, past Dub, southwards past Comur, past Tromma and eastwards past Fothromma, past Sláne and Gort Sláni, southwards past Druim Licce, past Áth Gabla, past Ardachad, northwards past Féraind, past Findabair, southwards past Aisse, past Druim Sálfind, past Druim Caín, past Druim mac nDega, past Eódond Mór and Eódond Bec, past Méthe Tog[maill] and Méthe Eóin; past Druim Cáemtechta, past Scúap and Imscúap, past Cend Ferna, past Baile, past Aile, past Báil Scena and Dáil Scena, past Ferste, past Ross Lochad, past Sále, past Lochmach, past Ánmag, past Deind, past Delt, past Dubglais, past Fid Mór*c*, past Colptha, past Crond in Cúailnge.

From Findabair in Cúailnge the armies of Ireland spread out over the province in quest of the Bull. For they had gone past all these places before reaching Findabair.

Here ends the introductory part. The story in due order now begins.

The Story in Due Order

When they had come on the first stage of their journey from Crúachain to Cúil Silinne, the site of Loch Cairrcín today, Medb told her charioteer to harness her nine chariots[1] for her that she might

---

a i.e. Loch Carrcín, and it got its name from Silend daughter of Madchar

b i.e. Cairpre

c i.e. Trúalli

---

[1] i.e. she was always accompanied by nine chariots, so that the dust raised by the great army should not soil her.

drive around the encampment and see who among them was reluctant and who was glad to go on the hosting.

Now his tent was pitched for Ailill and his equipment was placed therein, both beds and blankets. Fergus mac Róich was next to Ailill in his tent. Cormac Conn Longas, son of Conchobor, was next to him. Then came Conall Cernach, with Fiacha mac Fir Febe, the son of Conchobor's daughter, beside him. Medb, the daughter of Eochu Feidlech was on the other side of Ailill, with Finnabair, the daughter of Ailill and Medb, beside her and Flidais next to Finnabair. This was not counting the servants and attendants.

After she had surveyed the host, Medb came back and said that it would be vain for the rest to go on that expedition if the division of the Gailióin went also.

'Why do you belittle the men?' asked Ailill.

'I am not belittling them,' said Medb. 'They are splendid warriors. When the others were making their shelters, the Gailióin had already finished thatching their shelters and cooking their food. When the rest were eating, they had already finished their meal and their harpers were playing to them. So it is useless for them to go on this expedition,' said Medb, 'for it is they who will take credit for the victory of the army.'

'Yet it is for us they fight,' said Ailill.

'They shall not go with us,' said Medb.

'Let them stay here then,' said Ailill.

'Indeed they shall not,' said Medb. 'They will overpower us when we have come back and seize our land.'

'Well then, what shall be done with them,' asked Ailill, 'since neither their staying nor their going pleases you?'

'Kill them!' said Medb.

'I shall not deny that is a woman's counsel,' said Ailill.

'You speak foolishly,' said Fergus in a low voice. It shall not happen unless we are all killed, for they are allies of us Ulstermen.'

'Nevertheless,' said Medb, 'we could do it. For I have here with me my own household retinue numbering two divisions, and the seven Maines are here, my seven sons, with seven divisions. Their luck can protect them,' said she. 'Their names are Maine Máthramail, Maine Aithremail, Maine Mórgor, Maine Mingor, Maine Mó Epirt, who is also called Maine Milscothach, Maine Andóe and Maine Cotageib Uile—he it is who has inherited the appearance of his mother and his father and the dignity of them both.'

'That will not be,' said Fergus, 'There are here seven kings from Munster, allies of us Ulstermen, and a division with each king.

I shall give you battle in the middle of the encampment where we now are, supported by those seven divisions, by my own division and by the division of the Gailióin. But I shall not argue the point,' said Fergus. 'We shall arrange the warriors of the Gailióin so that they shall not prevail over the rest of the army. Seventeen divisions,' said Fergus, 'is the number here in our encampment, not counting the camp-followers and our boys and our women-folk— for each chief here in Medb's company has brought his wife. The eighteenth division is that of the Gailióin. Let them be distributed throughout all the host.'

'I care not,' said Medb, 'provided that they do not remain in the close battle array in which they now are.'

This then was done; the Gailióin were distributed among the host. Next morning they set out for Móin Choltna. There they met with eight score deer in a single herd. They encircled them and killed them. Wherever there was a man of the Gailióin, it was he who got a deer, for the rest of the host got only five of the deer. They came on then to Mag Trego and there they encamped and prepared food for themselves.

According to one version it was then that Dubthach chanted this lay:

'Admit that hitherto ye have not heard nor listened to the trance-speech of Dubthach. A fierce hosting lies before you, contending for Findbenn, the bull of Ailill's wife.

'There will come a leader of armies who will try to recover the cattle of Murthemne. Because of the companionship of the two swineherds, ravens on the battle-field will drink men's blood.

'The watchful river Crann will offer them resistance and will not let them cross into Murthemne until the work of warriors is finished in the mountain north of Ochaíne.

' "Quickly," said Ailill to Cormac, "come and hold back your son." None comes from the plains where the cattle graze but is affrighted (?) by the din of the army.

'In due course a battle will be fought here with Medb and a third of the army. Men's corpses will then lie here if the distorted one come to you.'

Thereupon the Némain, that is, the war-goddess, attacked them. That was not the quietest of nights for them with the trance-speech of the boorish Dubthach as he slept. The hosts rose up at once and the army was thrown into confusion until Medb came and quelled them.

Then, after the army had been led astray across bogs and streams, they went and spent the night in Granard in northern Tethba. For the sake of kinship Fergus sent a warning to the Ulstermen who were still suffering from their debility, all except Cú Chulainn and his father Súaltaim. When the warning message had come from Fergus, Cú Chulainn and his father went as far as Irard Cuillenn, that is, Crossa Caíl, there to watch for the enemy host.

'I have a premonition that the host will arrive tonight,' said Cú Chulainn to his father. 'Take a warning from us to the men of Ulster. I must go to Feidelm Noíchride'—he meant to tryst with her handmaiden who was secretly Cú Chulainn's concubine—'to fulfil my own pledge which I gave her.'

Then before he went, he twisted a withe into a ring and wrote an ogam inscription on its peg, and cast it over the top of a pillar-stone.

Then Fergus was given the task of leading the army along the path. He went far astray to the south to give the Ulstermen time to complete the mustering of their army. This he did out of affection for his own kin.

Ailill and Medb noticed this, and Medb said:

'O Fergus, this is strange. What manner of path do we travel? We go astray to south and to north, past every strange district.

'Ailill of Mag Aí with his army fears that you will betray him. Until now he heeded not where the path led.

'If you feel the pull of kinship, do not lead horses any longer. Perhaps someone else may be found to guide us on our way.'

Fergus answered:

'O Medb, what perturbs you? This is not anything resembling treachery. O woman, the land across which I shall lead you belongs to the men of Ulster.

'Not with intent to harm the hosting do I go in turn along each devious road, but that I may avoid the great one who guards Mag Murthemne.

'It is not to save my mind from weariness that I go thus aside from the path, but I am trying to avoid meeting Cú Chulainn mac Súaltaim even at a later time.'

They went on then to Irard Cuilenn, today called Crossa Caíl. The four sons of Irard mac Anchinne[1], Eirr and Indell with Foich and Fochlam their two charioteers, were those who always preceded the hosts to protect their brooches and their rugs and their mantles that the dust raised by the army might not soil them. These men found the withe Cú Chulainn had cast and they noticed the grazing made by the horses. For Súaltaim's two horses had cropped the grass to its roots in the earth while Cú Chulainn's horses had licked the soil down to the bedrock beneath the grass. Then these four men sat still till the host came up, and their musicians played to them. They handed the withe to Fergus mac Róich; he read out the ogam inscription that was on it.

When Medb arrived she asked:

'Why are you waiting here?'

'We are waiting,' said Fergus, 'because of yonder withe. There is on its peg an ogam inscription which reads: "Let none go past till there be found a man to throw a withe made of one branch as it is in the same way with one hand. But I except my friend Fergus." In truth,' said Fergus, 'it is Cú Chulainn who has cast it and it is his horses which grazed this plain.'

And he put the withe in the druid's hand and chanted this song:

'Here is a withe. What is its message for us? What is its secret meaning? And how many put it there? Was it few or many?

'Will it bring ruin on the army if they go past it? Find out, O ye druids, why the withe was left there.'

A druid answered:

'A hero cast it there, the swift cutting (?) of a hero, a source of perplexity to warriors, containment of chiefs with their followers. One man cast it there with one hand.

'Does not the king's army obey him unless they have broken faith? I know no reason why the withe was cast there save that one of you should cast a withe even as one man did.'

---

[1] or the four sons of Nera mac Núada meic Taccain, as is found in other versions.

Then said Fergus to them:

'If ye flout this withe or if ye go past it, though it be in a man's possession or in a locked house, it will go after the man who wrote the ogam inscription, and he will kill one of you before morning unless one of you cast a withe in like manner.'

'We do not wish, however, that any one of us should be killed straight away,' said Ailill. 'Let us go to the end of yon great wood to the south of us, Fid Dúin. We shall go no farther than that.'

The army then hewed down the wood to make a path for the chariots. That place is called Slechta. It is there that the Partraige (now) live.

—According to others, however, it was here that the dialogue between Medb and Feidelm Banfháith as we have related above took place, and it was after the answer Feidelm made to Medb that the wood was cut down. Thus: 'Look for me,' said Medb, '(to see) how will my expedition fare.'

'It is hard for me,' said the maiden. 'The wood prevents me from seeing them properly.'

'That can be arranged,' said Medb. 'We shall cut down the wood.'

So it was done, and Slechta is the name of that place.—

They spent the night then in Cúil Sibrille, that is, Cennannas. Heavy snow fell on them, reaching to the girdles of the men and the wheels of the chariots. They rose early on the morrow. That had not been a restful night for them because of the snow, nor had they prepared food for themselves that night.

But Cú Chulainn did not come early from his tryst; he remained until he had washed and bathed. Then he came on to the track of the army.

'Would that we had not gone thither nor betrayed the men of Ulster!' cried Cú Chulainn. 'We have let the enemy host come upon them unawares. Make an estimate of the host for us,' said Cú Chulainn to Lóeg, 'that we may know their number.'

Lóeg did so and said to Cú Chulainn:

'I am confused. I cannot estimate exactly.'

'If only I come, I shall not see them confusedly,' said Cú Chulainn.

'Get out of the chariot,' said Lóeg.

Cú Chulainn got out of the chariot and for a long time he estimated the number of the host.

'Even you,' said Lóeg, 'do not find it easy.'

'It is easier for me, however, than for you. For I have three gifts, namely, the gift of sight, the gift of understanding, the gift of reckoning. I have reckoned up the numbers here.[1] There are here in number eighteen divisions, but the eighteenth division, that is, the division of the Gailióin, has been distributed among the whole host so that it is confusing to count them.'

Then Cú Chulainn went round the host until he was at Áth nGrencha. There he cut down a forked branch with one blow of his sword and fixed it in the middle of the stream so that a chariot could not pass it on this side or on that. While he was thus engaged Eirr and Indell with their two charioteers, Fóich and Fochlam, came up with him. He cut off their four heads and impaled them on the four prongs of the forked branch. Hence the name Áth nGabla.[2]

Then the horses of the four men went towards the host, with their bloodstained trappings. The host thought that there had been a battle in the ford before them. A band went from them to survey the ford; they saw only the track of one chariot and the forked branch with the four heads and an ogam inscription on its side. At that point the whole army arrived.

'Are yonder heads those of some of our people?' asked Medb.

'They are of our people and of our choice men,' said Ailill.

One of them read aloud the ogam inscription that was on the side of the forked branch: 'One man has cast this forked branch with one hand, and ye shall not go past it unless one of you, but not Fergus, has cast it with one hand.'

'It is marvellous,' said Ailill, 'how quickly the four were slain.'

'Do not think that marvellous,' said Fergus, 'but rather the cutting of the forked branch from its root with one blow, and if its end shows one cutting, it is all the greater achievement, and (it is marvellous) that it should have been driven in in this manner, for no hole was dug for it but it was cast from the back of a chariot with one hand.'

'Deliver us in this difficulty, Fergus,' said Medb.

'Give me a chariot then,' said Fergus, 'that I may pull the branch out so that it may be seen if its end shows one cutting.'

Then Fergus smashed fourteen of their chariots but from his own chariot he drew the forked branch out of the ground and he saw that its end was one cutting.

---

[1] This is one of the three cleverest yet most difficult reckonings ever made in Ireland, the three being this reckoning of the men of Ireland made by Cú Chulainn in the Táin, the reckoning made by Lug of the Fomorians in the battle of Mag Tuired and the reckoning of the army in Bruiden Da Derga made by Ingcél, [marginal note]

[2] that is, at the place called Beloch Caille Móire to the north of Cnogba, [marginal note]

'We must take heed of the nature of the people to whom we are going,' said Ailill. 'Let all of you prepare food. Last night was not restful for you with the snow. And let some of the adventures and stories of the people to whom we go be related to us.'

So then they were told the adventures of Cú Chulainn.

Ailill asked:

'Is it Conchobar who has done this?'

'It is not indeed,' said Fergus. 'He would not have come to the marches unless he was accompanied by a number sufficient to give battle.'

'Was it Celtchar mac Uthidir?'

'It was not indeed,' said Fergus. 'He would not have come to the marches without a number sufficient to give battle around him.'

'Was it Eógan mac Durthacht?'

'It was not indeed,' said Fergus. 'He would not have come past the marches without thirty scythed chariots. The man who would have done the deed is Cú Chulainn,' said Fergus. 'It is he who would have cut down the tree with one blow from its root, and he who would have killed the four men as quickly as they were killed, and he who would have come to the border accompanied (only) by his charioteer.'

The Eulogy of Cú Chulainn

'What manner of man,' asked Ailill, 'is this Hound whom we have heard of among the Ulstermen? What age is that famous youth?'

'I can tell you that,' said Fergus. 'In his fifth year he went to the boys in Emain Macha to play. In his sixth year he went to learn feats of arms to Scáthach [1]and went to woo Emer.[1] In his seventh year he took up arms. At the present time he is seventeen years old.'

'Is he the most formidable among the Ulstermen?' asked Medb.

'More so than any one of them,' answered Fergus. 'You will not encounter a warrior harder to deal with, nor a spear-point sharper or keener or quicker, nor a hero fiercer, nor a raven more voracious, nor one of his age to equal a third of his valour, nor a lion more savage, nor a shelter in battle nor a sledge-hammer for smiting, nor a protector in fighting, nor doom of hosts, nor one better able to check a great army. You will not find there any man his equal in age like unto Cú Chulainn in growth, in dress, in fearsomeness, in

---

[1]–[1] note between columns

speech, in splendour, in voice and appearance, in power and harshness, in feats, in valour, in striking power, in rage and in anger, in victory and in doom-dealing and in violence, in stalking, in sureness of aim and in game-killing, in swiftness and boldness and rage, with the feat of nine men on every spear-point.'

'I reck little of that,' said Medb. 'He has but one body; he suffers wounding; he is not beyond capture. Moreover he is only the age of a grown girl and as yet his manly deeds have not developed.'

'Nay,' said Fergus. 'It were no wonder that he should perform a goodly exploit today, for even when he was younger, his deeds were those of a man.'

The Boyhood Deeds

'He was reared,' said Fergus, 'by his father and mother at the Airgthech in Mag Muirthemne. He was told the famous tales of the youths in Emain. For,' said Fergus, 'thrice fifty youths are usually there engaged in play. This is how Conchobor spends his time of sovereignty: one third of the day spent watching the youths, another third playing *fidchell*, another third drinking ale till he falls asleep therefrom. Though we have been exiled by him, (I still maintain that) there is not in Ireland a warrior more wonderful,' said Fergus.

'Cú Chulainn asked his mother to let him go to join the boys.

' "You shall not go," said his mother, "till you be escorted by some of the Ulster warriors."

"I think it too long to wait for that," said Cú Chulainn. "Point out to me in what direction is Emain."

' "To the north there," said his mother, " and the journey is hard. Slíab Fúait lies between you and Emain."

' "I shall make an attempt at it at all events," said Cú Chulainn.

'He went off then with his wooden shield and his toy javelin, his hurley and his ball. He kept throwing the javelin in front of him and catching it by the point before its end touched the ground.

'Then he went to the boys without binding them over to protect him. For no one used to come to them in their playing-field till his protection was guaranteed, but Cú Chulainn was not aware of the fact that this was tabu for them.

' "The boy insults us," said Follomon mac Conchobair. "Yet we know he is of the Ulstermen. Attack him."

'They threw their thrice fifty javelins at him, and they all stuck in his toy shield. Then they threw all their balls at him and he caught them, every single ball, against his breast. Then they threw their thrice fifty hurling-clubs at him. He warded them off so that they did not touch him, and he took a load of them on his back.

'Thereupon he became distorted. His hair stood on end so that it seemed as if each separate hair on his head had been hammered into it. You would have thought that there was a spark of fire on each single hair. He closed one eye so that it was no wider than the eye of a needle; he opened the other until it was as large as the mouth of a mead-goblet. He laid bare from his jaw to his ear and opened his mouth rib-wide (?) so that his internal organs were visible. The champion's light rose above his head.

'Then he attacked the boys. He knocked down fifty of them before they reached the gate of Emain. Nine of them came past me and Conchobar where we were playing chess. Cú Chulainn leapt over the chess-board in pursuit of the nine. Conchobar seized him by the forearm.

' "The boys are not well treated." said Conchobar.

' "It was right for me (to treat them so), master Conchobar," said he. "I came to play with them from my home, from my father and mother, and they were not kind to me."

' "What is your name?" said Conchobar.

' "I am Sétanta the son of Sualtaim and of Deichtire, your sister. It was not to be expected that I should be tormented there."

' "Why were the boys not bound over to protect you?" asked Conchobar.

' "I did not know of (the need of) that," said Cú Chulainn. "Undertake to protect me against them."

' "I agree," said Conchobar.

'But then he turned again and attacked the boys throughout the house.

' "What have you got against them now?" asked Conchobar.

' "Let me be bound over to protect them," said Cú Chulainn.

' "Undertake it then," said Conchobar.

' "I agree," said Cú Chulainn.

'So they all went into the playing field. And those boys who had been knocked down there rose to their feet, helped by their foster-mothers and their foster-fathers.'

'At one time,' said Fergus, 'when Cú Chulainn was a boy, he never slept in Emain.'

' "Tell me," said Conchobar to him, 'Why do you not sleep?"

11

' "I do not sleep unless my head and my feet are equally high."

'So a pillar-stone was placed by Conchobar at his head and another at his feet, and a special couch was made for him between them.

'On another occasion a certain man went to wake him and with his fist Cú Chulainn struck him on the forehead, driving the front of his forehead on to his brain, while with his arm he knocked down the pillar-stone.

' "Surely," said Ailill, 'that was the fist of a warrior and the arm of a strong man!"

'From that time on,' said Fergus, 'they never dared to wake him (but left him) till he woke of his own accord.'

The Death of the Boys

'Another time he was playing ball in the playing-field east of Emain, he alone on one side against the thrice fifty boys. He kept defeating them in every game in that way all the time. Eventually the boy began to belabour them with his fists and fifty of them died. Whereupon he fled and hid under the pillow of Conchobar's couch. The Ulstermen rose up around him but I and Conchobar stood up to defend him. The boy rose to his feet under the couch and on to the floor of the house he threw from him the couch together with the thirty warriors who were in it.

'Then the Ulstermen sat around him in the house and we arranged matters and made peace between the boys and him,' said Fergus.

The Fight between Eógan mac Durthacht and Conchobar

'There was strife between the Ulstermen and Eógan mac Durthacht. The Ulstermen went to battle while Cú Chulainn was left behind asleep. The Ulstermen were defeated. Conchobar and Cúscraid Menn Macha and many others besides were left on the field. Their groans awoke Cú Chulainn. Then he stretched himself so that the two flag-stones which were about him were smashed. Bricriu yonder witnessed this happening,' said Fergus. 'Then he arose. I met him in front of the fort as I came in severely wounded.

' "Hey! Welcome! master Fergus," said he. "Where is Conchobar?"

' "I do not know," said I.

'He went on his way then. The night was dark. He made for the battlefield. He saw in front of him a man with half a head carrying the half of another man on his back.

' "Help me, Cú Chulainn!" said he. "I have been wounded and I have brought half of my brother on my back. Take a turn with me in carrying him."

' "I will not," said he.

'Whereupon the other threw the burden he was carrying to him, but Cú Chulainn cast it off. They wrestled then and Cú Chulainn was thrown. He heard the war-goddess crying from among the corpses.

' "Poor stuff to make a warrior is he who is overthrown by phantoms!"

'Whereupon Cú Chulainn rose to his feet, and, striking off his opponent's head with his hurley, he began to drive the head like a ball before him across the plain.

' "Is my master Conchobar on this battle-field?"

Conchobar answered him. Cú Chulainn went towards him and saw him in the ditch with the earth around him on all sides hiding him.

' "Why have you come to the battle-field" said Conchobar, "where you may die of fright?"

'He lifted Conchobar out of the ditch then. Six of our strong men in Ulster could not have lifted him out more courageously.

' "Go before us to yonder house," said Conchobar, "and make a fire for me there."

'He kindled a big fire for him.

' "Well," said Conchobar, "if I now had a roast pig, I should live."

"I will go and fetch one," said Cú Chulainn.

'He went off then and saw a man at a cooking-pit in the middle of the wood, with one hand holding his weapons, the other cooking a pig. Great was the fearsomeness of the man. Nevertheless he attacked him and carried off his head and his pig. Afterwards Conchobar ate the pig.

"Let us go to our house," said Conchobar.

They met Cúscraid mac Conchobair. He too bore severe wounds, Cú Chulainn carried him on his back. The three of them went on to Emain Macha.

The fate of the twenty-seven men and the reason why none dared to wound the Ulstermen when they were in their debility.

'On another occasion the Ulstermen were in their debility. Among us,' said Fergus, 'women and boys do not suffer from the debility nor does anyone outside the territory of Ulster, nor yet

Cú Chulainn and his father, and so none dares to shed their blood for whosoever wounds them at once suffers himself from the debility or he wastes away or his life-span is shortened.

'Twenty-seven men came to us from the Isles of Faiche. While we were suffering the debility they climbed over into our back-court. The women in the fort cried out in warning. The boys who were in the playing-field came on hearing the cries, but when they saw the dark gloomy men, they all fled except Cú Chulainn alone. He cast hand-stones at them and belaboured them with his hurley. He killed nine of them but they dealt him fifty wounds, and then they went off.

'If a man did those deeds when he was five years old, it were no wonder that he should have come to the marches, and cut off the heads of yon four men.'

The killing of the Smith's Hound by Cú Chulainn and the reason why he is called Cú Chulainn

'Indeed we know that boy', said Conall Cernach, 'and we know him all the better in that he is a fosterling of ours. Not long after the deed which Fergus has just related, he performed another exploit.

'When Culann the smite prepared a feast for Conchobar, he asked Conchobar not to bring a great crowd with him for the feast he had made was not provided by his possession of land or estate but was gained by the work of his hands and his tongs. Then Conchobar set off together with fifty chariot-warriors, the noblest and most illustrious of the heroes.

'Conchobar visited the playing-field then. It was always his custom to pay the boys a fleeting visit to ask a greeting of them. There he saw Cú Chulainn playing ball against thrice fifty boys, and defeating them. When they were engaged in driving the ball into the hole, he would fill the hole with his balls and the boys would not be able to ward him off. When it was they who were throwing at the hole, he by himself would ward them off so that not even a single ball would go into it. When they were wrestling, he alone would throw the thrice fifty boys, yet not all of them together could surround him to throw him. When they were engaged in the game of stripping one another, he would strip them all stark-naked but they could not even take his brooch from his mantle.

'Conchobor marvelled at this. He asked if the boy's deeds would correspond (to his present ones) when he attained the age of man-hood. They all said that they would. Conchobor said to Cú Chulainn:

' "Come with me to the feast to which we are going since you are a guest."

' "I have not yet had my fill of play, master Conchobor," said the boy. "I shall follow you."

'When they had all come to the feast, Culann asked Conchobar:

' "Do you expect anyone to follow you?"

' "No," said Conchobor. He did not remember the arrangement with his fosterling to come after him.

' "I have a blood hound,[1]" said Culann. "There are three chains on him and three men holding each chain. He was brought from Spain. Let him be loosed to guard our cattle and our stock and let the fort be shut."

'At that point the boy arrived. The dog made for him. He still kept on with the play; he would throw his ball and then throw his hurley after it so that it struck the ball, neither stroke being greater than the other. And he threw his toy spear after them and caught it before it fell. And though the dog was approaching him, it interfered not with his play. Conchobor and his household were so dismayed by this that they could not move. They thought they would not reach him alive though the fort was open. Now when the hound came towards the boy, he cast aside his ball and his hurley, and he tackled the dog with both hands, that is, he put one hand on the apple of the hound's throat and the other at the back of his head, and dashed him against the pillar-stone that was beside him so that all the hound's limbs sprang apart. According to another version, however, he threw his ball into the hound's mouth and it drove his entrails out through him.

'The Ulstermen rose up to fetch the boy, some leaping over the wall of the court, others going out by the gate. They placed him in Conchobar's arms. A great alarm was raised by them at the thought that the son of the king's sister had almost been killed. At that point Culann entered the house.

' "Welcome, little lad, for your mother's sake. But as for myself, would that I had not prepared a feast! My livelihood is now a livelihood wasted, my husbandry a husbandry lost without my hound[2]. The servant who has been taken from me, that is, my

[1] i.e. a hound brought from overseas, i.e. the whelp of a mastiff, [foot note]

[2] That hound was not one of the three hounds that were in the brain of Conganchness, as some hold, for it was to take vengeance for Cú Roí's death on the men of Ulster that Conganchness had gone and that happened long after the Cattle-Raid, but Cú Chulainn was only seven years old when he killed the smith's hound. Thus the theory held by those people is false; the smith's hound had been brought from Spain, as is asserted in the text of the tale, [marginal note, hand M].

hound, maintained life and honour for me. He was defence and protection for my goods and my cattle. He guarded all my beasts for me in field and in house."

' "That is no great matter," said the boy. "A whelp of the same litter will be reared by me for you, and until such time as that hound grows and is fit for action, I myself shall be a hound to protect your cattle and to protect yourself. And I shall protect all Mag Murthemne; neither flock nor herd shall be taken thence from me without my knowing it."

' "Your name shall be Cú Chulainn (the Hound of Culann) then," said Catbhad.

' "I am glad that it should be my name," said Cú Chualinn.

'It were no cause of wonder that one who had done this when he was seven, should have performed a valiant deed now that he is seventeen years old,' said Conall Cernach.

The Death of Nechta Scéne's Three Sons

'He did still another exploit,' said Fiachu mac Fir Febe.

'Cathbad the druid was with his son Conchobar mac Nessa. There were with him a hundred active men learning the druid's art—that was the number that Cathbad used to instruct. One of his pupils asked him for what that day would be of good omen. Cathbad said that if a warrior took up arms on that day, his name for deeds of valour would be known throughout Ireland and his fame would last for ever.

'Cú Chulainn heard this. He went to Conchobar to ask for arms. Conchobar asked:

' "Who prophesied good fortune for you?"

' "Master Cathbad," said Cú Chulainn.

' "We know him indeed," said Conchobar.

'He gave him a spear and a shield. Cú Chulainn brandished them in the middle of the hall so that not one was left unbroken of the fifteen spare sets of weapons which were kept in Conchobar's household to replace broken weapons or to provide for the taking up of arms by someone. Finally Conchobar's own arms were given to him. They withstood him, and he brandished them and blessed the king whose arms they were, saying: "Happy the people and race over whom reigns the owner of these arms!"

'Then Cathbad came to them and asked:

' "Is the boy taking up arms?"

' "Yes," said Conchobar.

' "That is not lucky for the son of his mother," said he.

' "Why, was it not you who instructed him?"

' "It was not I indeed," said Cathbad.

' "What use is it for you to deceive me so, you sprite?" said Conchobar to Cú Chulainn.

' "O king of the Fían, it is no deceit," said Cú Chulainn. "He prophesied good fortune for his pupils this morning and I heard him from where I was on the south side of Emain, and then I came to you."

' "It is indeed a day of good omen," said Cathbad. "It is certain that he who takes up arms today will be famous and renowned, but he will, however, be short-lived."

' "A mighty thing!" said Cú Chulainn. "Provided I be famous, I am content to be only one day on earth."

'On another day a certain man asked the druids for what that day was a good omen.

"The name of one who goes (for the first time) into a chariot on this day," said Cathbad, "will be famed throughout Ireland for ever."

'Then Cú Chulainn heard this, and he came to Conchobar and said to him:

"Master Conchobar, give me a chariot."

'Conchobar gave him a chariot. Cú Chulainn put his hand between the two shafts and the chariot broke. In the same way he smashed twelve chariots. So finally Conchobar's chariot was given to him and it withstood the test.

'Thereafter he went into the chariot with Conchobar's charioteer. The charioteer, whose name was Ibor, turned the chariot under him.

' "Come out of the chariot now," said the charioteer. "These are fine horses."

' "I am fine too, lad," said Cú Chulainn. "Just go on around Emain and you shall be rewarded for it."

'The charioteer drove off and Cú Chulainn made him go along the road that he might greet the boys, "and so that the boys may wish me well." Then he besought him to go back over the road again. When they had come there Cú Chulainn said to the charioteer:

' "Ply the goad on the horses."

' "In what direction?" asked the charioteer.

' "As far as the road will lead," said Cú Chulainn.

'Thence they came to Slíab Fúait where they found Conall Cernach. It had fallen to Conall to guard the province that day. For each warrior of the Ulstermen spent a day in turn in Slíab

Fúait, to protect anyone who came that way with poetry or with challenge to battle, so that there he might be encountered and so that no one should go unnoticed into Emain.

' "I wish you prosperity, victory and triumph!" said Conall.

' "Go to the fort, Conall, and leave me here to watch now," said Cú Chulainn.

' "That will do," said Conall, "if it is (merely) to undertake the protection of one coming with poetry. However, if it be to fight some one, it is still too soon for you to do that."

' "Perhaps it will not be necessary at all," said Cú Chulainn. "Meanwhile let us go to take a look at the sand-bank of Loch Echtra. There are usually warriors staying there."

' "I am willing," said Conall.

'So they set out. Cú Chulainn threw a stone from his sling and the shaft of Conall Cernach's chariot broke.

' "Why have you thrown the stone, lad?" asked Conall.

' "To test my shooting and the accuracy of my shot," said Cú Chulainn, "And it is the custom with you Ulstermen that you do not drive on in a chariot which is unsafe. Go back to Emain master Conall, and leave me here to keep watch."

' "I am willing," said Conall.

'Conall Cernach did not go past that spot afterwards.

'Cú Chulainn went on to Loch Echtra but they found no one there. The charioteer told Cú Chulainn that they should go to Emain to be in time for the feasting there.

' "No," said Cú Chulainn. "What mountain is that over there?"

' "Slíab Monduirnd," said the charioteer.

' "Let us go to it," said Cú Chulainn.

'Then they went to it, and when they had reached the mountain, Cú Chulainn asked:

' "What white cairn is that over there on the mountain-top?"

' "Finncharn," said the charioteer.

' "What plain is that yonder?" asked Cú Chulainn.

' "Mag mBreg," said the charioteer.

'So he told him the name of every chief fort between Temair and Cennannas. He named, moreover, their meadowlands and their fords, their renowned places and their dwellings, their forts and their fortified heights. He showed him too the fort of the three sons of Nechta Scéne,[1] to wit, Fóill, Fannall and Túachell.

---

[1] from Inber Scéne [gloss H]. Fer Ulli mac Lugdach was their father and Nechtan Scéne their mother. The Ulstermen had killed their father which is the reason they were at war with the Ulstermen [marginal note M]

' "Is it they who say," asked Cú Chulainn, "that there are not more Ulstermen alive than they have killed of them ?"

' "It is they indeed," said the charioteer.

' "Let us go to meet them," said Cú Chulainn.

' "It is dangerous for us," said the charioteer.

' "Indeed it is not to avoid danger that we go," said Cú Chulainn.

'Then they set off, and they unyoked their horses at the confluence of a bog and a river, on the south above the fort of the sons of Nechta Scéne. And Cú Chulainn cast the withe that was on the pillar-stone as far as his arm could throw it out into the river and let it float downstream. This violated a tabu which bound the sons of Nechta Scéne who noticed what had been done and came towards them. But Cú Chulainn, after letting the withe drift with the current, fell asleep at the pillar-stone, having said to the charioteer :

"Do not wake me for a few, but wake me for several."

'However the charioteer was now sore afraid, and he harnessed the chariot and he tugged at the rugs and skin-coverings that were under Cú Chulainn, though he did not dare to waken him because Cú Chulainn had previously told him not to waken him for a few.

'Then came the sons of Nechta Scéne.

' "Who is here ?" said one of them.

' "A little lad who has come on an expedition in a chariot today," answered the charioteer.

' "May his first taking up of arms not bring him prosperity or success. He must not stay in our land and the horses must not graze here any longer," said the warrior.

' "Their reins are ready in my hand." said the charioteer. "You had no reason to show yourself unfriendly to him, and anyway," said Ibor to the warrior, "the lad is asleep."

' "I am no lad indeed," said Cú Chulainn, "but the lad who is here has come to seek battle with a man."

' "That pleases me well," said the warrior.

' "It will please you well now in yonder ford," said Cú Chulainn.

' "This is fitting for you," said the charioteer. "Beware of the man who comes against you. Fóill (Sly) is his name. If you reach him not with the first thrust, you will never reach him."

' "I swear by the god by whom my people swear, he shall not play that trick again on Ulstermen if once the broad spear of my master Conchobar reach him from my hand. It will mean an outlaw's hand, that is, death, for him."

'Then Cú Chulainn cast the spear at Fóill so that his back broke therefrom and he carried off his spoils and his severed head then.

' "Beware of the next man," said the charioteer. "Fannall (Swallow) is his name. He skims over water as lightly as a swan or a swallow."

' "I swear that he will not play that stick on Ulstermen again," said Cú Chulainn. "You have seen how I travel across the pool in Emain."

'Then they met in the ford. Cú Chulainn killed that man and carried off his spoils and his head.

' "Beware of the next man who comes to you," said the charioteer. "Túachell (Cunning) is his name, and it is no misnomer for no weapons wound him."

' "Here is the *deil chlis* for him to confound him so that it may riddle him like a sieve," said Cú Chulainn.

'Then he cast the spear at him and knocked him down. He went towards him and cut off his head. He carried off his head and his spoils to his own charioteer.

'Then he heard the cry of their mother, Nechta Scéne, bewailing them. He carried off the spoils and brought the three heads with him in his chariot and said:

' "I will not part from these tokens of my triumph until I reach Emain."

'Thereupon they set forth with their trophies. Cú Chulainn said to the charioteer:

' "You promised us a good drive, and we need it now because of the fight and because of the pursuit behind us."

'They drove on then to Slíab Fúait. So swift was the run they made across Brega after his urging of the charioteer that the chariot-horses used to outstrip the wind and birds in flight, and Cú Chulainn used to catch the stone he had thrown from his sling before it reached the ground.

'On reaching Slíab Fúait they found a herd of deer before them.

' "What are those nimble cattle over there?" asked Cú Chulainn.

' "Wild deer," said the charioteer.

' "Which would the Ulstermen deem best, that I should take them to them alive or dead?"

' "It is more wonderful (to take them) alive" said the charioteer. "Not every one can do so, but there is not one of them who cannot take them dead. But you cannot carry off any one of them alive," added the charioteer.

"Indeed I can," said Cú Chulainn. "Ply the goad on the horses and drive them to the bog."

'The charioteer did so, and the horses stuck fast in the bog. Cú Chulainn sprang out of the chariot and caught the deer that was nearest to him and the finest of the herd. He lashed the horses through the bog and subdued the deer immediately and tied it up between the two poles of the chariot.

'Again they saw before them a flock of swans.

' "Which would the Ulstermen deem best," asked Cú Chulainn, "that I should carry them alive to them or carry them dead?"

' "The bravest and most active carry them off alive," said the charioteer.

'Cú Chulainn then threw a small stone at the birds and brought down eight of them. Again he threw a big stone and struck twelve of them. All this was done by his 'return-stroke.'

' "Collect the birds for me," said Cú Chulainn to his charioteer. "If I go to get them, the wild deer will spring on you."

' "It is not easy for me to go there," said the charioteer. "The horses have become wild so that I cannot go past them. Nor can I go past the iron wheels of the chariot because of their sharpness, and I cannot go past the deer for his antlers have filled all the space between the two poles of the chariot."

' "Step from his antlers then," said Cú Chulainn. "I swear by the god by whom the Ulstermen swear, that I shall so nod at him and so glare at him that he will not move his head towards you and will not dare to stir."

'That was done then. Cú Chulainn fastened the reins and the charioteer collected the birds. Then Cú Chulainn tied the birds to the strings and cords of the chariot. In this wise he went to Emain Macha with a wild deer behind his chariot, a flock of swans fluttering over it and three severed heads in his chariot.

They reached Emain then.

"A chariot-warrior is driving towards you!" cried the watchman in Emain Macha. "He will shed the blood of every man in the fort unless heed be taken and naked women go out to meet him."

'Then he turned the left side of his chariot towards Emain which was tabu for it. And Cú Chulainn said.

"I swear by the god by whom Ulstermen swear that, unless some man is found to fight with me, I shall shed the blood of everyone in the fort."

"Send forth naked women to meet him!" ordered Conchobor.

'Then the women-folk of Emain came forth to meet him led by Mugain,[1] the wife of Conchobor mac Nessa, and they bared their breasts to him.

---

[1] or by Férach, according to other versions [gloss]

"These are the warriors who will encounter you today," said Mugain.[1]

'He hid his face. Then the warriors of Emain seized him and cast him into a tub of cold water. That tub burst about him. The second tub into which he was plunged boiled hands high therefrom. The third tub into which he went after that he warmed so that its heat and its cold were properly adjusted for him. Then he came out and the queen, Mugain, put on him a blue mantle with a silver brooch therein, and a hooded tunic, and he sat at Conchobor's knee which was his resting-place always after that.

'One who did that in his seventh year,' said Fíachu mac Fir Febe, 'it were no wonder that he should triumph over odds and overcome in fair fight now that his seventeen years are complete today.'

A different Version up to the Death of Órlám

'Let us go forward now,' said Ailill.

Then they reached Mag Mucceda. There Cú Chulainn cut down an oaktree in their path and on its side he wrote an ogam inscription which said that none should go past it until a warrior should leap across it in a chariot. They pitched their tents at that spot and they came to leap across it in their chariots. Thirty horses fell in the attempt and thirty chariots were broken there.

Bélach nÁne is the name of that place ever since.

The Death of Fráech

They remained there till the morrow. Fráech was summoned to them.

'Help us, Fráech,' said Medb. 'Deliver us in this strait. Go for us to meet Cú Chulainn to see if perhaps you may encounter him in battle.'

Fráech set forth, a company of nine men, early in the morning and reached Áth Fúait. He saw a warrior bathing in the river.

'Wait here,' said Fráech to his followers, 'till I fight with yonder man. He is not good in water.'

He took off his clothes and went into the water to Cú Chulainn.

'Do not come against me,' said Cú Chulainn. 'You will die if you do and I should be sorry to kill you.'

---

[1] or Férach [gloss]

'Indeed I shall go,' said Fráech, 'so that we may meet in the water, and give me fair play.'

'Arrange that as you please,' said Cú Chulainn.

'Let each of us clasp the other (and wrestle),' said Fráech.

For a long time they kept wrestling in the water, and Fráech was submerged. Cú Chulainn lifted him up again.

'Now this time will you yield and accept your life?' said Cú Chulainn.

'I will not,' said Fráech.

Cú Chulainn thrust him down again and Fráech died. He came to land. His people carried his body to the encampment. Ever after that ford was called Áth Fraích.

The whole encampment mourned for Fráech. They saw a band of women dressed in green tunics bending over the corpse of Fráech mac Idaid. They carried him off into the fairy mound which was called Síd Fraích ever afterwards.

Fergus leapt across the oak-tree in his own chariot.

They went on as far as Áth Taiten. There Cú Chulainn overthrew six of them, namely, the six Dungail Irruis.

Thence they went on to Fornocht. Medb had a young hound named Baiscne. Cú Chulainn threw a stone at it and took its head off. Druim Baiscne was the name of that place henceforth.

'It is a disgrace for you,' said Medb, 'that you do not hunt down that wicked hind who is killing you.'

So they went in pursuit of him then and the shafts of their chariots broke in the hunting.

The Death of Órlám

On the morrow they went over Iraird Culenn. Cú Chulainn went forward and came upon the charioteer of Órlám, son of Ailill and Medb, at a place called Tamlachta Órláim a little to the north of Dísert Lochait where he was cutting wood.

—According to another version, however, it was the shaft of Cú Chulainn's chariot that had broken and he had gone to cut a new shaft when he met the charioteer of Órlám. But according to this version it was the charioteer who cut the shafts.

'It is a bold action on the part of the Ulstermen if it is they who are yonder,' said Cú Chulainn, 'while the army is on their track.'

He went to the charioteer to reprimand him, thinking he was one of the Ulstermen. He saw the man cutting wood, that is, chariot-shafts.

'What are you doing here?' said Cú Chulainn.

'Cutting chariot-shafts,' said the charioteer. 'We have broken our chariots hunting yon wild deer, Cú Chulainn. Help me,' said the charioteer. 'Decide whether you will collect the shafts or strip them.'

'I will strip them,' said Cú Chulainn.

Then Cú Chulainn stripped the shafts between his fingers in the presence of the other, and he cleaned them both of bark and of knots.

'It was not your proper work that I set you,' said the charioteer who was sore afraid.

'Who are you?' asked Cú Chulainn.

'I am the charioteer of Órlám, son of Ailill and Medb,' said he. 'And who are you?'

'My name is Cú Chulainn,' said he.

'Woe is me!' said the charioteer.

'Fear nothing,' said Cú Chulainn. 'Where is your master?'

'He is on the mound yonder,' said the charioteer.

'Come on then with me,' said Cú Chulainn, 'for I do not kill charioteers.'

Cú Chulainn went to Órlám, killed him and cut off his head and brandished it before the host. He put the head then on the charioteer's back and said: 'Take that with you and go thus to the camp. If you do not go thus, I shall cast a stone at you from my sling.'

When the charioteer drew near the camp, he took the head from his back, and related his adventures to Ailill and Medb.

'It is not like catching a fledgling,' said she.

'And he said that if I did not bring the head to the camp on my back, he would break my head for me with a stone.'

The Death of the three Sons of Gárach

Then the three Meic Gárach remained at their ford. Their names were Lon, Úalu and Diliu, and Mes Lir, Mes Lóech and Mes Lethan were their three charioteers. They thought Cú Chulainn had gone too far in doing what he had done, namely, killing the king's two foster-sons and his son and brandishing his son's head before the host. (They came then) that they might kill Cú Chulainn in revenge for Órlám and so that they might themselves alone remove this cause of anxiety from the host. They cut three wooden rods for their charioteers so that the six of them together might do battle with Cú Chulainn. But then he killed all of them for they had broken the terms of fair play.

At that time Órlám's charioteer was standing between Ailill and Medb. Cú Chulainn threw a stone at him and his head broke and his brains gushed out over his ears. His name was Fer Teidil. So it is not true that Cú Chulainn never slew charioteers; but he did not kill them unless they were at fault.

The Death of the Marten and of the Pet Bird

Cú Chulainn threatened in Méithe that, wherever afterwards he should see Ailill or Medb, he would cast a stone from his sling at them. He did so indeed; he threw a stone from his sling and killed the marten on Medb's shoulder south of the ford. Hence is the name Méithe Togmaill. And north of the ford he killed the bird that was on Ailill's shoulder. Hence the name Méithe nEóin.

—Or, according to another version, both marten and bird were on Medb's shoulder and their heads were struck off by the stones cast.

Then Reúin was drowned in his lake; hence the name Loch Reóin.

'Your opponent is not far from you,' said Ailill to the Maines.

They rose to their feet and gazed around. When they sat down again Cú Chulainn struck one of them and smashed his head.

'That was no successful expedition! It ill befitted you to boast,' said Maenén the jester. 'I should have cut his head off.'

Then Cú Chulainn cast a stone at him and smashed his head.

In this manner then these men were killed: first of all Órlám on his height, then the three Meic Gárach at their ford, Fer Teidil at his *dedil* and Maenén on his hill.

'I swear by the god by whom my people swear,' said Ailill, 'that I shall cut in twain whatever man shall make a mock of Cú Chulainn here. Come on now, I beg you, travelling by day and by night until we reach Cúailnge. That man will kill two thirds of your army (if he continue) in this way.'

Then the harpers of Caín Bile came to them from Ess Ruaid to entertain them with music. But they thought that the harpers had come from the Ulstermen to spy on them. So they hunted them until they went before them into the pillar-stones at Lía Mór in the north, transformed into deer, for (in reality) they were druids possessed of great occult knowledge.

The Death of Lethan

Lethan came on to his ford over the Níth in Conaille, and he indeed waited to encounter Cú Chulainn. He was grieved by what Cú

Chulainn had already done. Cú Chulainn cut off his head and left it there beside the body. Hence is the name Áth Lethan on the Níth. And their chariots broke when they met on the ford beside it. Hence is the name Áth Carpat. Mulcha, Lethan's charioteer, fell on the shoulder of the hill that lies between Áth Lethan and Áth Carpat. Hence comes the place-name Gúala Mulcha.

While the army was going over Mag mBreg Allecto came for a while, that is, the Mórrígan, in the form of a bird which perched on the pillar-stone in Temair Cúailnge and said to the bull:

'Does the restless Black Bull know (it) without destructive falsehood? . . . I have a secret that the Black Bull will know if he graze (?) . . . on the green grass . . . Fierce is the raven, men are dead, a sorrowful saying . . . every day the death of a great tribe . . .'

Then the bull went with fifty heifers to Slíab Cuillinn, and his herdsman, Forgaimen, followed him. The bull threw off the thrice fifty boys who used to play on his back and killed two thirds of them. And before he went he he pawed the earth in Tír Margéni in Cúailnge.

Cú Chulainn did not kill anyone between the Saili Imdoirchi in the district of Conaille until they reached Cúailnge. Cú Chulainn was then on the mountain Cuinche. He threatened that wherever he saw Medb he would cast a stone at her head. This was not easy for him, for Medb travelled surrounded by half the army and with a screen of shields over her head.

The Death of Lócha

A handmaid of Medb's called Lócha went with a great company of women to fetch water. Cú Chulainn thought that she was Medb. He threw a stone at her from Cuinche and killed her on her plain. Hence comes the place-name Réid Lócha in Cúailnge.

From Findabair Cúailnge the army scattered and set the country on fire. They gathered together all the women, boys, girls and cows that were in Cúailnge and brought them all to Findabair.

'Your expedition was not successful,' said Medb. 'I do not see that you have the bull.'

'He is not in the province at all,' said they all.

Lóthar. Medb's cowherd was summoned to them.

'Where do you think the bull is?' she asked.

'I am afraid to tell,' said the cowherd. 'The night that the Ulstermen fell into their debility the bull went away with sixty heifers and he is now in Dubchaire in Glenn Gat.'

'Go,' said Medb, 'and take a withe between each pair of you.'

They did so then, and hence the glen is called Glenn Gat.

Then they brought the bull to Findabair.   When the bull caught sight of Lóthar the cowherd, he rushed at him and disembowelled him with his horns.   Then together with his thrice fifty heifers the bull made for the encampment and fifty warriors were killed by him.

That is the Death of Lóthar on the Foray.

Then the bull went away from them out of the camp, but they knew not where he had gone and they were grieved.   Medb asked the cowherd if he knew where the bull was.

'I fancy that he might be in the recesses of Slíab Cuillinn.'

So they turned back after ravaging Cúailnge but they did not find the bull there.   The river Cronn rose up against them as high as the tops of the trees.   They spent the night by the river-bank. And Medb ordered some of her people to go across.

The Death of Úalu

On the morrow a valiant hero called Úalu went and took a great flagstone on his back to go across the water.   But the river turned him over and he lay with his stone on his belly.   His grave and his headstone are on the road beside the stream.   Lia Úalann is its name.

Afterwards they went round the river Cronn as far as its source, and they would have gone between its source and the mountain only that Medb would not allow it.   She preferred that they should go across the mountain so that the track they made might remain there for ever as an insult to the men of Ulster.   So they remained there three days and three nights until they had dug up the earth in front of them (to make a pass through the mountain) which was called Bernas Bó Cúailnge.

Then Cú Chulainn killed Cronn and Cóemdele and fought a furious (?) combat.   A hundred warriors died by his hand ... together with Roán and Roae, the two historians of the Táin. A hundred and forty-four kings were slain by him beside that same stream.

After that they came through the pass Bernas Bó Cúailnge with the stock and cattle of Cúailnge, and they spent the night in Glenn Dáil Imda in Cúailnge.   Botha is the name of that place because they made huts (*botha*) to shelter them there.   On the morrow they went on to the river Colptha.   They heedlessly tried to cross it but it rose in flood against them and carried off to sea a hundred of their chariot-warriors. Clúain Carpat is the name of the district where they were drowned.

They went round the river Colptha then to its source at Belat Alióin and spent the night at Liasa Liac. It is so called because they made sheds (*liasa*) for their calves there between Cúailnge and Conaille. They came through Glenn Gatlaig and the river Glais Gatlaig rose in flood against them. Before that its name was Sechaire, but from that time it was called Glais Gatlaig because they had taken their calves across bound together with withes. They spent the night in Druim Féne in Conaille.

Those then were their journeyings from Cúailnge to Machaire according to this version. But other authors and books give a different account of their wanderings from Findabair to Conaille, which is as follows:

The Harrying of Cúailnge

When they had all arrived with their booty and assembled at Findabair Cúailnge, Medb said:

'Let the army be divided here. All the cattle cannot be taken by one route. Let Ailill go with half of them by Slige Midlúachra. Fergus and I will go by Bernas Bó nUlad.'

'The half of the drove that has fallen to our share is not lucky for us,' said Fergus. 'The cattle cannot be taken across the mountain unless they are divided.'

So it was done. Whence comes the name Bernas Bó nUlad.

Then Ailill said to Cuillius, his charioteer:

'Spy for me today on Medb and Fergus. I do not know what has brought them thus together. I shall be glad if you can bring me a proof.'

Cuillius arrived when they were in Cluichri. The lovers remained behind while the warriors went on ahead. Cuillius came to where they were, but they did not hear the spy. Fergus's sword happened to be beside him and Cuillius drew it out of its scabbard, leaving the scabbard empty. Then he came back to Ailill.

'Well?' said Ailill.

'Well indeed,' said Cuillius. 'Here is a proof for you.'

'That is well,' said Ailill.

They exchanged smiles.

'As you thought,' said Cuillius, 'I found them both lying together.'

'She is right (to behave thus),' said Ailill. 'She did it to help in the cattle-driving. Make sure that the sword remain in good condition. Put it under your seat in the chariot, wrapped in a linen cloth.'

Then Fergus rose up to look for his sword.

'Alas!' he cried.

'What ails you?' asked Medb.

'I have wronged Ailill,' said he. 'Wait here until I come out of the wood, and do not wonder if it is a long time until I return.'

Now in fact Medb did not know of the loss of the sword. Fergus went off, taking his charioteer's sword in his hand. In the wood he cut a wooden sword. Hence the Ulstermen have the place-name Fid Mórdrúalle.

'Let us go on after the others,' said Fergus.

All their hosts met in the plain. They pitched their tents. Fergus was summoned to Ailill to play chess. When he came into the tent Ailill began to laugh at him.

Fergus said:

'Well for the man who is being laughed at if he be not deluded by the foolish violence of his fateful deed. By the point of my sword, halidom of Macha, swiftly shall we wreak vengeance on swords following on a cry (for help) from the Gaileóin had not a woman's triumph misdirected (me); following on a tryst bloody and grave-strewn and with blunt-edged spears between a great host with [their] commanders, there shall be fought a battle [extending] to the mountain of Nessa's grandson (Cú Chulainn) by a stout host, and the battle shall scatter the headless trunks of men.'

Then Ailill spoke:

'Do not wage battle after the loss of your sword . . . It defends Medb against many tribes . . .

'Sit down then,' said Ailill, 'so that we may play a game of chess. Your arrival is welcome.'

Then Ailill said:

'Play chess and draughts before a king and a queen. They have prepared a game for great eager armies It matters not (?) what stake you lay . . . I am well-skilled. Perhaps in truth the first guilt will lie on the women . . . Findabair loves the bold Fergus, Fergus mac Rossa Róich with lowing cattle and great armies surrounded (?) by tribes with great possessions, Fergus with the beauty of a king, the fierceness of a dragon, the venomous breath of a viper, the powerful blow of a lion . . . '

Then they began to play chess. They moved the gold and silver chessmen across the bronze chessboard.

Ailill was heard speaking:

'It is not the due of a king . . . '

Medb was heard to say:

'Cease those uncouth speeches. A noble lady is not the secret love of a stranger . . . I am not given to destruction and unjust judgments . . .'

Then Fergus was heard saying:

'Alas! With many words they wage war facing many tribes, and with secret counsesl they will be nourished (?) and with treasure they will be bewitched (?), and with spears they will be cleared away . . . that is, you will be obeyed.'

They remained there that night and on the following morning they heard Ailill say:

'A great champion comes to face the mighty army by Cronn, the river of Nessa's grandson. The men of Connacht will fight against an opponent. There will flow streams of blood from headless necks in a bloody and grave-strewn meeting of heroes. Many waters rise up against the beardless champion who will come from Ulster to the fray.'

Then Medb spoke:

'Do not contend, O arrogant son of Máta. . . . men are herded together, women are carried off . . . great armies propose to come from the battle-field of Cúailnge and the hosts sleep on.'

Fergus was heard:

'Let a great prince (?) be seized . . . Let them swear by their people, let them make promises to their queens, let them fight against their enemies.'

'Medb was heard saying:

'Let what he says be done, let it be done.'

Medb spoke:

'He judges in submission to you for many armies. Let them advance while Ailill is in your power . . .'

They set forth on their way to the river Cronn, and Mane mac Ailella was heard to say:

'If I am quickly sent forth against a fair opponent of many feats, he will ward off father and mother on horned cattle . . .'

Then Fergus was heard saying:

'Do not go, O valorous boy. They will give no other counsel until a beardless lad shall strike your head from your neck . . . '

'Let me go in front with the banished Ulstermen,' said Fergus, 'to make sure that the lad gets fair play, with the cattle before us and the army in our rear, and the women folk behind the army.'

Then Medb was heard saying:

'Hark, O Fergus! for the sake of your honour ... ward off (the enemy) with your fine army. Do not drive away the Ulstermen ... In Mag nAí you prevail over a meeting of companies.'

Fergus spoke:

'Alas! O foolish Medb whose voice I do not hear ... I am not the son of a weakling ... I shall not strike a great blow upon the tribes. Cease to cast stones at me ...'

Cú Chulainn came to Áth Cruinn to meet them.

'My friend Láeg,' said he to his charioteer, 'the armies are coming towards us.'

Láeg spoke:

'I swear by the gods that I shall perform a great deed in front of chariot-warriors in the small remnant of the battle. They are carried on slender steeds with silver yokes and golden wheels (on their chariots) ... You will march against kings. They will conquer with their power of leaping.'

Cú Chulainn spoke:

'Take heed, O Láeg, that you grasp the reins with the great victory of Macha ... I beseech the rivers to come to my help. I call upon heaven and earth and especially the river Cronn to aid me.'

The plaintive river Cronn offers them resistance and will not let them cross into Muirthemne until the work of warriors is finished in the mountain north of Ochaíne.

Thereupon the river rose in flood as high as the tree-tops.

Maine, the son of Ailill and Medb came forward before the others. Cú Chulainn slaughtered him on the ford and thirty horsemen of his household were submerged in the water. Cú Chulainn overthrew thirty-two of their brave warriors again at the river. They pitched their tents at that ford. Lugaid mac Nóis uí Lomairc Allchomaig accompanied by thirty horsemen came on a fleeting visit to parley with Cú Chulainn.

'Welcome, Lugaid,' said Cú Chulainn. 'If birds fly over Mag Murthemne you shall have a barnacle goose and a half. Or else if fish swim into the estuaries you shall have a salmon and a half. Or else you shall have three sprigs, a sprig of cress, a sprig of laver, a sprig of seaweed. A man shall take your place (to fight) at the ford.'

'That is welcome,' said Lugaid. 'I wish all goodness of the tribe for the lad.'

'Your army is fine,' said Cú Chulainn.

'You will not suffer even though the company you bring against them is few,' said Lugaid.

'Grant me fair play and goodly combat,' said Cú Chulainn. 'O friend Lugaid, do the army hold me in fear?'

'I swear by the god of my people,' said Lugaid, 'that not one man or two dare go outside the camp to make water unless they go in companies of twenty or of thirty.'

'It will be a fine thing for them,' said Cú Chulainn, 'if I begin to pelt them with stones from my sling. If every man's strength is put forth against me, it will be right for you, Lugaid, (to remember) your alliance with the men of Ulster. Tell me now what it is that you want.'

'I want a truce from you for my company.'

'You shall have that provided that they bear a special sign (that I may recognize them.) And tell my friend Fergus that his company too should bear a special sign. Tell the physicians to make their company also bear a sign and let them swear to preserve my life and send me food every night.'

Lugaid left him then. Now it chanced that Fergus was in his tent with Ailill. Lugaid called him out and gave him the message.

Ailill was heard speaking:

'*Cair iss i sanassaib* . . . Let us go with a small army, to a choice tent and an encampment . . .'

'I swear by the god of my people that it is not so,' said Fergus, 'unless I ask the lad. Come, Lugaid, go and ask him if Ailill and his division of three thousand may join together with my company. Take him an ox and a flitch of bacon and a barrel of wine.'

Then Lugaid goes to him and gives him that message.

'I do not mind if he go,' said Cú Chulainn.

So the two companies joined them. They remained there until night. Cú Chulainn wounded thirty of their warriors with stones from his sling.

—Or, as some books tell it, they remained there for twenty nights.

'Your journeyings will be unpleasant,' said Fergus. 'The Ulstermen will recover from their debility and they will crush us into the dust and gravel. We are ill-placed for battle. Come on to Cúil Airthir.'

It happened that Cú Chulainn went that night to speak with the men of Ulster.

'What tidings have you?' asked Conchobar.

'Women are taken captive,' said he, 'cattle are driven away, men are slain.'

'Who takes them captive? Who drives them away? Who kills them?'

'... The man foremost in slaughter and killing, Ailill mac Máta, carries them off and Fergus mac Róich, the brave one, who wields a sword ...'

'That is not of much benefit to you,' said Conchobar. 'Today we have been smitten (by the *cess*) as before.'

Thereafter Cú Chulainn left them. He saw the army going forth. Ailill spoke:

'Alas! I see a chariot with bright points ... he will slay men in fords and capture cows, and the thirty will act when the army has come from Laigin. Blood will flow from headless necks. They will fall fighting for the cattle of the Ulstermen in the ford.'

Cú Chulainn killed thirty of their warriors at Áth Durn. They made no stop then until at nightfall they reached Cúil Airthir. He killed thirty of them at that spot and they pitched their tents there.

Ailill's charioteer, Cuillius, was at the ford early in the morning washing the wheels of the chariot. Cú Chulainn hit him with a stone and killed him. Hence the place-name Áth Cuillne in Cúil Airthir.

They travelled on then and spent the night in Druim Féine in Conaille, as we have related above.

Cú Chulainn attacked them there. On each of the three nights that they were there he killed a hundred of them. He let fly at them with his sling from Ochaíne near them.

'Our army will not long survive with Cú Chulainn attacking us in this fashion,' said Ailill. 'Let an offer of terms from us be made to him, namely, that he shall have an extent of Mag nAí equal to Mag Muirthemne, the best chariot in Mag nAí and the equipment of twelve men. Or, if he prefer, this plain in which he was reared and thrice seven *cumala*. And all that has been destroyed in his household or among his cattle shall be made good, and he shall be compensated for it. And let him take service with me, it is better for him than to be in the service of a princeling.'

'Who will go on that mission?' they asked.

'Mac Roth yonder.'

Mac Roth, the messenger of Ailill and Medb—he it is who could go all round Ireland in one day—went to Delga on that mission, for Fergus believed that Cú Chulainn was in Delga.

'I see a man coming towards us,' said Láeg to Cú Chulainn. 'He has yellow hair. He wears the linen garments of his office. In his hand a great club and at his waist an ivory-hilted sword. He wears a hooded tunic with red insertion.'

'That is one of the king's warriors,' said Cú Chulainn.

Mac Roth asked Láeg whose vassal he was.

'Vassal to yonder man below,' said Láeg.

Cú Chulainn was sitting stark-naked in the snow which reached up to his thighs, examining his shirt for lice. So Mac Roth asked Cú Chulainn whose vassal he was.

'Vassal of Conchobor mac Nessa,' said Cú Chulainn.

'Have you no more definite description?'

'That is sufficient,' said Cú Chulainn.

'Where is Cú Chulainn then?' asked Mac Roth.

'What would you say to him?' said Cú Chulainn.

So Mac Roth told him the whole message as we have (already) related.

'Even if Cú Chulainn were here near at hand, he would not agree to that. He will not exchange his mother's brother for another king.'

Once again Cú Chulainn was visited (by Mac Roth) and he was told that he would be given the noblest of the (captured) women and the dry kine on condition that he should not ply his sling on them by night even if he killed them by day.

'I will not agree,' said Cú Chulainn. 'If our base-born women are carried off, then our noble women will work at querns, and if our milch cows are taken away we shall be left without milk.'

A third time Cú Chulainn was visited by Mac Roth and he was told that he would get the base-born women and the milch cows.

'I will not agree,' said Cú Chulainn. 'The Ulstermen will take their base born women to bed and base offspring will be born to them, and they will use their milch cows for meat in the winter.'

'Is there anything else then?' asked the messenger.

'There is,' said Cú Chulainn, 'but I shall not tell you. It will be agreed to if some one (else) tell you.'

'I know what it is,' said Fergus. 'The man has arranged that I should make it known. But indeed it is of no advantage to you. These then are the terms: that for a day and a night the cattle shall not be taken away from the ford on which he shall fight in single combat, in the hope that help may come from the Ulstermen to him. And I find it strange,' said Fergus, 'that they are so long in recovering from their debility.'

'It is better for us indeed, said Ailill, 'to lose one man every day than a hundred men every night.'

The death of Etarcomol and the terms offered by the men
of Ireland as told to Cú Chulainn by Fergus:

Then Fergus went on that mission.   Etarcomol, the son of Ed
and Leithrinn, fosterson of Ailill and Medb, followed Fergus.

'I do not wish you to go,' said Fergus, 'and it is not out of hatred
of you that I say so, but I dislike the thought of a fight between you
and Cú Chulainn because of your pride and insolence and because of
the fierceness and violence, the boldness and fury of your opponent,
Cú Chulainn.   No good will come of your encounter.'

'Can you not protect me from him ?' said Etarcomol.

'I can,' said Fergus, 'provided that you do not provoke a quarrel.'

They set off then for Delga in two chariots.   At that time Cú
Chulainn was playing draughts with Láeg: the back of his head was
towards them and Láeg was facing them.

'I see two chariots coming towards us,' said Láeg.   'There is a
tall dark man in the first chariot.   He has dark bushy hair.   He
wears a purple cloak in which is a golden brooch, and a hooded
tunic with red insertion.   He carries a curved shield with a scalloped
rim of white gold.   In his hand he holds a broad spear with per-
forations from point to upper shaft (?).   Across his thighs a sword as
long as a boat's rudder.'

'That great rudder carried by my master Fergus is empty,' said
Cú Chulainn, 'for there is no sword in the scabbard, only a sword of
wood.   I have been told,' said Cú Chulainn, 'that Ailill came unawares upon Fergus and Medb as they slept, and he took away
Fergus's sword and gave it into the keeping of his charioteer, and a
wooden sword was put into its scabbard.'

At that point Fergus arrived.

'Welcome, master Fergus,' said Cú Chulainn.   'If fish swim into
the estuaries you shall have a salmon and a half; or else if a flock
of birds fly over the plain you shall have a barnacle goose and the
half of another; or you shall have a handful of cress or seaweed, a
handful of laver, a drink from the sand.   I shall to go the ford to
encounter an opponent if he challenge (you) and you shall be guarded
until you shall have slept.'

'I trust your welcome,' said Fergus, 'but it is not for food that I
have come.   I know what provisions you have here.'

Then Cú Chulainn received the message from Fergus, and Fergus
departed.

Etarcomol remained behind gazing at Cú Chulainn.

'What are you looking at ?' said Cú Chulainn.

'You,' said Etarcomol.

'An eye can soon glance over that,' said Cú Chulainn.

'So I see,' answered Etarcomol. 'I see no reason why anyone should fear you. I see in you no horror or fearfulness or superiority in numbers. You are merely a handsome youth with wooden weapons and fine feats of arms.'

'Though you revile me' said Cú Chulainn, 'I will not kill you because of Fergus. But for your being under his protection, I would have sent back your distended loins and your dismembered body behind your chariot to the encampment.'

'Do not threaten me thus,' said Etarcomol. 'As for the wonderful agreement you made, namely, to engage in single combat, it is I who will be the first of the men of Ireland to fight with you tomorrow.'

Then he went away, but he turned back again from Méithe and Ceithe, saying to his charioteer:

'I boasted in the presence of Fergus that I would encounter Cú Chulainn tomorrow. It is not easy for me, however, to wait until then. Turn the horses back again from the hill.'

Láeg saw what was happening and said to Cú Chulainn:

'The chariot is coming again and has turned its left side to us.'

'That is a challenge which must be met,' said Cú Chulainn. 'Let us go down to meet him at the ford and find out (what he wants).

'I do not wish to do what you ask;' said Cú Chulainn (to Etarcomol).

'You must do it, however,' said Etarcomol.

Cú Chulainn struck the sod beneath his feet and he fell prostrate with the sod on his belly.

'Begone!' said Cú Chulainn. 'I am loath to dip my hands in your blood. I should have cut you into pieces just now but for Fergus.'

'We shall not part like this,' said Etarcomol, 'until I carry off your head or until I leave my head with you.'

'The latter is what will happen,' said Cú Chulainn.

Then Cú Chulainn struck him with his sword under his armpits so that his garments fell off him, but he did not cut his skin.

'Begone then!' said Cú Chulainn.

'No,' said Etarcomol.

Cú Chulainn touched him then with the edge of his sword and cut his hair off as cleanly as if it had been shaved off with a razor. He did not even scratch his skin. Then since the fellow was troublesome and pertinacious, he struck him on the crown of his head and clove him down to the navel.

Fergus saw the chariot go past with only one man in it. He turned back to scold Cú Chulainn.

'It was wicked of you, you whippersnapper,' said he, 'to violate my protection (of Etarcomol). You think my club is short.'

'Do not be angry with me, master Fergus,' said Cú Chulainn,' . . . Do not reproach me, master Fergus.'

He bowed down and let Fergus's chariot go past him three times.

'Ask his charioteer if I was the one who instigated the fight.'

'Indeed it was not you,' said Etarcomol's charioteer.

'He said,' went on Cú Chulainn, 'that he would not go away till he carried off my head or left his own head with me. Which would you prefer, master Fergus?'

'Indeed I prefer what has been done,' said Fergus, 'for it is he who was insolent.'

Then Fergus put a spanceling band through Etarcomol's heels and dragged him behind his own chariot to the camp. Whenever Etarcomol's body went over rocks, one half would part from the other; when the path was smooth, the two parts would come together again.

Medb looked at him.

'That was not kind treatment for a young hound, Fergus,' said Medb.

'It is no source of annoyance to me,' said Fergus, 'that the mongrel should have waged battle with the great hound for whom he was no match.'

Then Etarcomol's grave was dug and his headstone was planted in the ground; his name was written in ogam and he was mourned.

That night Cú Chulainn did not attack them with his sling.

The Death of Nad Crantail

'What man have you got to encounter Cú Chulainn tomorrow?' asked Lugaid.

'They will give you him tomorrow,' said Maine son of Ailill.

'We can get no one to encounter him,' said Medb. 'Let us make a truce with him till a man be sought for him.'

A truce was granted them.

'Whither will you send,' asked Ailill, 'to seek a man to encounter Cú Chulainn?'

'There is no one in Ireland to be got for him,' said Medb, 'unless Cú Roí mac Dáire or Nad Crantail the warrior be brought.'

One of Cú Roí's followers was in the tent.

'Cú Roí will not come,' said he. 'He thinks that enough of his people have already come.'

'Let a message be sent to Nad Crantail then.'

Maine Andoí went to Nad Crantail. They related their tidings to him.

'Come with us for the sake of the honour of Connacht.'

'I will not,' said he, 'unless Findabair is given to me.'

He came with them then. They brought his weapons in a cart from the east of Connacht to the encampment.

'You shall get Findabair,' said Medb, 'as a reward for encountering yonder man.'

'I shall do so,' said he.

That night Lugaid came to Cú Chulainn.

'Nad Crantail is coming to meet you tomorrow. Alas for you! You will not stand out against him.'

'That is no matter,' said Cú Chulainn.

—According to another version it was then that Cú Chulainn chanted the verse: 'If Nad Crantail should fall.'—

On the morrow Nad Crantail went forth from the camp, taking with him nine stakes of holly, sharpened and charred. Cú Chulainn was there engaged in fowling, with his chariot beside him. Nad Crantail cast a stake at Cú Chulainn. Cú Chulainn sprang on to the top of that stake but it did not hinder him in his fowling. Similarly with the other eight stakes. When Nad Crantail cast the ninth stake, the flock of birds flew away from Cú Chulainn who went in pursuit of them. Then, like a bird himself, he stepped on to the points of the stakes, going from one stake to another, pursuing the birds that they might not escape him. They were all certain, however, that Cú Chulainn was fleeing from Nad Crantail.

'That Cú Chulainn of yours,' said Nad Crantail, 'has taken to flight before me.'

'It was to be expected,' said Medb, 'if goodly warriors opposed him, that the sprite would not hold out against bold men.'

Fergus and the Ulstermen were grieved to hear this. Fiacha mac Fir Febe was sent by them to upbraid Cú Chulainn.

'Tell him,' said Fergus, 'that it was fine for him to attack the warriors as long as he acted bravely. It is better for him, however, to hide himself when he flees from a single opponent, for it is no greater dishonour for him than for the rest of the Ulstermen.'

'Who boasted that I fled?' asked Cú Chulainn.

'Nad Crantail,' said Fiacha.

'If he had boasted of the feat I had performed in his presence, it would have become him better,' said Cú Chulainn. 'But he would not boast if only he had a weapon in his hand. You know that I kill no man unarmed. So let him come tomorrow and stand between Ocháine and the sea, and however early he come, he shall find me waiting there and I shall not flee from him.'

Cú Chulainn ended the meeting, and he cast his mantle around him after his night watch, but he did not notice the great pillar-stone as big as himself which was beside him and he covered it over between himself and his mantle and sat down beside it.

Then Nad Crantail arrived. His weapons were brought by him in a wagon.

'Where is Cú Chulainn?' he asked.

'There he is over there,' said Fergus.

'That is not how he appeared to me yesterday,' said Nad Crantail. 'Are you the famous Cú Chulainn?'

'And what if I am?' said Cú Chulainn.

'If you are,' said Nad Crantial, 'then until I carry the head of a little lamb to the camp, I shall not take back your head which is the head of a beardless boy.'

'I am not Cú Chulainn at all,' said Cú Chulainn. 'Go round the hill to him,'

Cú Chulainn came to Láeg.

'Smear a false beard on me. The champion refuses to fight with me since I am beardless.'

So it was done for him. He went to meet Nad Crantail on the hill.

'I think that better,' said Nad Crantail. 'Grant me fair play now.'

'You shall have it provided that we know it.' said Cú Chulainn.

'I will throw a cast at you,' said Nad Crantail, 'and do not avoid it.'

'I shall avoid it only by leaping upwards,' said Cú Chulainn.

Nad Crantail threw a cast at him and Cú Chulainn leapt upwards as it came.

'You do ill to avoid the cast,' said Nad Crantail.

'Avoid my cast upwards also,' said Cú Chulainn.

Cú Chulainn threw the spear at him but it was upwards he threw so that the spear came down on the crown of Nad Crantail's head and went through him to the ground.

'Indeed,' he cried, 'you are the best warrior in Ireland! I have twenty-four sons in the encampment. Let me go and tell them what hidden treasures I have. And I shall come back so that you may behead me for I shall die if the spear is taken out of my head.'

'Good,' said Cú Chulainn, 'provided that you come back again.'

Then Nad Crantail went to the encampment. They all came forth to meet him.

'Where is the head of the distorted one that you have brought?' they all asked.

'Stay, O warriors, until I tell my tale to my sons and go back again to fight with Cú Chulainn.'

He went off to meet Cú Chulainn and cast his sword at him. Cú Chulainn leapt up so that the sword struck the pillar-stone and broke in two. Cú Chulainn was distorted as he had been when with the boys in Emain. Thereupon Cú Chulainn leapt on to Nad Crantail's shield and cut off his head. He struck him again on his headless neck (and split him) down to the navel and Nad Crantail fell in four sections to the ground.

Then Cú Chulainn spoke these words:

'If Nad Crantail has fallen, there will be increase of strife. Alas that I do not now give battle to Medb with a third of the host!'

The Finding of the Bull according to this Version

Then Medb went with a third of the army to Cuib in search of the bull and Cú Chulainn followed them. She went along Slige Midlúachra then as far as Dún Sobairche to harry the Ulstermen and the Cruithne.

Cú Chulainn caught sight of Buide mac Báin from Slíab Cuilinn with the bull and fifteen heifers. Sixty warriors of Ailill's household formed his company, each man wrapped in a mantle. Cú Chulainn came towards them.

'Whence have you brought the cattle?' asked he.

'From yonder mountain,' answered the warrior.

'Tell me, where is their cow-herd?' said Cú Chulainn.

'He is where we found him,' said the warrior.

Cú Chulainn gave three leaps to follow them as far as the ford, seeking to have speech with them. Then he spoke to their leader.

'What is your name?' said he.

'One who hates you not, who loves you not, Buide mac Báin,' said he.

'Here is this spear for Buide,' said Cú Chulainn.

He cast a small spear at him and it went into his armpit, and his liver on the other side broke in two at the impact of the spear. Cú Chulainn killed him at his ford. Hence the place-name Áth mBuide.

Thereupon the bull was brought into the encampment.

Then they decided in debate that if Cú Chulainn were deprived of his javelin, he would be no more formidable (than anyone else).

The Death of Redg the Satirist

Then Redg the satirist went, on Ailill's advice, to ask Cú Chulainn for the javelin, that is, Cú Chulainn's spear.

'Give me your spear,' said the satirist.

'No indeed,' said Cú Chulainn, 'but I will give your treasure.'

'I shall not accept that,' said the satirist.

So he wounded the satirist since he did not accept what was offered him, and Redg said that he would bring dishonour on him (by satire) unless he got the javelin. So Cú Chulainn threw the javelin at him and it went right through his head.

'This treasure was quickly delivered indeed,' said the satirist.

Hence the name Áth Tolam Sét.

There is also a ford to the east of that place where the copper from the spear landed. Umarrith (Umaṡruth) is the name of that ford.

It was in Cuib that Cú Chulainn killed all those that we have mentioned, namely, Nath Coirpthe at his trees, Cruthen on his ford, Meic Búachalla at their cairn, Marc on his hill, Meille in his stronghold, Bodb in his tower, Bogaine in his marsh.

Cú Chulainn turned back again into Mag Muirthemne. He preferred to guard his own homeland. After going there he killed the men of Crochen (or Crónech), that is, Focherda, he cast off twenty men. He come upon them as they were setting up camp, ten cupbearers and ten warriors.

Medb turned back again from the north when she had remained there for a fortnight, ravaging the province, and when she had fought a battle against Findmór the wife of Celtchar mac Uthidir. After the destruction of Dún Sobairche in the territory of Dál Riada against Findmór she carrried off fifty women captives. Wherever in Cuib Medb planted her horsewhip is named Bile Medba. Every ford and every hill by which she spent the night is named Áth Medba and Dindgna Medba.

Then they all met at Focherd, Ailill and Medb and the men who drove the bull. His herdsman took the bull from them but by beating their shields with sticks they drove the bull across into a narrow pass and the cattle trampled the herdsman into the ground. His name was Forgemen.   And the hill there is called Forgemen.

Their only anxiety that night was to get some one from among them to contend with Cú Chulainn at the ford.

'Let us ask Cú Chulainn for a truce,' said Ailill.

'Let Lugaid go on that mission,' said they all.

So Lugaid went to speak with him.

'What do the army think of me now? asked Cú Chulainn.

'They think that the request you made of them is a great disgrace, namely, that they should return to you your women and girls and half your cattle.   But they think it more grievous than anything else that you should go on killing them and yet be provided with food by them.'

Then every day for a week a man fell there at Cú Chulainn's hands.   Terms of fair play were broken against him; twenty men were sent to attack him all together, but he killed them all.

'Go to him, Fergus,' said Ailill, 'and ask if he will allow us to move camp.'

So they went then to Crónech.   In that place there fell by him in single combat two men called Roth, two called Lúan, two female thieves, ten jesters, ten cupbearers, ten men called Fergus, six called Fedelm and six called Fiachrach.   All these were killed by him in single combat.   Then when they had pitched their tents in Crónech, they debated as to what they should do about Cú Chulainn.

'I know what is right in this matter,' said Medb.   'Send a message asking him to grant a truce with the host and say that he shall have half the cattle that are here.'

That message was taken to him.

'I shall do so,' said Cú Chulainn, 'on condition that you do not violate the agreement.'

The Meeting of Cú Chulainn and Finnabair

'Let a proposal be made to him,' said Ailill.   'He shall have Finnabair provided he keep away from the host.'

Maine Aithremail went to him, and he went first to Láeg.

'Whose vassal are you?' he asked.

Láeg did not address him.   Maine asked him the same question three times.

'I am Cú Chulainn's vassal,' said Láeg, 'and do not plague me lest perchance I strike your head off.'

'What a bad-tempered fellow!' said Maine turning away from him.

So then Maine went to speak to Cú Chulainn. Cú Chulainn had taken off his shirt and was sitting in the snow up to his waist while around him the snow had melted a man's length, so great was the fierce ardour of the warrior. Maine asked him three times in the same way whose vassal he was.

'Conchobor's vassal, and do not plague me. If you bother me any more, I shall cut off your head as the head is cut off a blackbird'.

'It is not easy to speak to these two,' said Maine.

He left them then and told Ailill and Medb what had happened.

'Let Lugaid go to him,' said Ailill, 'and speak to him (and offer him) the maid.'

So Lugaid went and gave Cú Chulainn the message.

'Friend Lugaid,' said Cú Chulainn, 'this is a trick.'

'It is the word of a king,' said Lugaid. 'There will be no trickery.'

'So be it done,' said Cú Chulainn.

Thereupon Lugaid went from him and told that answer to Ailill and Medb.

'Let the jester go disguised as me,' said Ailill, 'wearing a king's crown on his head. And let him stand far away from Cú Chulainn that he may not recognize him. And the girl shall go with him and he shall betroth her to Cú Chulainn. They shall come away quickly then and very likely you will deceive Cú Chulainn in that way and he will not hinder you until such time as he comes with the Ulstermen to the great battle.'

So the jester went, accompanied by the maid, to Cú Chulainn and from afar off he addressed him. Cú Chulainn went to meet them. But in fact he recognized by the man's speech that he was a jester. He threw at him a sling-stone which he had in his hand and it went into the jester's head and drove his brains out. He came to the girl. He cut off her two plaits and thrust a stone through her mantle and her tunic. Then he thrust a stone through the middle of the jester. Their two pillar-stones are still there, Finnabair's stone and the jester's stone. Cú Chulainn left them thus.

Messengers came from Ailill and Medb in search of their people, for it seemed to them that they had long been gone. They were found in that plight. The whole story spread through the camp. Thereafter there was no truce between them and Cú Chulainn.

The Combat of Munremar and Cú Roí

When the hosts were there in the evening, they saw one stone thrown at them from the east and another thrown to meet it from the west.   The stones collided in the air and they kept falling between Fergus's camp and that of Ailill and that of the Érainn.   This performance went on until the same time next day, and the hosts were standing, holding their shields over their heads to protect them from the battle-stones, until the plain was full of stones. Hence the name Mag Clochair.

In fact it was Cú Ruí mac Dáire who had done this; he came to help his followers and he was in Cotail facing Munremar mac Gerrcinn.   Munremar had come from Emain Macha to Ard Róich to the assistance of Cú Chulainn.   Cú Roí knew that there was no one in the army who could withstand Munremar.   So they both carried on this performance (with the stones).

The host begged them to desist.   Then Munremar and Cú Roí made peace and Cú Roí went to his house while Munremar returned to Emain Macha and did not come (again) until the day of the great battle.   Cú Roí, however, did not come until the fight with Fer Diad.

'Ask Cú Chulainn,' said Medb and Ailill, 'to allow us to move camp.'

They were given permission and they moved camp.

By this time the debility of the Ulstermen was at an end.   As they awoke from their torpor, some of them kept still attacking the army until they were once more smitten by their affliction.

The Death of the Youths

Then the youths of Ulster took counsel together in Emain Macha.

'Alas for us,' said they, 'that our friend Cú Chulainn should be left unaided!'

'Tell me,' said Fiachna Fuilech mac Fir Febi, a brother of Fiachach Fialdána mac Fir Febi, 'shall I have a band of fighters from among you so that I may go and help him thus?'

Thrice fifty boys, a third of the youths of Ulster, went with him, carrying their hurleys.   The army saw them approaching across the plain.

'There is a great host coming towards us across the plain,' said Ailill.

Fergus went to see them.

'Those are some of the boys of Ulster,' he said, 'and they are coming to help Cú Chulainn.'

'Let a band of armed men go to meet them,' said Ailill, 'but without Cú Chulainn's knowledge, for if they meet with him, you will not withstand them.'

Thrice fifty warriors went to encounter them.   Both sides fell and not one of those splendid boys escaped alive at Lia Toll.   Hence the place-name Lia Fiachrach meic Fir Febi for it is there he fell.

'Take counsel,' said Ailill.   'Ask Cú Chulainn to let you leave this place for you will hardly escape from him now that his hero's flame has sprung forth.'

For it was usual with him that when his hero's flame sprang forth his feet would turn to the back and his hams turn to the front and the round muscles of his calves would come on to his shins, while one eye sank into his head and the other protruded.   A man's head would go into his mouth.   Every hair on him would be as sharp as a spike of hawthorn and there would be a drop of blood on every hair.   He would recognise neither comrades nor friends.   He would attack alike before him and behind him.   Hence the men of Connacht named Cú Chulainn the Distorted One.

The Bloodless Fight of Rochad

Cú Chulainn sent his charioteer to Rochad mac Fathemain of Ulster to ask him to come to his aid.   Now it happened that Finnabair was in love with Rochad for he was the handsomest of the Ulster warriors of the day.   The charioteer went to Rochad and asked him to come and help Cú Chulainn if he had recovered from his debility, and he suggested that they should set a snare for the host to entrap some of them and kill them.   Rochad came from the north with a hundred men.

Scan the plain for us today,' said Ailill.

'I see a troop coming across the plain,' said the watchman, 'and a youthful warrior among them.   He towers shoulder-high above the other warriors.'

'Who is that, Fergus?' asked Ailill.

'Rochad mac Fathemain,' said he, 'and he comes to help Cú Chulainn.   I know what you must do,' said Fergus.   'Send a hundred men with the maid yonder as far as the middle of the plain, and let the maid go in front of them.   A messenger shall go and speak to Rochad and ask him to come alone to talk to the maid, and then let him be seized and that will save us from attack by his followers.'

This was done then.   Rochad went to meet the messenger.

'I have come to you from Finnabair to ask you to go and speak with her.'

So he went alone to speak with her. The host rushed about him on all sides; he was captured and seized. His followers took to flight. Afterwards he was released and bound over not to attack the host until he came with all the Ulstermen. He was promised that Finnabair should be given to him, and then he went away from them.

That is the Bloodless Fight of Rochad.

The Death of the Royal Mercenaries

'Let Cú Chulainn be asked for a truce for us,' said Ailill and Medb.

Lugaid went with that message and Cú Chulainn granted the truce.

'Send a man to the ford for me tomorrow,' said Cú Chulainn.

There were with Medb six royal mercenaries, that is, six royal heirs of Clanna Dedad, to wit, three called Dub from Imlech, and three called Derg from Sruthair.

'Why should we not go against Cú Chulainn?' said they.

So they went to meet him on the morrow and Cú Chulainn killed the six of them.

The Death of Cúr

Then Cúr mac Da Lath was asked by them to encounter Cú Chulainn. He from whom Cúr drew blood died before the ninth day.

'If he kill Cú Chulainn,' said Medb, 'it means victory. If he is himself killed, it will be a relief to the host. It is not pleasant to consort with Cúr eating and sleeping.'

So Cúr went forth. But he disliked going to encounter a beardless whipper-snapper of a boy.

'In truth,' said he, 'ye make little account of me. Had I known that I was sent against this man, I should not have stirred to meet him. I should think it enough to send a boy of his own age from my followers to encounter him.'

'Nay,' said Cormac Cond Longas. 'It would be a wonderful thing for us were you yourself to repel him.'

'However that be,' said Cúr, 'since I have been entrusted with this task, ye shall go on your way early tomorrow for it will not take me long to kill that young deer.'

So early in the morning on the morrow he went to meet Cú Chulainn, and he told the host to start on their journey for it would be a joyful expedition for him to go and meet Cú Chulainn.

So he went off. Cú Chulainn at that time was practising feats.

A List of the Feats

The ball-feat, the blade-feat, the feat with horizontally-held shield, the javelin-feat, the rope-feat, the feat with the body, the cat-feat, the hero's salmon-leap, the cast of a wand, the leap across . . . , the bending of a valiant hero, the feat of the *gae bolga*, the feat of quickness (?), the wheel-feat, the eight-men feat, the over-breath feat, the bruising with a sword, the hero's war-cry, the well-measured blow, the return-stroke, the mounting on a spear and straightening the body on its point, with the bond of a valiant champion.

For a third of the day Cúr was plying his weapons against him protected by the boss of his shield, and no blow or thrust reached Cú Chulainn in the wild excitement of his feats, nor did he realise that the man was attacking him until Fiacha mac Fir Febe cried to him:

'Beware of the man who is attacking you!

Cú Chulainn glanced at Cúr and cast the ball-feat which he held in his hand so that it went between the boss and the centre of the shield and back through the fellow's head.

—According to another version it was in (the battle of) Imslige Glendamnach that Cúr fell.—

Fergus turned to the host.

'If your surety binds you,' said he, 'stay here until tomorrow.'

'Not here,' said Ailill, 'but we shall go back to our encampment.'

Then Láth mac Da Bró was asked to fight him even as Cúr had been asked. He too fell. Fergus turned again to enforce their surety. So they remained there until there were slain Cúr mac Da Láth and Láth mac Da Bró and Foirc mac Trí nAignech and Srubgaile mac Eóbith. These men were all killed in single combat.

The Death of Fer Báeth

'Go for me, friend Láeg, to the encampment and consult Lugaid mac Nóis uí Lomairc, and find out who is coming to fight me tomorrow. Question him closely and greet him.'

Láeg went off then.

'Welcome!' said Lugaid. 'Cú Chulainn is indeed in unlucky plight, fighting single handed against the men of Ireland.'

'Who is coming to fight him tomorrow?'

'It is Fer Báeth—bad luck to him in his fighting!—who goes to meet him tomorrow, Fer Báeth, the comrade of us both. He has been given Finnabair for doing so and sway over his own people.'

Láeg returned to where Cú Chulainn was.

'My friend Láeg is not glad of the answer he got,' said Cú Chulainn.

Láeg recounted it all to him, telling him how Fer Báeth had been summoned to Ailill and Medb in their tent and told to sit beside Finnabair and that she would be given to him as a reward for fighting with Cú Chulainn, for he was her chosen lover. They considered that he was a match for Cú Chulainn for they had both learnt the same art of war with Scáthach. Fer Báeth was plied with wine until he was intoxicated. He was told that they prized that liquor for only fifty wagon-loads of it had been brought by them. And the maiden used to serve him his share of the wine.

'I do not wish to go,' said Fer Báeth. 'Cú Chulainn is my foster brother and bound to me by solemn covenant. Nevertheless I shall go and oppose him tomorrow and cut off his head.'

'You will be the man to do it,' said Medb.

Cú Chulainn told Láeg to go and ask Lugaid to come and speak with him. Lugaid came to him.

'So it is Fer Báeth who comes to oppose me tomorrow,' said Cú Chulainn.

'It is he indeed,' said Lugaid.

'It is an evil day,' said Cú Chulainn. 'I shall not survive this encounter. We two are of equal age, of equal swiftness and of equal weight. Leave me now so that we may meet, and tell him that it is unworthy of his valour that he should come against me. Ask him to come and meet me and speak to me tonight.'

Lugaid told this to Fer Báeth. Since Fer Báeth did not avoid the conflict, he went that night accompanied by Fiacha mac Fir Febe, to renounce his friendship with Cú Chulainn. Cú Chulainn adjured him by his foster-brotherhood and by their common foster-mother Scáthach.

'I must fight,' said Fer Báeth. 'I have promised to do so.'

'Renounce your bond of friendship then,' said Cú Chulainn.

Cú Chulainn went away from him in anger. He trampled a sharp shoot of holly into his foot and it came up to his knee and appeared there. Cú Chulainn pulled it out.

'Do not go away, Fer Báeth, until you see what I have found.'

'Throw it here,' said Fer Báeth.

Then Cú Chulainn threw the holly shoot after Fer Báeth and it struck the depression at the back of his neck and went out through his mouth, and he fell on his back in the glen.

'That is indeed a throw,' said Fer Báeth.

From this comes the place-name Focherd Muirthemne.

—Or (according to another version), Fiacha said: 'Your throw is lucky today, Cú Chulainn.' Whence the place-name Focherd Muirthemne.—

Fer Báeth fell dead at once in the glen.   Whence the place-name Glend Fir Baíth.

Fergus was heard saying:

'O Fer Báeth, foolish is your expedition on this spot wherein is your grave. Ruin has reached you there . . . in Cróen Corand.

The hill is named Fríthe; forever it will be Cróenech in Muirthemne.   Henceforth its name will be Focherd, the place in which you fell, O Fer Báeth.'

'Your opponent has fallen,' said Fergus.   'Tell me, will that man give compensation tomorrow?'

'He will indeed,' said Cú Chulainn.

Cú Chulainn sent Láeg again to find out how matters stood in the camp and whether Fer Báeth was alive.

Lugaid said:

'Fer Báeth has died, and tell Cú Chulainn to come presently to talk with me.'

The Combat of Láiríne mac Nóis

'Let one of you go speedily tomorrow to meet your opponent,' said Lugaid.

'No one will be got,' said Ailill, 'unless ye employ some trickery in this matter.   Give wine to every man that comes to you until he is gladdened in mind, and tell him: "That is all that is left of the wine that was brought from Cruachain.   We are grieved that you should have only water to drink in the camp."—and let Finnabair be placed at his right hand, and tell him: "You shall have her if you bring back to us the head of the distorted one." '

A message was sent to each warrior on his night, and he was told that.   But Cú Chulainn killed each of them in turn.   At last no one could be got to oppose him.

Láríne mac Nóis, brother of Lugaid King of Munster, was summoned to them. His pride was over-weening. He was plied with wine and Finnabair was placed at his right hand. Medb looked at the two.

'I think that couple well matched,' said she. 'A marriage between them would be fitting.'

'I shall not oppose you,' said Ailill. 'He shall have her if he bring me the head of the distorted one.'

'I shall do so indeed,' said Láiríne.

Thereupon Lugaid arrived.

'What man have ye got to send to the ford tomorrow?'

'Láiríne is going,' said Ailill.

Then Lugaid went to speak with Cú Chulainn. They met in Glend Fir Baíth. Each greeted the other in friendly fashion.

'This is why I have come to speak with you,' said Lugaid. There is a boorish fellow, foolish and arrogant, yonder, my brother who is called Láiríne. He is being tricked about the same girl. By our friendship do not kill him, do not leave me without my brother, for he is being sent to you in order that we two may quarrel. But I am willing for you to give him a sound thrashing, for it is against my wishes he goes.'

On the morrow Láiríne came to meet Cú Chulainn and the maiden came with him to encourage him. Cú Chulainn came unarmed to attack him, and forcilby took his weapons from Láiríne. Then he seized him with both hands and squeezed him and shook him until he drove his excrement out of him and the water of the ford was turbid with his dung and the air of the firmament was polluted with his stench.

Then Cú Chulainn threw him into Lugaid's arms.

As long as Láiríne lived, his inward parts never recovered. He was never without chest-disease; he never ate without pain. Yet he is the only man of all those who met Cú Chulainn on the Táin who escaped from him, even though it was a poor escape.

The Conversation of the Mórrígan with Cú Chulainn

Cú Chulainn saw coming towards him a young woman of surpassing beauty, clad in clothes of many colours.

'Who are you?' asked Cú Chulainn.

'I am the daughter of Búan the king,' said she. 'I have come to you for I fell in love with you on hearing your fame, and I have brought with me my treasures and my cattle.'

'It is not a good time at which you have come to us, that is, our condition is ill, we are starving (?). So it is not easy for me to meet a woman while I am in this strife.'

'I shall help you in it.'

'It is not for a woman's body that I have come.'

'It will be worse for you', said she, 'when I go against you as you are fighting your enemies. I shall go in the form of an eel under your feet in the ford so that you shall fall.'

'I prefer that to the king's daughter,' said he. 'I shall seize you between my toes so that your ribs are crushed and you shall suffer that blemish until you get a judgment blessing.'

'I shall drive the cattle over the ford to you while I am in the form of a grey she-wolf.'

'I shall throw a stone at you from my sling so and smash your eye in your head, and you shall suffer from that blemish until you get a judgment blessing.'

'I shall come to you in the guise of a hornless red heifer in front of the cattle and they will rush upon you at many fords and pools yet you will not see me in front of you.'

'I shall cast a stone at you,' said he, 'so that your legs will break under you, and you shall suffer thus until you get a judgment blessing.'

Whereupon she left him.

—(According to one version) he was a week at Áth nGreacha and every day a man fell by him at Áth nGrencha, that is, at Áth Darteisc.

The Death of Lóch Mac Mo Femis

Then Lóch mac Emonis was summoned like the others and he was promised the extent of Mag Muirthemne in the arable land of Mag nAí, the equipment of twelve men, and a chariot worth seven *cumala*. But he scorned to encounter a mere lad. He had a brother, namely Long mac Ebonis. The same payment was offered to him, the maiden, the raiment, chariot and land.

Long went to meet Cú Chulainn. Cú Chulainn killed him and he was brought back dead and set down before his brother Lóch.

Then Lóch said that if he knew that it was a bearded man who killed his brother he would himself kill him in revenge.

'Attack him vigorously,' said Medb to her men, 'over the ford from the west, so that ye may cross the river, and let terms of fair play be broken against him.'

The seven Maines, the warriors, went first and saw him on the brink of the ford to the west. That day Cú Chulainn put on his festive apparel. The women kept climbing on the men's shoulders to get a glimpse of him.

'I am grieved,' said Medb, 'that I do not see the lad around whom they gather there.'

'You would be no more joyful for seeing him,' said Lethrend, Ailill's groom.

She came then to the ford where he was.

'Who is that man yonder, Fergus?' asked Medb.

'A lad who defends with sword and shield . . . if it be Cú Chulainn.'

So Medb too climbed on the men to get a look at him.

Then the women told Cú Chulainn that he was jeered at in the camp since he was beardless and goodly warriors did not oppose him, only mere boys. It were better for him to put on a beard of blackberry juice. So this he did in order to seek combat with a grown man, that is, with Lóch.

Then Cú Chulainn took a handful of grass and chanted a spell over it and they all thought that he had a beard.

'Yes,' said the women, 'Cú Chulainn is bearded. It is fitting that a warrior should fight with him.'

This they said in order to goad Lóch.

'I shall not fight with him until the end of seven days from today,' said Lóch.

'It is not right for us to leave him unattacked for that length of time,' said Medb. 'Let us send a band of warriors to seek him out every night in the hope of catching him unawares.'

It was done thus. Every night a band of warriors would go looking for him and he used to kill them all. These are the names of those that fell there: seven called Conall, seven called Óengus, seven called Úargus, seven called Celtre, eight called Fiac, ten called Ailill, ten called Delbaeth, ten called Tasach. Those were his deeds during that week at Áth nGrencha.

Medb sought counsel as to what she would do against Cú Chulainn, for she was sorely perturbed by the number of her army that was slain by him. The plan she decided on was to send brave and arrogant men to attack him all together when he should come to a rendez-vous with her to parley with her. For she had made a tryst with Cú Chulainn for the next day to make a mock peace with him and so capture him. She sent a messenger to him asking him to come and meet her, and stipulated that he should come unarmed for she herself would come to him accompanied only by her women attendants.

The messenger, Traigthrén, went to where Cú Chulainn was and gave him Medb's message. Cú Chulainn promised that he would do as she asked.

'How do you intend to go and meet Medb tomorrow, Cú Chulainn,' asked Láeg.

'As Medb asked me,' said Cú Chulainn.

'Many are Medb's treacherous deeds,' said the charioteer. 'I fear that she has help behind the scenes.'

'What should we do then?' said he.

'Gird your sword at your waist,' said the charioteer, 'so that you may not be taken unawares. For if a warrior is without his weapons, he has no right to his honour-price, but in that case he is entitled only to the legal due of one who does not bear arms.'

'Let it be done so then,' said Cú Chulainn.

The meeting was in Ard Aignech, which is today called Fochaird.

Then Medb came to the meeting and she set in ambush for Cú Chulainn fourteen men, the most valorous of her own household. These are they: two called Glas Sinna, sons of Briccride, two called Ardán, sons of Licc, two called Glas Ogna, sons of Crond, Drúcht and Delt and Dathen, Téa and Tascur and Tualang, Taur and Glese.

Then Cú Chulainn came to meet her. The men rose up to attack him and all together they threw fourteen spears at him. Cú Chulainn took shelter from them and not a spear touched his skin or surface. Then he attacked them and killed the fourteen men. Those are the fourteen men of Fochaird, and they are (also) the men of Crónech for they were killed in Crónech at Fochaird.

Of this deed Cú Chulainn said:

'Splendid is my heroic deed. I strike fearsome blows against a brilliant spectral army. I wage battle against many hosts to destroy valiant warriors together with Ailill and Medb . . . There comes treachery, coldly impetuous, to strike against valiant warriors who take wise well-judged counsel from one who can well advise them to perform heroic deeds.'

So it was from that exploit that Focherd remained as the name of the place, that is, *fó cerd*, good was the feat of arms which Cú Chulainn performed there.

Then Cú Chulainn came and found them pitching camp and he killed two men called Daigre, two called Ánle and four Dúngais Imlich among them. So Medb began to incite Lóch.

'It is a great shame for you,' said she, 'that the man who killed your brother should be destroying our army and that you do not go to do battle with him. For we are sure that a sharp, boastful lad like yonder fellow will not stand out against the rage and fury of such as you, and anyway it was the same fostermother and teacher who taught you both the arts of war.'

So Lóch, since he saw that Cú Chulainn had a beard, came to attack him to avenge his brother's death.

'Come to the upper ford,' said Lóch. 'We shall not meet in the polluted ford where Long fell.'

When Cú Chulainn came to the ford, the men drove the cattle across.

'There will be lack of water here today,' said Gabrán, the poet.

Hence the names Áth Darteisc and Tír Mór Darteisc ever since for that place. Then when the combatants met on the ford and began to fight and to strike one another and when each began to belabour the other, the eel twined itself in three coils round Cú Chulainn's feet so that he fell prostrate athwart the ford. Lóch attacked him with the sword until the ford was blood-red with his gore.

'That is indeed a wretched performance in the presence of the enemy!' said Fergus. 'Let one of you taunt the man, my men,' said he to his people, 'lest he fall in vain.'

Bricriu Nemthenga mac Carbada rose up and began to incite Cú Chulainn.

'Your strength is exhausted,' said he, 'if a puny opponent overthrows you now that the Ulstermen are on their way to you, recovered from their torpor. It is hard for you to undertake a hero's deed in the presence of the men of Ireland and to ward off a formidable opponent with your weapons in that way.'

Whereupon Cú Chulainn arose and struck the eel and its ribs were broken within it, and the cattle rushed eastwards over the army, carrying off the tents on their horns, so great was the thunderfeat of the two warriors in the ford.

The she-wolf attacked him and drove the cattle on him westwards. He threw a stone from his sling and her eye broke in her head.

Then she went in the guise of a red hornless heifer and the cattle stampeeded into the streams and fords. Cú Chulainn said then:

'I cannot see the fords for the streams.'

He cast a stone at the red hornless heifer and her leg broke.

Thereupon Cú Chulainn chanted:

'I am here all alone, guarding the flocks. I neither hold them back nor let them go. In the cold hours I stand alone to oppose many peoples.

'Let some one tell Conchobar that it is time for him to come to my aid. The sons of Mágu have carried off their cows and shared them out amongst them.

'One man alone may be defended but a single log will not catch fire. If there were two or three, then their firebrands would blaze up.

'My enemies have almost overcome me, so many single combats have I fought. I cannot now wage battle against splendid warriors as I stand here alone.'

Then it was that Cú Chulainn did against the Mórrígan the three things that he had threatened her with in the Táin Bó Regamna. And he overcame Lóch in the ford with the *gáe bolga* which the charioteer threw to him downstream. He attacked him with it and it entered his body through the anus, for Lóch had a horn-skin when he was fighting with an opponent.

'Retreat a step from me,' said Lóch.

Cú Chulainn did so, so that it was on the other side (of the ford) that Lóch fell. Hence the place-name Áth Traiged in Tír Mór.

Then the terms of fair play were violated against Cú Chulainn on that day when five men came simultaneously to attack him, namely, two called Crúaid, two called Calad and one named Derothor. Single-handed Cú Chulainn slew them. The place is called Cóicsius Focherda and Cóicer Óengoirt. Or else it is because Cú Chulainn was fifteen days in Focherd that the name Cóicsius Focherda comes in the Táin. Cú Chulainn pelted them (with sling-stones) from Delga so that no living creature, neither man nor beast, could get past him to the south between Delga and the sea.

The Healing of the Mórrígan

While Cú Chulainn lay thus in great weariness, the Mórrígan came to him in the guise of an old crone, one-eyed and half-blind and engaged in milking a cow with three teats. He asked her for a drink. She gave him the milk of one teat.

'She who gave it will at once be whole,' said Cú Chulainn. 'The blessing of gods and of non-gods be on you!'

—The magicians were their gods but the husbandmen were their non-gods.—

Thereupon her head was made whole.

Then she gave him the milk of the second teat, and her eye was healed.

She gave him the milk of the third teat, and her leg was cured.

—And it is suggested that on each occasion he said: 'The judgment of blessing be on you!'—

'But you told me,' said the Mórrígan, 'that I should never get healing from you.'

'Had I known that it was you,' said Cú Chulainn, 'I should never have healed you.'

—In another version the name of this tale in the Táin is Ríamdrong Con Culainn for Tarthesc.—

Then Fergus demanded of his sureties that Cú Chulainn should get fair play. So they came to oppose him in single combat, and he killed the five men of Cend Coriss or of Dún Chind Coross which is now called Delgu Murthemne.

Then Cú Chulainn killed Fota in his field; Bó Mailce on his ford; Salach in his marsh, Muinne in his stronghold; Lúar in Lethbera and Fer Toíthle in Toíthle. Wherever any one of those men fell their names have remained for ever in those districts.

Cú Chulainn also killed Traig and Dorna and Derna, Col and Mebal and Eraise at Méthe and Cethe on this side of Áth Tíre Móir. These were three druids and their wives.

Then Medb sent out a hundred men of her household to kill Cú Chulainn but he slew them all at Áth Chéit Chúile.

Whereupon Medb said:

'Indeed we deem it a crime that our people should be slain!'

Whence the place-names Glais Chró and Cuillenn Cind Dún and Áth Céit Chúle.

The Scythed Chariot and Breslech Mór Maige Muirthemne

Then the four provinces of Ireland pitched their camp at the place called Breslech Mór in Mag Muirthemne. They sent their share of the cattle and booty on ahead southwards to Clithar Bó Ulad.

Cú Chulainn took up position at the mound in Lerga close beside them, and his charioteer, Láeg mac Ríangabra, kindled a fire for him in the evening of that night. Cú Chulainn saw afar off, over the heads of the four provinces of Ireland, the fiery glitter of the bright gold weapons at the setting of the sun in the clouds of evening. Anger and rage filled him when he saw the host, because of the multitude of his foes and the great number of his enemies. He seized his two spears and his shield and his sword. He shook his shield and brandished his spears and waved his sword, and he uttered a hero's shout deep in his throat. And the goblins and sprites and spectres of the glen and demons of the air gave answer for terror of the shout that he had uttered. And Némain, the war goddess, attacked the host, and the four provinces of Ireland made a clamour of arms round the points of their own spears and weapons so that a hundred warriors among them fell dead of fright and terror in the middle of the encampment on that night.

As Láeg was there he saw a single man coming straight towards him from the north-east across the encampment of the men of Ireland.

'A single man approaches us now, little Cú,' said Láeg.

'What manner of man is there?' asked Cú Chulainn.

'A man fair and tall, with a great head of curly yellow hair. He has a green mantle wrapped about him and a brooch of white silver in the mantle over his breast. Next to his white skin he wears a tunic of royal satin with red-gold insertion reaching to his knees. He carries a black shield with a hard boss of white-bronze. In his hand a five-pointed spear and next to it a forked javelin. Wonderful is the play and sport and diversion that he makes (with these weapons). But none accosts him and he accosts none as if no one could see him.'

'That is true, lad,' said he. 'That is one of my friends from the fairy mounds come to commiserate with me, for they know of my sore distress as I stand now alone against the four great provinces of Ireland on the Foray of Cúailnge.'

It was indeed as Cú Chulainn said. When the warrior reached the spot where Cú Chulainn was he spoke to him and commiserated with him.

'Bravo, Cú Chulainn,' said he.

'That is not much indeed,' said Cú Chulainn.

'I shall help you,' said the warrior.

'Who are you?' asked Cú Chulainn.

'I am your father, Lug mac Ethlend, from the fairy mounds.'

'My wounds are indeed grievous. It were time that I should be healed.'

'Sleep now for a little while, Cú Chulainn,' said the warrior, 'your heavy slumber at the mound in Lerga for three days and three nights, and during that time I shall fight against the hosts.'

Then he chanted a low melody to him which lulled him to sleep until Lug saw that every wound he bore was quite healed.

Then Lug spoke:

The Incantation of Lug

'Arise, O son of mighty Ulster now that your wounds are healed . . . Help from the fairy mound will set you free . . . A single lad is on his guard . . . Strike . . . and I shall strike with you. They have no strong length of life, so wreak your furious anger mightily on your vile (?) enemies. Mount your safe chariot, so then arise.'

For three days and three nights Cú Chulainn slept. It was right that the length of his sleep should correspond to the greatness of his weariness. From the Monday after Samain until the Wednesday after the festival of Spring Cú Chulainn had not slept except when he dozed for a little while after midday, leaning against his spear with his head resting on his clenched fist and his fist holding his spear and his spear on his knee, but he kept striking and cutting down, slaying and killing the four great provinces of Ireland during all that time. Then the warrior from the fairy mound put plants and healing herbs and a curing charm in the wounds and cuts, in the gashes and many injuries of Cú Chulainn so that he recovered during his sleep without his perceiving it at all.

It was at this time that the youths came southwards from Emain Macha, thrice fifty of the kings' sons of Ulster led by Fallamain, the son of Conchobar. Thrice they gave battle to the host and three times their own number fell by them, but the youths fell too, all except Fallamain mac Conchobair. Fallamain vowed that he would never go back to Emain until he carried off Ailill's head with its golden diadem. No easy task was it that faced him. For the two sons of Beithe mac Báin, the sons of Ailill's fostermother and fosterfather, came up with him and wounded him so that he fell dead at their hands.

That is the Death of the Youths from Ulster and of Fallamain mac Conchobair.

Cú Chulainn, however, lay in a deep sleep at the mound in Lerga until the end of three days and three nights. Then he rose up from his sleep and passed his hand over his face and blushed crimson from head to foot. His spirits were as high as if he were going to an assembly or a march or a tryst or a feast or to one of the great assemblies of Ireland.

'How long have I been asleep now, O warrior?' asked Cú Chulainn.

'Three days and three nights,' answered the warrior.

'Woe is me then!' said Cú Chulainn.

'Why is that?' asked the warrior.

'Because the hosts have been left unattacked for that length of time,' said Cú Chulainn.

'They have not indeed,' said the warrior.

'Why, how was that?' asked Cú Chulainn.

'The youths came south from Emain Macha, thrice fifty of the kings' sons of Ulster, led by Fallamain mac Conchobair and during the three days and three nights that you were asleep, they fought three times with the hosts, and three times their own number fell by them and the youths themselves fell, all except Fallamain mac Conchobair. Fallamain swore that he would carry off Ailill's head, but that proved no easy task for he was killed himself.'

'Alas that I was not in my full strength, for had I been, the youths would not have fallen as they did, nor would Fallamain have fallen.'

'Fight on, little Cú, it is no reproach to your honour, no disgrace to your valour.'

'Stay here with us tonight, O warrior,' said Cú Chulainn, 'that together we may take vengeance on the host for the death of the boys.'

'Indeed I shall not stay,' said the warrior, 'for though a man do many valorous and heroic deeds in your company, the fame and glory of them will redound not on him but on you. Therefore I shall not stay. But exert your valour, yourself alone, on the hosts, for not with them lies any power over your life at this time.'

'What of the scythed chariot, my friend Láeg?' said Cú Chulainn. 'Can you yoke it and have you its equipment? If you can yoke it and have its equipment, then do so. But if you have not its equipment, do not yoke it.'

Then the charioteer arose and put on his warlike outfit for chariot-driving. Of this outfit which he donned was his smooth tunic of skins, which was light and airy, supple and filmy, stitched and of deerskin, which did not hinder the movement of his arms outside. Over that he put on his overmantle black as raven's feathers. Simon Magus had made it for Darius King of the Romans, and Darius had given it to Conchobar and Conchobar had given it to Cú Chulainn who gave it to his charioteer. This charioteer now put on his helmet, crested, flat-surfaced, rectangular with variety of every colour and form, and reaching past the middle of his shoulders. This was an adornment to him and was not an encumbrance. His hand brought to his brow the circlet, red-yellow like a red-gold plate of refined gold smelted over the edge of an anvil, which was a sign of his charioteer status to distinguish him from his master. In his right hand he took the long spancel of his horses and his ornamented goad. In his left he grasped the thongs to check his horses, that is, the reins of his horses which controlled his driving.

14

Then he put on his horses their iron inlaid armour, covering them from forehead to forehand and set with little spears and sharp points and lances and hard points, and every wheel of the chariot was closely studded with points, and every corner and edge, every end and front of the chariot lacerated as it passed. Then he cast a protective spell over his horses and over his companion, so that they were not visible to anyone in the camp, yet everyone in the camp was visible to them. It was right that he should cast this spell, for on that day the charioteer had three great gifts of charioteering, to wit, *léim dar boilg, foscul ndírich* and *imorchor ndelind*.

Then the champion and warrior, the marshalled fence of battle of all the men of earth who was Cú Chulainn, put on his battle-array of fighting and contest and strife. Of that battle-array which he put on were the twenty-seven shirts, waxed, board-like, compact, which used to be bound with strings and ropes and thongs next to his fair body that his mind and understanding might not be deranged whenever his rage should come upon him. Outside these he put on his hero's battle-girdle of hard leather, tough and tanned, made from the choicest part of seven yearling ox-hides which covered him from the thin part of his side to the thick part of his armpit. He wore it to repel spears and points and darts and lances and arrows, for they used to glance from it as if they had struck on stone or rock or horn. Then he put on his apron of filmy silk with its border of variegated white gold against the soft lower part of his body. Outside his apron of filmy silk he put on his dark apron of pliable brown leather made from the choicest part of four yearling ox-hides with his battle-girdle of cows' hides about it. Then the royal hero took up his weapons of battle and contest and strife. Of these weapons were his eight small swords together with his ivory-hilted bright-faced sword. He took his eight little spears with his five-pronged spear. He took his eight little javelins with his ivory-handled javelin. He took his eight little darts together with his *deil chliss*. He took his eight shields together with his curved dark-red shield into the boss of which a show boar would fit, with its sharp, keen razor-like rim all around it, so sharp and keen and razor-like that it would cut a hair against the current. Whenever the warrior did the 'edge-feat' with it, he would slash alike with shield or spear or sword. Then he put on his head his crested war-helmet of battle and strife and conflict. From it was uttered the shout of a hundred warriors with a long-drawn-out cry from every corner and angle of it. For there used to cry from it alike goblins and sprites, spirits of the glen and demons of the air before him and above him and around him wherever he went, prophesying the shedding of the blood of warriors and champions. He cast around him his protective cloak made of raiment from Tír Tairngire, brought to him from his teacher of wizardry.

Then a great distortion came upon Cú Chulainn so that he became horrible, many-shaped, strange and unrecognizable. All the flesh of his body quivered like a tree in a current or like a bulrush in a stream, every limb and every joint, every end and every member of him from head to foot. He performed a wild feat of contortion with his body inside his skin. His feet and his shins and his knees came to the back; his heels and his calves and his hams came to the front. The sinews of his calves came on to the front of his shins, and each huge round knot of them was as big as a warrior's fist. The sinews of his head were stretched to the nape of his neck and every huge immeasurable, vast, incalulable round ball of them was as big as the head of a month-old child. Then his face became a red hollow (?). He sucked one of his eyes into his head so deep that a wild crane could hardly have reached it to pluck it out from the back of his skull on to his cheek. The other eye sprang out on to his cheek. His mouth was twisted back fearsomely. He drew back his cheek from his jawbone until his inward parts were visible. His lungs and his liver fluttered in his mouth and his throat. His upper palate clashed against the lower in a mighty pincer-like movement (?) and every stream of fiery flakes which came into his mouth from his throat was as wide as a ram's skin. The loud beating of his heart against his ribs was heard like the baying of a bloodhound . . . or like a lion attacking bears. The torches of the war-goddess, virulent rain-clouds and sparks of blazing fire, were seen in the air over his head with the seething of fierce rage that rose in him. His hair curled about his head like branches of red hawthorn used to re-fence a gap in a hedge. If a noble apple-tree weighed down with fruit had been shaken about his hair, scarcely one apple would have reached the ground through it, but an apple would have stayed impaled on each separate hair because of the fierce bristling of his hair above his head. The hero's light rose from his forehead, as long and as thick as a hero's fist and it was as long as his nose, and he was filled with rage as he wielded the shields and urged on the charioteer and cast sling-stones at the host. As high, as thick, as strong, as powerful and as long as the mast of a great ship was the straight stream of dark blood which rose up from the very top of his head and dissolved into a dark magical mist like the smoke of a palace when a king comes to be waited on in the evening of a winter's day.

After being thus distorted, the hero Cú Chulainn sprang into his scythed chariot, with its iron points, its thin sharp edges, its hooks and its steel points, with its nails which were on the shafts and thongs and loops and fastenings in that chariot. Thus was the chariot: it had a framework of narrow and compact opening, high enough for great feats, sword-straight, worthy of a hero. In it would fit eight sets of royal weapons, and it moved as swiftly as a swallow or as the wind or as a deer across the level plain. It was drawn by two swift horses, fierce and furious, with small round pointed heads, with pricked ears, with broad hoofs, with roan breast, steady, splendid, easily harnessed to the beautiful shafts (?) of Cú Chulainn's chariots. One of these horses was lithe (?) and swift-leaping, eager for battle, arched of neck, with great hoofs which scattered the sods of the earth. The other horse had a curling mane, and narrow, slender feet and heels.

Then Cú Chulainn performed the thunderfeat of a hundred and the thunderfeat of two hundred, the thunderfeat of three hundred and the thunderfeat of four hundred. And at the thunderfeat of five hundred he ceased for he thought that that was a sufficient number to fall by him in his first attack and in his first contest of battle against the four provinces of Ireland. And in that manner he came forth to attack his enemies and drove his chariot in a wide circuit outside the four great provinces of Ireland. And he drove his chariot furiously so that the iron wheels sank deep into the ground casting up earth sufficient to provide fort and fortress, for there arose on the outside as high as the iron wheels dykes and boulders and rocks and flagstones and gravel from the ground. He made this warlike encirclement of the four great provinces of Ireland so that they might not flee from him nor disperse around him until he pressed them close to take vengeance on them for the deaths of the youths of Ulster. And he came across into the middle of their ranks and three times he threw up great ramparts of his enemies' corpses outside around the host. And he made upon them the attack of a foe upon his foes so that they fell, sole of foot to sole of foot, and headless neck to headless neck, such was the density of the carnage. Three times again he encircled them in this way leaving a layer of six corpses around them, that is, the soles of three men to the necks of three men, all around the encampment. So that the name of this tale in the Táin is Sesrech Breslige, the Sixfold Slaughter. It is one of the three slaughters in which the victims cannot be numbered, the three being Sesrech Breslige and Imshlige Glennamnach and the battle at Gáirech and Irgáirech. But on this occasion hound and horse and man suffered alike.

—Other versions say that Lug mac Eithlend fought beside Cú Chulainn in the battle of Sesrech Breslige.

Their number is not known nor is it possible to count how many of the common soldiery fell there, but their leaders alone have been reckoned. Here follow their names: two men called Crúaid, two called Calad, two called Cír, two called Cíar, two called Ecell, three called Crom, three called Caurath, three called Combirge, four called Feochar, four called Furachar, four called Cass, four called Fota, five called Caurath, five called Cerman, five called Cobthach, six called Saxan, six called Dách, six called Dáire, seven called Rochaid, seven called Rónán, seven called Rúrthech, eight called Rochlad, eight called Rochtad, eight called Rindach, eight called Cairpre, eight called Mulach, nine called Daigith, nine called Dáire, nine called Dámach, ten called Fiac, ten called Fiacha, ten called Fedelmid.

Seven score and ten kings did Cú Chulainn slay in the battle of Breslech Mór in Mag Muirthemne, and a countless number besides of hounds and horses, of women and boys and children, and of the common folk. For not one man in three of the men of Ireland escaped without his thigh-bone or the side of his head or one eye being broken or without being marked for life. Then Cú Chulainn, after he had fought that battle against them, came from them with no wound or gash inflicted upon himself or his charioteer or on either of his horses.

The Description of Cú Chulainn

Cú Chulainn came on the morrow to survey the host and to display his gentle and beautiful form to women and girls and maidens, to poets and men of art, for he held not as honourable or dignified the dark magical appearance in which he had appeared to them the previous night. So for that reason he now came on this day to display his beautiful fair appearance.

Beautiful indeed was the youth who thus came to display his form to the hosts, namely, Cú Chulainn mac Súaltaim. He seemed to have three kinds of hair: dark next to his skin, blood-red in the middle and hair like a crown of gold covering them outside. Fair was the arrangement of that hair with three coils in the hollow in the nape of his neck, and like gold thread was each fine hair, loose-flowing, bright-golden, excellent, long-tressed, splendid and of beautiful colour, which fell back over his shoulders. A hundred bright crimson ringlets of flaming red-gold encircled his neck.

Around his head a hundred strings interspersed with carbuncle-gems. Four shades (?) in each of his cheeks, a yellow shade and a green, a blue shade and a purple. Seven brilliant gem-like pupils in each of his noble eyes. Seven toes on each of his feet; seven fingers on each of his hands with the grasp of a hawk's claws and the grip of a hedghog's claws in each separate toe and finger.

So on that day he donned his festive apparel, namely, a fair mantle, well-fitting, bright purple, fringed, five-folded. A white brooch of silver inset with inlaid gold over his white breast as it were a bright lantern that men's eyes could not look at by reason of its brilliance and splendour. Next to his skin he wore a tunic of silky satin reaching to the top of his dark apron, dark-red, soldierly, of royal satin. He carried a dark-red purple shield with five concentric circles of gold and a rim of white bronze. At his girdle hung, ready for action, a golden-hilted, ornamented sword with great knobs of red gold at its end. In the chariot beside him was a long shining-edged spear together with a sharp attacking javelin with rivets of burning gold. In one hand he held nine heads, in the other ten, and these he brandished at the hosts. Those were the trophies of one night's fighting by Cú Chulainn.

Then the women of Connacht climbed up on the hosts and the women of Munster climbed on men's shoulders that they might behold the appearance of Cú Chulainn. But Medb hid her face and dared not show her countenance, but through fear of Cú Chulainn she sheltered under a cover of shields.

That is why Dubthach Dóel Ulad said (these verses):

'If this is the distorted one, men's corpses will lie here and cries will be heard around the courts. There will be tales in the lands(?).

'Headstones will be erected over graves. More and more kings will be slain. Not well do ye fight on the battle-field against that champion.

'I see how he drives around with eight severed heads on the cushions of his chariot. I see the shattered spoils he brings and ten heads as trophies.

'I see how your woman-folk raise their heads above the battle (to see him), but I see that your great queen does not seek to come to the fight.

'Were I your counseller, then warriors would lie in ambush all around him so that they might cut short his life, if this is the distorted one.'

Then Fergus chanted these verses:

'Take Dubthach Déoltengaid away. Drag him to the rear of the army. He has done nought of good since he slew the maidens (in Ulster).

'He performed a wicked and ill-omened deed when he killed Fiacha, the son of Conchobar. Nor was the slaying of Coirpre, son of Fedelmid, any less wicked.

'Dubthach, the son of Lugaid mac Casruba, does not contend for the lordship of Ulster, but this is how he treats them; those not killed he sets at loggerheads.

'The Ulster exiles will grieve if their beardless lad is slain. If the Ulster army come upon you, they will turn back the herds.

'The debility of the Ulstermen will be greately prolonged before they finally recover.

'Messengers will bring great tidings. Great queens will be there. Men's wounded bodies will be mangled and many slaughtered.

'Corpses will be trampled underfoot. Vultures will feast. Shields will lie flat on the battle fields. Marauders will find shelter.

'Warriors' blood will be spilt on the ground by this army of curs in human shape. If they get there, the exiles will penetrate far into Ulster.

'He cannot heed the prophecy of what lies before you. Take Dubthach Dóeltenga away.'

Thereupon Fergus hurled Dubthach away from him and he landed flat on his face outside those who stood there.

Then Ailill was heard saying:

'O Fergus, do not fight against the women and cattle of Ulster. I can see by their mountain passes that many will be killed there. Strike even though they will be struck down only one by one. He slays them in the ford every day.'

Then Medb was heard:

'O Ailill, arise with war-bands . . . (Your) sons will kill in passes (?) and on fords, in great sandy places and in dark pools. And Fergus the brave and the exiled warriors will be victorious. After the battle there will be restitution . . .'

Then Fergus spoke:

'Do not listen to the foolish counsels of a woman. Hear them not . . .'

Then Gabrán the poet spoke:

'Speak no words . . . do not earn hatred.'

'Refuse not your opponent. Come to meet him at the ford,' said Fergus. 'Hear Ailill!' said Medb.

Ailill was heard speaking:

'Fergus knows . . .'

Then Fergus was heard:

'O Medb, do not send the great heroes of your mighty exiles . . .'

The Mis-throw at Belach Eóin

Fíacha Fíaldána Dimraith came to have speech with the son of his mother's sister, whose name was Maine Andóe. Dócha mac Mágach came with Maine Andóe and Dubthach Dóel Ulad came with Fíacha Fíaldána Dimraith. Dócha cast a spear at Fíacha and it went into Dubthach. Then Dubthach cast a spear at Maine and it went into Dócha.

The mothers of Dubthach and Dócha were also two sisters.

Hence the name Imroll Belaig Eúin, the Miscast at Belach Eúin.

—Or, according to another version, the origin of the name Imroll Belaig Eúin is as follows:

The hosts came to Belach Eúin. Both armies halted there. Diarmait mac Conchobair came from the north from Ulster.

'Send a messenger,' said Diarmait, 'asking Maine to come with one man to parley with me, and I shall go with one man to meet him.'

Then they met.

'I have come from Conchobar,' said Diarmait, 'to ask you to tell Medb and Ailill that they must let all the cattle (they have taken) go and their depredations will be overlooked. And let the bull from the west be brought hither to the bull (Donn Cúailnge) that they may encounter each other, for so Medb has promised.'

'I shall go and tell them,' said Maine.

So he gave the message to Medb and Ailill.

'These terms cannot be got from Medb,' said Maine.

'Well then, let us exchange weapons,' said Diarmait, 'if you prefer.'

'I am willing,' said Maine.

Each of them cast a spear at the other and both of them died, so that Imroll Belaig Eóin is the name of that place.

The army rushed upon the opposing force. Three score of them fell on each side. Hence the name Ard in Dírma.

The Death of Taman the Jester

Ailill's people put his king's crown on Taman the Jester. Ailill himself did not venture to wear it. Cú Chulainn cast a stone at him at the place called Áth Tamuin and smashed his head. Whence the names Áth Tamuin and Tuga im Thamun.

The Death of Óengus mac Óenláime

Then Óengus mac Óenláime Gaibe, a bold warrior of the Ulstermen, turned back the whole army at Moda Loga (which is the same name as Lugmod) as far as Áth Da Ferta. He did not allow them to go farther and he pelted them with stones.

Learned men say that he would have driven them on before him to be put to the sword at Emain Macha if only they had encountered him in single combat. But they did not grant him fair play. They killed him as he fought against odds.

The Meeting of Fergus and Cú Chulainn

'Let one of you come to meet me at Áth Da Ferta,' said Cú Chulainn.

'It will not be I!' 'It will not be I!' cried one and all from the place where they were. 'No scapegoat is owed by my people, and even if he were, it is not I who would go in his stead as a victim.'

Then Fergus was begged to go against him. But he refused to encounter his foster-son, Cú Chulainn. He was plied with wine then until he was greatly intoxicated, and again he was asked to go and fight. So then he went forth since they were so earnestly importuning him.

Then Cú Chulainn said:

'It is with (a feeling of) security you come against me, master Fergus, seeing that you have no sword in your scabbard.'

—For, as we have already told, Ailill had stolen it from the scabbard.—

'I care not indeed,' said Fergus. 'Even if there were a sword in it, it would not be wielded against you. Retreat a step from me, Cú Chulainn.'

'You in turn will retreat before me,' said Cú Chulainn.

'Even so indeed,' answered Fergus.

Then Cú Chulainn retreated before Fergus as far as Grellach Dolluid so that on the day of the great battle Fergus might retreat before him.

Afterwards Cú Chulainn dismounted (from his chariot) in Grellach Dolluid.

'Go after him, Fergus!' they all cried.

'Nay,' said Fergus. 'Until my turn come round I shall not go, for it is no easy task for me. That man is too lively for me.'

They went on then and pitched camp in Crích Rois. Ferchú Loingsech, who had been exiled by Ailill, heard of this and came to encounter Cú Chulainn. Thirteen men was the number of his force. Cú Chulainn killed them at the place called Cingit Ferchon. Their thirteen headstones mark the spot.

The Fight with Mand

Medb sent Mand Muresci, the son of Dáire of the Domnannaig, to fight against Cú Chulainn. Mand was own brother to Damán, the father of Fer Diad. This Mand was a violent fellow, excessive in eating and sleeping. He was scurrilous and foul-spoken like Dubthach Dóel Ulad. He was strong and active and mighty of limb like Munremar mac Errcind. He was a fierce champion like Triscod, the strong man of Conchobar's household.

'I shall go forth unarmed and crush him in my bare hands, for I scorn to use weapons against a beardless whippersnapper.'

So Mand went to attack Cú Chulainn who, with his charioteer, was on the plain keeping a look-out for the host.

'A man comes towards us,' said Láeg to Cú Chulainn.

'What manner of man?' asked Cú Chulainn.

'A dark, strong, fierce man who comes unarmed.'

'Let him go past,' said Cú Chulainn.

Thereupon Mand came to them.

'I have come to fight against you,' said Mand.

Then they fell to wrestling for a long time and thrice did Mand throw Cú Chulainn, so that the charioteer urged him on, saying:

'If you were striving for the hero's portion in Emain,' said Láeg, 'you would be powerful over the warriors there.'

So then his hero's rage and his warrior's fury arose in Cú Chulainn, and he dashed Mand against the pillarstone and shattered him into fragments.

Hence the name Mag Mandachta, that is, Mand Échta, which means the death of Mand was there.

The next day Medb sent twenty-nine men against him to Cú Chulainn's bog. Fuiliarn is the name of the bog which is on this side of Áth Fir Diad. These men were Gaile Dáne and his twenty-seven sons and his sister's son, Glas mac Delgna. At once they cast their twenty-nine spears at Cú Chulainn. Then as they all reached for their swords, Fíacha mac Fir Febe came after them out of the encampment. He leapt from his chariot when he saw all their hands raised against Cú Chulainn, and he struck off their twenty-nine forearms.

Then said Cú Chulainn:

'What you have done is timely help.'

'Even this little,' said Fíacha, 'is in breach of our covenant for us Ulstermen. If any one of them reach the encampment (to tell of it), our whole division will be put to the sword.'

'I swear my people's oath,' said Cú Chulainn, 'that now that I have drawn my breath, not one of those men shall get there alive.'

Thereupon Cú Chulainn killed the twenty-nine men, with the two sons of Ficce helping him in the killing. These were two brave warriors of Ulster who had come to exert their might against the host. That was their exploit on the Foray until they came with Cú Chulainn to the great battle.

In the stone in the middle of the ford there is still the mark of the boss of their (twenty-nine) shields and of their fists and knees. Their twenty-nine headstones were erected there.

The Fight of Fer Diad and Cú Chulainn

Then they debated among themselves as to which man would be capable of repelling Cú Chulainn. The four provinces of Ireland named and confirmed and decided whom they should send to the ford to meet Cú Chulainn. They all declared that it was the horn-skinned man from Irrus Domnann, the one whose attack cannot be endured, the battle-stone of doom, Cú Chulainn's own dear foster-brother. Cú Chulainn possessed no feat that Fer Diad had not, except only the feat of the *gáe bulga*. And they thought that Fer Diad could avoid even that and protect himself from it, for he had a horn-skin which weapons and swords could not pierce.

Medb sent messengers for Fer Diad, but he did not come with those messengers. Then Medb sent to fetch him poets and artists and satirists who might satirise him and disgrace him and put him to shame, so that he would find no resting-place in the world until he should come to the tent of Medb and Ailill on the Foray. So for fear that he should be put to shame by them Fer Diad came with those messengers.

Finnabair, the daughter of Medb and Ailill was placed at his side. It was she who handed Fer Diad every goblet and cup; it was she who gave him three kisses with every one of those cups; it was she who gave him fragrant apples over the bosom of her tunic. She kept saying that Fer Diad was her beloved, her chosen lover from among all the men of the world.

When Fer Diad was sated and cheerful and merry, Medb said:

'Well now, Fer Diad, do you know why you have been summoned to this tent?'

'I know not indeed,' said Fer Diad, 'except that the nobles of the men of Ireland are here, so why should it be less fitting for me to be here than any other nobleman?'

'That is not why, indeed,' said Medb, 'but (you have been summoned for us) to give you a chariot worth thrice seven *cumala*, the equipment of twelve men, the equivalent of Mag Muirthemne in the arable land of Mag nAí, permission to remain at all times in Crúachu with wine poured for you there, and your descendants and your race to be free for ever from tax or tribute, and my leaf-shaped brooch of gold in which there are ten score ounces and ten score half-ounces and ten score crosachs and ten score quarters bestowed on you, and Finnabair, my daughter and Ailill's, as your wedded wife, and my own intimate friendship. And in addition to that, if you require it, you will get the gods as guarantee.'

'Those gifts are great,' said they all.

'That is true,' said Fer Diad. 'They are indeed great. But great though they be, Medb, you will keep them yourself if I am to go and fight with my foster-brother.'

'O my men,' said Medb, intending to stir up strife and dissension and speaking as if she had not heard Fer Diad at all, 'what Cú Chulainn said is true.'

'What did he say, Medb?' asked Fer Diad.

'He said, my friend, that he thought you should fall by his choicest feat of arms in the province to which he would go.'

'It was not right for him to say that for he never found weakness or cowardice in me, day or night. I swear by my people's god that I shall be the first man to come tomorrow morning to the ford of combat.'

'A blessing on you!' said Medb. 'I prefer that rather than finding weakness or cowardice in you. Every man has kindly feeling for his own people. So is it any more fitting for him to work for Ulster's weal since his mother was of Ulster, than for you to seek the good of Connacht, for you are the son of a Connacht king?'

Even as they bound their covenants and made this compact, they made a song there:

'You shall have a reward of many bracelets, and a share of plain and forest, together with freedom for your posterity from today until doomsday. O Fer Diad mac Damáin, you shall receive beyond all expectation. It is right for you to accept what all others accept.'

'I shall not accept anything without surety for no warrior without skill in casting am I. It will be an oppressive task for me tomorrow. The exertion will be hard for me. A Hound called the Hound of Culann, it will not be easy to resist him. Hard the task, great the disaster.'

'What avails it for you to delay? Bind it as it may please you by the right hand of kings or princes who will go surety for you ... You shall have all that you ask, for it is certain that you will kill him who will come to encounter you.'

'I shall not consent unless I get six sureties—let it not be less— before performing my exploits in the presence of the army. Were I to have my wish ... I shall go to fight with brave Cú Chulainn.'

'O Medb great in boastfulness! The beauty of a bridegroom does not touch you. I am certain that you are master in Crúachu of the mounds. Loud your voice, great your fierce strength. Bring me satin richly variegated. Give me your gold and your silver in the amount that they were offered to me.'

'Take landowner or reaver, take the bardic folk as sureties. You will certainly have them. Take Morand as security if you wish for fulfilment (of my promises). Take Cairbre Nia Manand, and take our two sons.'

'I shall take those sureties as guarantees, and I shall sing a requiem for brave Cú Chulainn.'

'You are the heroic leader to whom I shall give my circular brooch. You shall have until Sunday, no longer shall the respite be. O strong and famous warrior, all the finest treasures on earth shall thus be given to you. You shall have them all.'

'Finnabair of the champions, the queen of the west of Inis Elga, when the Hound of the Smith has been killed, you shall have, O Fer Diad.'

A wonderful warrior of the Ulstermen, Fergus mac Róig, was present when they made that compact. Fergus came to his tent.
'Woe is me for the deed that will be done tomorrow morning!'
'What deed is that?' asked those in the tent.
'The killing of my noble foster-son, Cú Chulainn.'
'Why, who makes such a boast?'
'His own dear foster-brother, Fer Diad mac Damáin. Why do ye not take my blessing and one of you go with a friendly warning to Cú Chulainn in the hope that he might not come to the ford tomorrow morning.'
'We swear,' said they, 'that even if you yourself were at the ford, we would not go there to you.'
'Well, driver,' said Fergus, 'harness our horses and yoke the chariot.'
The charioteer arose and harnessed the horses and yoked the chariot.
They came forward to the ford of combat where Cú Chulainn was·
'A single chariot is coming towards us, little Cú,' said Láeg.
For the charioteer had his back turned to his master.—He used to win every second game of draughts and chess from his master. Apart from that he acted as sentinel and watchman on the four airts of Ireland.
'What manner of chariot?' asked Cú Chulainn.
'A chariot like a great palace, with yoke of solid gold and a strong panel of copper, with its shafts of bronze, its frame with

narrow compact opening, high and sword-straight, fit for a hero, drawn by two black horses, active, spirited, vigorous, easily yoked, ... A single royal, wide-eyed warrior is driven in the chariot. He has a thick, forked beard reaching down past the soft lower part of his navel. It would protect fifty warriors on a day of storm and rain if they were under the deep shelter of the hero's beard. He carries a curved variegated shield with white shoulder piece and three beautiful concentric circles. A litter-bed for four bands of ten men would fit upon the hide which stretches across the broad circumference of the warrior's shield. He has a long, hard-edged, broad, red sword in a sheath with interlaced design of bright silver ... Over the chariot he holds a strong, three-ridged spear with rings and bands of pure white silver.'

'It is not hard to recognize him,' said Cú Chulainn. 'That is my master Fergus, coming to give me a friendly warning against all the four provinces of Ireland.'

Fergus arrived and descended from his chariot. Cú Chulainn bade him welcome.

'Your arrival is welcome, master Fergus,' said Cú Chulainn.

'I trust that welcome,' said Fergus.

'You may well trust it,' said Cú Chulainn. 'If a flock of birds fly across the plain, you shall have a wild goose and a half: or if fish come to the estuaries, you shall have a salmon and a half, or else a handful of watercress, a handful of laver and a handful of seaweed, and after that a drink of cold sandy water.'

'That is a meal fit for an outlaw,' said Fergus.

'That is so. I have an outlaw's portion,' said Cú Chulainn, 'for from the Monday after Samain until now I have not spent a night entertained as guest, but have been strongly holding back the men of Ireland on the Foray of Cúailnge.'

'If we had come for hospitality,' said Fergus, 'we should be all the better pleased to get it, but that is not why we have come.'

'Why then have you come?' asked Cú Chulainn.

'To tell you that a warrior will come to fight and do combat with you tomorrow morning,' said Fergus.

'Let us know who it is and hear it from you,' said Cú Chulainn.

'It is your own foster-brother, Fer Diad mac Damáin,'

'I vow that he is not the one we would prefer to meet,' said Cú Chulainn, 'not through fear of him indeed, but rather because of our great love for him.'

'It is right to fear him,' said Fergus, 'for he has a horn-skin when he fights with an opponent, and neither weapons nor sharp points can pierce it.'

'Do not say that,' said Cú Chulainn, 'for I swear the oath of my people that his every joint and limb will bend beneath my sword-point as pliantly as a rush in mid-stream, if he once appear before me on the ford.'

As they spoke thus, they made a lay:

'O Cú Chulainn—clear covenant—I see that it is time for you to rise. Fer Diad mac Damáin of the ruddy countenance comes here to meet you in his wrath.'

'I am here strongly holding back the men of Ireland—no easy task. I do not retreat one step to avoid encounter with a single opponent.'

'It is not that I attribute cowardice to you, O famed Cú Chulainn, but Fer Diad of the many followers has a horn-skin against which no fight or combat can prevail.'

'When I and Fer Diad the valorous meet at the ford, it will not be a fight without fierceness. Our sword-fight will be wrathful.'

'Strong is his hand which wreaks his anger with his hard red sword. There is the strength of a hundred in his body; brave is the hero. The point of weapons wounds him not, the edge of weapons cuts him not.'

'Hold your peace! Do not argue the matter, O Fergus of the mighty weapons. Over every land and territory there will be no fight against overwhelming odds for me.'

'O Cú Chulainn of the red sword, I should prefer above any reward that you were the one to take the spoils of proud Fer Diad eastwards.'

'I vow clearly, though I am not given to vaunting, that I shall be the one to triumph over the son of Damán mac Dáire.'

'It was I who, in requital for the wrong done me by the Ulster-man, collected and brought these forces to the east. With me the heroes and the warriors came from their own lands.'

'Were it not that Conchobar lies in his debility, our meeting would indeed be hard. Medb of Mag in Scáil has never come on a more uproarious march.'

'A greater deed now awaits your hand—to fight with Fer Diad mac Damáin.   Have with you, O Cú Chulainn, weapons harsh and hard and famed in song.'

After that, Cú Chulainn asked:
'Why have you come, master Fergus?''
'That is my message,' said Fergus.
'It is a happy augury,' said Cú Chulainn, 'that it was not someone else from among the men of Ireland who brought that message. But unless all the four provinces of Ireland join together (to attack me), I think nothing of a warning against the coming of a single warrior.'
Thereafter Fergus came back to his tent.
Concerning Cú Chulainn:
'What will you do tonight?' asked Láeg.
'What indeed?' said Cú Chulainn.
'Fer Diad will come against you freshly beautified, washed and bathed, with hair plaited and beard shorn, and the four provinces of Ireland will come with him to watch the fight.   I should like you to go to where you will get the same adorning, to the spot where Emer Fholtchaín is, to Cairthenn Clúana Da Dam in Slíab Fuait.'
So on that night Cú Chulainn came to that place and spent the night with his own wife.
His doings apart from that are not recorded here now, but those of Fer Diad.
Fer Diad came to his tent.   Sullen and dispirited were those in Fer Diad's tent that night.   They felt certain that when the two world champions met, they would both fall, or else that the result would be the fall of their own lord.   For it was no easy matter to encounter Cú Chulainn on the Foray.
That night great anxieties preyed upon Fer Diad's mind and kept him awake.   One great anxiety was the fear that he would lose all the treasures and the maid offered to him for engaging in single combat.   For if he did not fight that one man, he must fight with six warriors on the next day.   But there weighed upon him a greater anxiety than all that: he was sure that if he once appeared before Cú Chulainn on the ford, he would no longer have power over his own body or soul.
And Fer Diad arose early on the morrow.
'My lad,' said he, 'harness our horses and yoke the chariot.'
'On my word,' said the charioteer, 'it is no more advisable for us to go on this expedition than not to go at all.'

15

As Fer Diad spoke to the charioteer, he made this little song to urge him on:

'Let us go to this encounter, to contend with this man, until we reach that ford above which the war-goddess will shriek. Let us go to meet Cú Chulainn, to wound his slender body, so that a spear-point may pierce him and he may die thereof.'

'It were better for us to stay here. The threats ye will exchange will not be mild. There will be one to whom sorrow will come. Your fight will be short. An encounter with a fosterling of the Ulstermen is one from which harm will come. It will long be remembered. Woe to him who goes on that course!'

'What you say is wrong, for diffidence does not become a warrior. You must not show timidity. We shall not stay here for you. Be silent, lad! We shall presently be brave, for stoutness of heart is better than cowardice. Let us go to the encounter.'

The charioteer harnessed the horses and prepared the chariot, and they drove forward out of the camp.

'My lad,' said Fer Diad, 'it is not right for us to go without bidding farewell to the men of Ireland. Turn back the horses and chariot to face the men of Ireland.'

Three times the charioteer turned horses and chariot to face the men of Ireland. Medb was urinating on the floor of the tent.

'Is Ailill asleep now?' asked Medb.

'No indeed,' said Ailill.

'Do you hear your new son-in-law bidding you farewell?'

'Is that what he is doing?' asked Ailill.

'It is indeed,' said Medb. 'But I swear my people's oath that he who is so bidding you farewell will not return to you on his own feet.'

'Because of what we have gained by this marriage,' said Ailill, 'we care not if both of them fall, provided that Cú Chulainn is killed by him. But indeed we should be the better pleased if Fer Diad escaped.'

Fer Diad came forward to the ford of combat.

'Look and see, lad, if Cú Chulainn is at the ford.' said Fer Diad.

'He is not,' said the charioteer.

'Look closely for us,' said Fer Diad.

'Cú Chulainn is no small hidden trifle, wherever he might be.' said the charioteer.

'That is so, driver. Until today Cú Chulainn never heard of a brave warrior or a noble opposing him on the Foray, and when he did hear of one, he went from the ford.'

'It is shameful to revile him in his absence, for do you remember how ye both fought against Germán Garbglas above the shores of the Tyrrhene Sea and you left your sword with the enemy hosts, and how Cú Chulainn slew a hundred warriors to get it back for you, and how he gave it to you?   And do you remember where we were that night?'

'I do not know,' said Fer Diad.

'We were in the house of Scáthach's steward,' said the charioteer, 'and you were the first of us to go eagerly and proudly into the house.   The churlish fellow struck you in the small of your back with the three-pronged fork and pitched you out the door.   Cú Chulainn came in and struck the fellow with his sword and clove him in twain.   As long as ye remained in that stead, I acted as your steward.   If it were that day now, you would not say that you were a better warrior than Cú Chulainn.'

'You have done wrong (not to speak before this), driver,' said Fer Diad, 'for if you had told me that at first, I should not have come to the fight.   Why do you not pull the shafts of the chariot under my side and the skin-coverings beneath my head that I may sleep a while?'

'Alas!' said the charioteer, 'such a sleep is the sleep of a doomed one faced by stag and hounds.'

'Why then, driver, are you not capable of keeping watch for me?'

'I am,' said the driver, 'and unless they come out of the clouds and the air to attack you, none shall come from east or from west to fight with you without due warning.'

The shafts of his chariot were pulled beneath his side, and his skin-coverings placed under his head, and yet he slept not at all.

Now as regards Cú Chulainn:

'Good, my friend Láeg, harness the horses and prepare the chariot. If Fer Diad is awaiting us, he will deem it long.'

The charioteer arose.   He harnessed the horses and he yoked the chariot.   Cú Chulainn mounted the chariot and they drove forward towards the ford.

As for Fer Diad's charioteer, he was not long on the watch when he heard the rumble of a chariot approaching them.   As he awoke his master, he made this lay:

'I hear the sound of a chariot with fair yoke of silver. (I perceive) the form of a man of great size, rising above the front of the strong chariot.

'Past Broinfeirste Broine they advance along the road, past the side of Baile in Bile. Victorious is their triumph.

'A plundering Hound drives, a bright chariot-fighter harnesses, a noble hawk lashes his steeds towards the south. I am certain that he will come . . . He will give us battle.

'Woe to him who is on the hill awaiting the worthy Hound. Last year I foretold that he would come at some time, the Hound of Emain Macha, the Hound with beauty of every colour, the Hound of spoils, the Hound of battle. I hear him and he hears (us).

A description of Cú Chulainn's chariot, one of the three principal chariots in story-telling, on the Foray of Cúailnge:

'How does Cú Chulainn look to you?' said Fer Diad to his charioteer.

'I see,' he answered, 'a beautiful roomy chariot of white crystal, with solid gold yoke, with great sides of copper, with shafts of bronze, with *lungeta* of white gold, with framework of narrow compact opening and fair awning, a framework in which heroic feats are displayed and which would hold seven sets of weapons fit for princes. Beautiful is the seat for its lord which that chariot contains, the chariot of Cú Chulainn which travels with the swiftness of a swallow or a great deer hastening across a plain on high ground, such is the speed and swiftness with which they drive for it is towards us they travel. That chariot is drawn by two horses with small round heads, round-eyed, prick-eared, broad-hoofed, red-chested, steady, splendid, easily harnessed . . . One of these horses is strong, swift-jumping, battlesome, with great hoofs and skittish . . The other horse has curling mane, narrow slender feet, small heels, . . . The chariot has two dark black wheels and there is a chariot-pole of bronze with enamel of beautiful colour. There are two ornamented golden bridles.

'In the chief place in that chariot is a man with long curling hair. He wears a dark purple mantle and in his hand he grasps a broad-headed spear, bloodstained, fiery, flaming. It seems as if he has three heads of hair, to wit, dark hair next to the skin of his head, blood-red hair in the middle and the third head of hair covering him like a crown of gold. Beautifully is that hair arranged, with three coils flowing down over his shoulders. Like golden thread whose colour has been hammered out on an anvil or like the yellow of bees in the sunshine of a summer day seems to me the gleam of each separate hair. Seven toes on each of his feet; seven fingers on each of his hands.[1] In his eyes the blazing of a huge fire. His horses' hoofs maintain a steady pace.

In front of him is a charioteer fully worthy of his master. He has curling jet-black hair, a great head of hair. He wears a full-skirted hooded cape with an opening at his elbows and a light-grey mantle. [2]In his hand he holds a beautiful golden horsewhip[2] with which he goads the horses along whatever road the valorous warrior[3] in the chariot travels . . .

And Fer Diad said to his charioteer:

'Arise, lad,' said Fer Diad. 'Too highly do you extol that man. Prepare the weapons for our encounter with him at the ford.'

'If I were to turn my face in the direction to which my back is now turned, I think that the shafts of the chariot would pierce the nape of my neck.'

'O lad,' said Fer Diad, 'too highly do you extol Cú Chulainn, for he has not given you a reward for your praise.'

And as he described him, he said:

'It is time now for help for this is no deed of friendship (?). Be silent. Do not praise him for he is no overhanging doom. If you see the hero of Cúailnge with his proud feats, then he shall be dealt with by us. Since it is for reward, he shall soon be destroyed.'

'If I see the hero of Cúailnge with his proud feats, he does not flee from us but towards us he comes. Though skilful, he is not grudging. For his excellence we praise him. He runs and not slowly but like the swift thunderbolt.'

'So greatly have you praised him that it is almost ground for a quarrel. Why have you chosen him (for praise) since he came forth from his dwelling? Now they are challenging him and attacking him, and only cowardly churls come to attack him.'

Not long afterwards they met in the middle of the ford, and Fer Diad said to Cú Chulainn:

'Where do you come from, Cúa?'

---

[1] A warrior's grasp in his hands (gloss)

[2]–[2] In his hand a goad of white silver (alternative reading incorporated in text)

[3] He is his friend (gloss, incorporated in text)

For *cúa* is the word for squinting in old Irish and Cú Chulainn had seven pupils in his royal eyes, two of which were asquint. But this was more an adornment than a disfigurement to Cú Chulainn, and if he had had a greater bodily blemish, Fer Diad would undoubtedly have taunted him with that. And as Fer Diad proclaimed this, he made a lay and Cú Chulainn made answer until the lay was ended.

'Whence do you come, O Cúa, to fight with fresh strength? Your flesh will be blood-red above the steam of your horses. Woe to him who comes as you do, for it will be as vain as the kindling of a fire with one stick of firewood. You will be in need of healing if you reach your home again.'

'I have come, a wild boar of troops and herds, before warriors, before battalions, before hundreds, to thrust you beneath the waters of the pool. In anger against you and to prove you in a many-sided encounter, so that harm may come to you as you defend your life.'

'How shall we meet? Shall we groan over corpses as we meet at the ford? Shall it be with strong spear-points or with hard swords that you will be slain before your hosts if your time has come?

'Before sunset, before nightfall, if you are in straits ... When you meet with Boirche, the battle will be bloody. The Ulstermen are calling you. They have taken you unawares (?) Evil will be the sight for them. They will be utterly defeated.'

'You have come to the gap of danger. The end of your life is at hand. Sharp weapons will be wielded on you. It will be no gentle purpose. A great champion will slay (you). Two shall meet in conflict. You shall not be the leader of even three men from now until doomsday.

'When we were with Scáthach, by dint of our wonted valour we would fare forth together and traverse every land. You were my loved comrade, my kith and kin. Never found I one dearer to me. Sad will be your death.

'Leave off your warning. You are the most boastful man on earth. You shall have neither reward nor remission for you are no outstanding hero. Well I know that you are but a nervous lad, you with the heart of a fluttering bird, without valour, without vigour.

'Too much do you neglect your honour that we may not do battle, but before the cock crows your head will be impaled on a spit. O Cú Chulainn of Cúailnge, frenzy and madness have seized you. All evil shall come to you from us, for yours is the guilt.'

Then Cú Chulainn asked his charioteer to urge him on when he was overcome and to praise him when he was victorious fighting against his opponent. So his charioteer said to him:

'Your opponent goes over you as a tail goes over a cat. He belabours you as flax-heads (?) are beaten in a pond. He chastises you as a fond woman chastises her son.'

Then they betook themselves to the 'ford-feat,' and did all that Scáthach had taught both of them. They performed wonderful feats.

After that Cú Chulainn leapt on to Fer Diad's shield, and Fer Diad cast him off three times into the ford, so that the charioteer kept on inciting him once more. Cú Chulainn swelled and grew big as a bladder does when inflated. His size increased so that he was bigger than Fer Diad.

'Look out for the *gai bulga*!' cried the charioteer and cast it to him downstream. Cú Chulainn caught it between his toes and cast it at Fer Diad into his anus. It was as a single barb it entered but it became twenty-four (in Fer Diad's body). Thereupon Fer Diad lowered his shield. Cú Chulainn struck him with the spear above the shield, and it broke his ribs and pierced Fer Diad's heart.

'Strong is the spear-shaft cast by your right hand. My ribs like spoils are broken; my heart is gore. Well did I fight, but I have fallen, O Cúa!'

'Alas, O noble warrior! O brave Fer Diad! O strong and beautiful smiter, your arm was victorious.'

'Our friendship was fair, O delight of my eyes! Your shield had a golden rim. Your sword was beautiful.

'Your ring of white silver on your noble hand. Your chess-set of great worth. Your cheeks were rosy and beautiful.

'Your curling yellow hair was thick—a fair jewel. Your girdle, supple and ornamented, you wore around your side.

'Alas! my loved one, that you should fall at the hand of Cú Chulainn! Your shield which you wore against force afforded you no protection.

'Our fight . . . our sorrow, the din of our battle. Fine was the great champion. Every army was defeated and trampled underfoot. Alas! O noble warrior, Fer Diad!

'All was play and pleasure until I met with Fer Diad in the ford. Alas for the noble champion laid low there at the ford.

'All was play and sport until I met with Fer Diad at the ford. I thought that beloved Fer Diad would live after me for ever.'

While the enemy hosts were going south from Áth Fir Diad, Cú Chulainn lay there wounded until Senoll Úathach came to him ahead of the others and Senoll was there with the two Meic Ḟice. They brought Cú Chulainn back to the streams of Conaille Muirthemne to heal and bathe his wounds therein.

These are the names of those rivers: Sás, Buan Bithshlán, Finnglas, Gleóir, Bedg, Tadg, Talaméd, Rind, Bir, Breinide, Cumang, Cellend, Gaenemain, Dichu, Muach, Miliuc, Den, Delt, Dubglaise.

While Cú Chulainn went to bathe in those rivers, the army went south past him and made their encampment at Imorach Smiromrach. Mac Roth left the army and went north to watch out for the men of Ulster, and he came to Slíab Fúait to find out if he might see anyone pursuing them. He told them that he saw only one chariot.

The Chief Episodes of the Táin

The Hard Fight of Cethern mac Fintain, the Tooth-fight of Fintan, the Red Shame of Mend, the Bloodless Fight of Rochad, the Humorous Fight of Iliach, the Missile-throwing of the Charioteers, the Trance of Aimirgin, the Repeated Warning of Súaltaim, the

Mustering of the Ulstermen, the Trance of Dubthach, the Trance of Cormac Con Longes, the Array of the Companies, the Final Decision in Battle, the Fight of the Bulls, the Adventures of Dub Cúailnge on the Foray.

The Hard Fight of Cethern

'I see a chariot coming across the plain from the north today,' said Mac Roth, 'and (in the chariot) a grey-haired man, unarmed except for a silver spike which he holds in his hand. It seems as if the mist of May surrounds the chariot. With the spike he pricks both charioteer and horses, for he thinks he will scarcely reach the host alive. Before him runs a brindled hunting-dog.'

'Who is that, Fergus?' asked Ailill. 'Is it likely to be Conchobar or Celtchair?'

'It is not likely,' said Fergus. 'But I think it might be Cethern, the generous, red-sworded son of Fintan.'

And so indeed it was.

Then Cethern attacked them throughout the encampment and killed many. And he himself was grievously wounded and came from the fighting to Cú Chulainn, with his entrails lying about his feet. Cú Chulainn had compassion on him for his wounding.

'Get me a physician,' said Cethern to Cú Chulainn.

A litter-bed of fresh rushes with a pillow on it was prepared for him. Then Cú Chulainn sent Láeg to Fiacha mac Fir Febe in the encampment of the banished Ulstermen to seek physicians, and said that he would kill them all even if they were to take refuge underground in the encampment unless they came to him to cure Cethern. The physicians found this no pleasant prospect for there was none in the camp whom Cethern would not wound. However the physicians came forth to see Cethern.

The first physician who came to him examined him.

'You will not live,' said he.

'Neither will you,' said Cethern, and struck him a blow with his fist which caused his brains to gush out over his ears. In the same way he killed fifty physicians, or he killed fifteen of them. The last man received only a glancing blow which caused him to swoon. He was later rescued by Cú Chulainn.

They sent messengers then to Fíngin, the seer-physician, Conchobar's own physician, asking him to come and examine Cú Chulainn and Cethern.

'It is not right for you,' said Cú Chulainn to Cethern, 'to kill the physicians. It will not be possible to get any (more) of them to come to you.'

'It was not right for them to give me a bad prognosis.'

For each physician who examined him used to say that he would not live, that he was not curable, so then Cethern used to strike him with his fist.

They saw Fíngin's chariot approaching, for he had been told that Cú Chulainn and Cethern were in distress.

Cú Chulainn went to meet him.

'Examine Cethern for us,' said Cú Chulainn, 'but do so from a distance, for he has killed fifteen of their physicians.'

Fíngin came to Cethern. He examined him from afar off.

'Examine me,' said Cethern. 'This first thrust that I received I find painful.'

'Those are wounds inflicted by a proud and foolish woman,' said Fíngin.

'It is likely that it is so,' said Cethern. 'There came to me a tall beautiful woman with pale, tender face and long cheeks. She had long fair hair and two golden birds on her shoulder. She wore a dark purple hooded mantle. On her back she carried a shield five hands in breadth and overlaid with gold. In her hand a javelin, keen, sharp-edged and light. A sword with pointed hilt across her shoulders. Great was her beauty. She it was who first came to me and wounded me.'

'Aye indeed,' said Cú Chulainn. 'That was Medb from Crúachu.'

'These are slight wounds inflicted unwillingly by a kinsman. They will not prove fatal,' said the physician.

'That is so,' said Cethern. 'A warrior came to me. He carried a curved shield with scalloped rim. In his hand a spear with bent point, across his shoulders an ivory-hilted sword. He had a crest of hair and wore a brown cloak in which was a silver pin wrapped about him. He got a slight wound from me.'

'I know him,' said Cú Chulainn. 'That was Illann, the son of Fergus mac Róig.'

'This is the attack of two warriors,' said the physician.

'That is true,' said Cethern. 'Two men came to me. They bore long shields, each with two hard chains of silver and a silver boss. They had two five-pronged spears round which was a silver ring. They had thick heads of hair and each man wore a necklet of silver.'

'I know them,' said Cú Chulainn. 'Those were Oll and Oichne, the two foster-sons of Ailill and Medb. They never go to an assembly but that they are sure to kill someone. It was they who wounded you.'

'Two other warriors came to me,' said Cethern. 'They had splendid bright equipment and they themselves were manly.'

'I know them,' said Cú Chulainn. 'Those were Bun and Mecon of the king's household.'

'These wounds are grave,' said the physician. 'They have gone right through your heart and pierced it tranversely. I cannot undertake to heal them. Yet I have such skill that they may not prove fatal.'

'This is the bloody onset of the two sons of the King of Caill,' said the physician.

'That is true,' said Cethern. 'There came to me two grey-haired warriors, each carrying a wooden vessel on his back. Indeed,' said Cethern, 'this spear pierced one of them.'

'I know them,' said Cú Chulainn. 'They were noble warriors from Medb's great household. They were Bróen and Láiréne, the two sons of three lights, the two sons of the King of Caill.'

'This is the attack of three warriors,' said Fíngin, the physician.

'That is true,' said he. 'There came to me three men of equal size, linked together with a chain of bronze . . .'

'Those were the three warriors of Banba, followers of Cú Raí mac Dáire.'

'This is the onset of three champions,' said Fíngin.

'That is true,' said he. 'Three champions came to me bearing the equipment of warriors. Each had a silver chain around his neck and carried a handful of javelins. Each man of them thrust a spear into me, and I thrust this spear into each of them.'

'Those were three of the warriors of Irúath,' said Cú Chulainn.

'For their fierceness they were chosen to kill you,' said the physician. 'Indeed they have severed the sinews of your heart within you so that it rolls about in you like a ball of thread in an empty bag.'

'I cannot cure (you) (?),' said Fíngin.

'This is the attack of three bloody-minded men,' said Fíngin.

'That is so,' said Cethern. 'Three tall stout men came to me. They were inciting me even before they reached me. They had three grey heads of hair.'

'Those were the three stewards of Medb and Ailill, Scenb and Rand and Fodail,' said Cú Chulainn.

'These are three hostile blows,' said Fíngin.

'True,' said Cethern. 'Three warriors came to me. Each had a head of thick black hair and wore a vari-coloured cape. They carried in their hands three iron clubs.'

'Those were the three called Fráech Baíscne, the three table-servants of Medb,' said Cú Chulainn.

'This is the attempt of two brothers,' said Fíngin.

'That is true,' said Cethern. 'There came to me two choice warriors. They wore dark-grey mantles and carried curved shields with scalloped rim. Each had in his hand a broad shining spear on a slender shaft.'

'I know them,' said Cú Chulainn. 'They were Cormac Colomon ind Ríg, and Cormac Maíle Ogath.'

'Numerous indeed are the wounds they both inflicted on you,' said the physician. 'They have pierced your throat and their spears moved about within you.'

'These are the wounds inflicted by two brothers,' said the physician.

'That is likely,' said Cethern. 'Two warriors came to me. One had curling yellow hair, the other curling brown hair. They bore white shields ornamented with animal designs in gold. Each had a white-hilted sword across his shoulder. They wore hooded tunics with red insertion.'

'I know them,' said Cú Chulainn. 'Those were Maine Aithremail and Maine Máithremail.'

'These are the thrusts delivered by father and son,' said the physician.

'That is so,' said Cethern. 'There came to me two huge men with shining eyes, wearing golden diadems on their heads. Each man had at his waist a golden-hilted sword. Scabbards reaching to the haft of each sword and a ring[1] of variegated gold around each.'

'I know them,' said Cú Chulainn. 'That was Ailill with his son, Maine Condasgeb Uile.'

'What prognosis do you give me, master Fíngin?' asked Cethern.

'In truth,' said Fíngin, 'you should not exchange your grown cows for yearlings now. As long as your attackers were numbered only in twos and threes, it were easy to cure you. But when you bear wounds inflicted by many, you are destined to die in any case,'

With that Fíngin turned the chariot away from him.

'You pronounce judgment on me like the rest,' (said Cethern).

So he struck Fíngin a blow of his fist so that he fell across the shafts of the chariot and the whole chariot resounded.

[1] reading Stowe

Then said Cú Chulainn:

'That is a wicked kick of yours for an old man (?).'

Hence is still the name Úachtar Lúa in Crích Rois.

'You should have attacked enemies rather than physicians,' said Cú Chulainn.

Then the physician Fíngin offered Cethern a choice: either to lie sick for a year and then survive, or straightaway to have sufficient strength for three days and three nights to attack his enemies. The latter is what Cethern chose.

Then Cú Chulainn asked for marrow for the physician to cure Cethern. He made a marrow-mash from the bones of the cattle he encountered. Hence the name Smirommair in Crích Rois.

After absorbing the marrow, Cethern slept for a day and a night.

'I have no ribs,' complained Cethern. 'Put the ribs of the chariot-frame in me.'

'You shall have that,' said Cú Chulainn.

'If I had my own weapons,' said Cethern, 'the deeds I should perform would be remembered for ever.'

'What I see now seems fine,' said Cú Chulainn.

'What do you see?' asked Cethern.

'I think it is the chariot of your wife Find Bec, the daughter of Eochu, coming towards us.'

They saw the woman bringing Cethern's weapons in the chariot.

Cethern seized his weapons and attacked the host then with the framework of his chariot bound to his belly to give him more strength.

That physician, who had escaped from Cethern and lain unconscious among the corpses of the other physicians now carried a warning of Cethern's arrival into the encampment.

Then through fear of Cethern, Ailill's crown was put upon the pillar-stone. Cethern rushed at the pillar-stone and drove his sword through it and his fist after the sword. Hence the place-name Lia Toll in Crích Rois.

'This is a trick!' he cried. 'I shall not cease to attack you until I see this diadem of Ailill on one of you.'

Then for a day and a night he attacked them, until Maine put the diadem on his head and came forward in his chariot. Cethern threw after Maine his shield which split him and his charioteer and went right through the horses into the ground.

Then the host hemmed Cethern in on all sides and he attacked them and fell dead among them so doing.

The Tooth-Fight of Fintan

Fintan came then to avenge his son's death on them. Thrice fifty armed men was the number of his company. They had two spear-heads on each shaft and they were wrapt in mantles. Fintan fought seven battles with the enemy and none of his men escaped, only he himself and his son. Then through fear of Fintan his son was separated from him and was rescued by Ailill under a shelter of shields on condition that Fintan should not attack them until he came with Conchobar to the great battle.

So Fintan made a truce with them for delivering his son to him.

The Red Shame of Mend

Then there came to them Mend mac Sálchada with a band of thirty armed men. Twelve of them fell at Mend's hand and twelve of his own people fell too. Mend himself was grievously wounded while his men were red with blood. Hence the name Ruadrucca Mind, the Red Shame of Mend.

Afterwards they evacuated the encampment for Mend and he killed no more of them save only the twelve. He was told that no guilt attached to them for they had not gone near his dwelling by the Boyne in Coirenna. For in fact it was no disgrace to yield the encampment to him until he should come with Conchobar to the great battle.

The Bloodless Fight of Rochad

Then there came to them Rochad Rigderg mac Faithemain of Ulster with thirty armed men. He took up his position on a hillock near them, and his arrival was announced in the encampment. Then Finnabair said that he was her first love.

'If you have loved him,' said Ailill and Medb, 'crave a truce of him until such time as he comes with Conchobar to the great battle, and spend tomorrow night with him.'

All this was done, though it was not easy to get him to come. Rochad's tent was pitched for him at the place called Finnabair, and he spent the night with the girl.

This was told to the seven kings from Munster. One of them said:

'I was promised this girl on the surety of fifteen men, in requital for coming on this hosting.'

Kiosk 3
James Hardiman Library
Issue Receipt

NUI Galway
OÉ Gaillimh

Thank You for using the self service system.
Please note the due date of your loan.

Customer ID: 00804E0E825D2804

Items that you have checked out

Title: T Hin b H C H ailnge
ID: 31111402979270
Due: !!21/06/2018 17:30:00 IST!!

Title:
Ulidia : proceedings of the First International
Conference on the Ulster Cycle of Tales,
Belfast and Emain Macha, 8-12 April 1994 /
ID: 31111300377776
Due: !!21/06/2018 17:30:00 IST!!

Title:
Excavations at Navan Fort 1961-71 : County
Armagh /
ID: 31111401879844
Due: !!31/03/2018 17:30:00 IST!!

Title: Navan Fort : archaeology and myth /
ID: 31111401755119
Due: !!31/03/2018 17:30:00 IST!!

Total items: 4
/03/2018 21:47

Users with outstanding fines or unreturned
books will not receive exam results

All seven of them confessed that the same bargain had been made with each of them. So they went to take revenge for it on the sons of Ailill in Glenn Domain where they were guarding the rear of the army.

Medb rushed to the rescue. So did the division of the Leinstermen. So too Ailill and Fergus. Seven hundred fell there in the battle of Glenn Domain.

That is Bángleó Rochada and Imślige Glenndomnach.

Finnabair heard of this, namely, that seven hundred men had died because of her. She fell dead there of shame. Hence the place-name Finnabair Sléibe.

The Humorous Fight of Iliach.

There came then to them at Áth Feidle Iliach, the grandfather of Lóegaire Búadach who was son of Connad Buide meic Iliach. Iliach was being cared for with filial piety by his grandson in Ráith Immail. He announced to the host that they would die at his hand in revenge.

So he came in this wise: in his shaky, worn-out chariot, without rugs or covering, drawn by two old sorrel nags. And he filled his chariot with stones as high as the skin-coverings.

He kept striking all those who came to gaze at him, stark-naked as he was, long-membered, with the *clapar* down through the frame of the chariot. Then the host noticed in what manner he came and they mocked the naked man. Dócha mac Mágach checked the jeering of the rabble. And for that Iliach told Dócha that at the day's end he, Dócha, should take Iliach's sword and strike his head off, provided only that Iliach had exerted all his strength against the host.

At that point Iliach noticed the marrow-mash. He was told that it had been made from the bones of the cows of Ulster. So then he made another marrow-mash from the bones of the men of Connacht beside it, so that the two marrow-mashes are there together.

Then in the evening Dócha struck off Iliach's head and carried it to his grandson. He made peace with him and Láegaire kept Iliach's sword.

That is Mellgleó Iliach, (so called) because the host laughed at him.

The Missile-throwing of the Charioteers

The army came to Tailtiu then. The charioteers of Ulster, in number thrice fifty, attacked them. Three times their own number fell by the charioteers, and they themselves fell.

Roí Arad is the name of the spot where they fell together with their tackle on the Foray.

The Trance of Aimirgin

This then is the trance of Aimirgin in Tailtiu. In his trance Aimirgin pelted them so that no man could be found to raise his head in Tailtiu.

Then came Cú Raí mac Dáire to the host to fight against Cú Chulainn. He was told how Cú Chulainn had opposed the men of Ireland single-handed during the three months of winter. Cú Raí thought it did not befit a man to attack one stabbed and wounded, for Cú Chulainn had been wounded and lost much blood. So then Cú Raí hurled stones directly against Aimirgin, instead of Cú Chulainn, and the stones collided in the air. Cú Raí asked Aimirgin to let the cattle go past Tailtiu. Aimirgin permitted it. However it was not to be wondered at that they were carried off with difficulty.

Cú Raí promised Aimirgin that he would not remain with the host from that time on. So it was done. Cú Raí went away from the host at once.

When Aimirgin saw that they challenged him by turning the left board of their chariots to Tailtiu and Ráith Airthir, he began once more to pelt them.

This is one of the three (slaughters) which cannot be counted, namely, the great number of them that he killed. And his son Conall Cernach remained by him, furnishing him with stones and darts.

The Repeated Warning of Súaltaim

While these events which we have related were taking place, Súaltaim from Ráith Súaltaim in Mag Muirthemne heard how his son had been harassed by the twelve sons of Gaile Dána and his sister's son. Then said Súaltaim:

'Is it the sky that cracks, or the sea that overflows its bounderies, or the earth that splits, or is it the loud cry of my son fighting against odds?'

Then he went to his son. But Cú Chulainn was not pleased that he should come to him, for though he was wounded, Súaltaim would not be strong enough to avenge him.

'Go to the men of Ulster,' said Cú Chulainn, 'and let them give battle to the warriors at once.   If they do not, vengeance will never be taken on them.'

Then his father saw that there was not on Cú Chulainn's body a spot which the tip of a rush could cover which was not pierced, and even his left hand which the shield protected bore fifty wounds. Súaltaim came to Emain and called out to the men of Ulster:

'Men are slain, women carried off, cattle driven away!'

His first shout was from the side of the court, his second from the ramparts of the royal residence, his third from the Mound of the Hostages in Emain.

No one answered, for it was tabu for the Ulstermen that any of them should speak before Conchobar, and Conchobar, spoke only before the three druids.

'Who carries them off?   Who drives them away?   Who slays them?' asked the druid.

'Ailill mac Máta slays them, carries them off, drives them away, with the guidance of Fergus mac Róig,' said Súaltaim.   'Your people have been harassed as far as Dún Sobairche.   Their cows, their women-folk and their cattle have been carried off.   Cú Chulainn has not let them come into Mag Muirthemne and Crích Rois during the three months of winter.   Bent hoops (of wood) hold his mantle (from touching him).   Dry wisps plug his wounds. He has been wounded and bled profusely (?).'

'It were right,' said the druid, 'that one who so incited the king should die.'

'It is right that he should,' said Conchobar.

'It is right,' said the Ulstermen.

'What Súaltaim says is true,' said Conchobar.   'From the Monday on the eve of Samain until the Monday on the eve of Spring we have been ravaged.'

Thereupon Súaltaim leapt forth, unsatisfied with the answer he had got, and he fell on to his shield and the scalloped rim of the shield cut off his head.   The horse brought his head on the shield back into Emain, and the head uttered the same words. —Though others say that he had been asleep on the stone and on waking had fallen from it on to his shield.

'Too loud was that shout indeed,' said Conchobar.   '(I swear by) the sea before them, the sky above them, the earth beneath them that I shall restore every cow to its byre and every woman and boy to their own homes after victory in battle.'

Then Conchobar laid an injunction on his son Findchad Fer Bend. —He was so called because he bore horns of silver.

16

The Muster of the Ulstermen

'Arise, O Findchad! I send you to Dedad in his inlet, to Leamain, to Fallach, to Illann mac Fergusa, to Gabar, to Dorlunsa, to Imchlár, to Feidlimid Cilair Cétaig, to Fáeladán, to Rochaid mac Faithemain at Rigdonn, to Lugaid, to Lugda, to Cathbath in his inlet, to the three Cairpres, to Aela, to Láeg at his causeway, to Geimen in his valley, to Senoll Úathach at Diabul Arda, to Cethern mac Fintain at Carlag, to Torathor, to Mulaig in his fortress, to the royal poet Aimirgin, to the Úathadach Fodoblaid, to the Mórrígan at Dún Sobairche, to Ieth, to Roth, to Fiachna at his mound, to Dam Dremed, to Andiaraid, to Maine mac Braitharge, to Dam Derg, to Mod, to Maithes, to Irmaithes, to Corp Cliath, to Gabarleig in Líne, to Eochaid Sainmech in Saimne, to Eochaid Lathach at Latharna, to Uma mac Remarbisi in Fedan, to Muinremur mac Gerrgind, to Senlobair at Canainn Gall, to Follamain, to Lugaid rí Fer mBolc, to Laige Líne, to Búaidgalach, to Ambúach, to Fergna, to Barrene, to Áine, to Errgi Echbél at his hill, to Celtchar mac Cuithechair in Lethglais, to Láegaire Milbél at Breo Láegairi, to the three sons of Dromscalt mac Dregamm, to Drenda, to Drendas, to Cimb, to Cimling, to Cimmene, to Fána Caba, to Fachtna mac Senchath in his rath, to Senchaid at Senchairthe, to Briccir, to Bricirne, to Breic, to Buan, to Bairech, to Óengus mac Leiti, to Fergus mac Leiti, to Óengus Fer mBolg, to Bruachur, to Alamiach the warrior at Slánge, to the three sons of Fiachna in Cúailnge, to Conall Cernach in Midlúachair, to Connad mac Morna in Callainn, to Cú Chulainn mac Súaltaim in Muirthemne, to Aimirgin at Eas Rúaid, to Lóeg, to Léiri, to Menn mac Salcholca at Coirenna, to Cú Rí mac Armargin in his rath, to Óengus Fer Benn Umai, to Ogma Grianainech, to Brecc, to Eo mac Oircne, to Toillchenn to Saithe, to Mogoll Echbél in Magna, to Conla Sáeb, to Úarba, to Láegaire Búadach in Immail, to Alile Amargine in Tailtiu, to Furbaide Fer Benn, to Seil, to Manes, to Cúscraid Menn Macha, to Fingin at Finngabra, to Cremath, to Blae Fichit, to Blae Brugaich, to Fesair, to Eógan mac Durthacht in Fernmag, to Ord, to Seirid, to Serthe, to Oblán, to Cuilén, to Curether at Liana, to Eithbenne, to Fernél, to Finnchath at Slíab Betha, to Talgobain at Bernas, to Menn mac Fer Calca, of Maig Dula, to Íroll, to Bláirige at Tibraite mac Ailchatha, to Ialla Ingraimme of Mag Dobla, to Ros mac Ailchatha, to Mane mac Cruinn, to Nindich mac Cruinn, to Dipsemilid, to Mál mac Rochraidi, to Muinne mac Munremair, to Fiatach Fer nDoirre mac Dubthaig, to Muirne Menn.

It was not difficult, however, for Findchad to deliver that summons, for all of the province of Conchobar, every lord among them, was awaiting Conchobar. All those who were east or north or west of Emain came now to Emain Macha. When they had assembled they heard that Conchobar had recovered from his debility in Emain. They went on past Emain to the south in pursuit of the (enemy) host.

The first stage of their journey was from Emain to Iraird Cuillenn.

'What are you waiting for here?' asked Conchobar.

'We are waiting for your sons,' said the host. 'They have gone with a company of soldiers to Tara to seek Erc, the son of Cairbre Nia Fer and of Feidelm Noíchride. We shall not leave this spot, until the two companies come to join us.'

'I shall not wait, indeed,' said Conchobar, 'until the men of Ireland learn that I have recovered from the debility in which I have been.'

So Conchobar and Celtchair went off with thrice fifty chariot fighters, and brought back eight score (enemy) heads from Áth Airthir Mide. Hence the name Áth Féne. These men had been there keeping guard against Conchobar's army. Their share of the booty was eight score women. Their heads were brought there and Conchobar and Celtchair sent them to the encampment.

Then Celtchair said to Conchobar:

'Ramparts with bloodstained sides and a valorous king ... with spoils of war ... On Conchobar's behalf we prepare for battle. His warriors rouse themselves. Battle will be fought (?) at Gáirech and Irgáirech,' said he.

—Or it may have been Cúscraid Menn Macha, the son of Conchobar, who chanted this song of exhortation on the night before the great battle, after Lóegaire Búadach had chanted his song: 'Arise, kings of Macha. Be on your guard etc.', and it may have been sung in the eastern encampment.

That was the night when Dubthach Dóel Ulad saw a vision in which the army stood at Gáirech and Irgáirech, and in his trance he spoke:

The Vision of Dubthach

'A wonderful morning for a battle, a wonderful time when armies will be thrown into confusion, kings will be overthrown, men's necks will be broken and the sand will be red with blood. Three armies will be overcome in the wake of the army led by Conchobar.

They will defend their womenfolk. Their herds will come on the morning after. Heroes will be slain. Hounds will be checked. Horses will be destroyed . . . from the assemblies of great tribes.'

Thereupon he awoke from his trance.

The war-goddess attacked the host. A hundred of them fell dead. When they fell silent (?) they heard Cormac Con Longes once more—Or it may have been Ailill mac Máta chanting in the encampment in the west.

The Trance of Ailill

'Great is the truce, the truce of Cuillenn. Great the parleys, the parleys of Delend. Great the cavalcades (?), the cavalcades of Asal. Great the afflictions, the afflictions of Túath Bressi.'

The March of the Companies

Now while these prophetic visions were happening the men of Connacht, on the advice of Ailill and Medb and Fergus, decided to send messengers to see if the men of Ulster had reached the plain.

Then said Ailill:

'Go, Mac Roth, and find out for us if those men are in this plain of Meath where we now are, I have carried off their cattle and their prey. They will give me battle if they so wish. But if they have not reached the plain, I shall not await them here any longer.'

So Mac Roth went to reconnoitre the plain. He returned again to Ailill and Medb and Fergus. The first time Mac Roth gazed into the distance around Slíab Fúait, he saw that all the wild beasts had come out of the wood into the whole plain.

'The second time I looked out over the plain,' said Mac Roth, 'I saw that a dense mist had filled the glens and valleys, so that the hills between them rose up like islands in lakes. Then I saw sparks of fire flashing in that dense mist, and I seemed to see the variegation of every colour in the world. Then I saw the lightning and I heard the din and the thunder, and I felt a great wind which almost blew the hair from my head and threw me on my back, and yet the wind that day was not strong.'

'What was that, Fergus?' said Ailill. 'Identify it.'

'It is not hard for me to recognize what it is,' said Fergus. 'Those are the men of Ulster now recovered from their debility. It was they who rushed into the wood. It was the multitiude, the greatness and the violence of the warriors that shook the wood. It is from them the wild beasts fled into the plain. The dense mist you saw which filled the valleys was the breath of those champions which filled the glens and made the hills to rise among them like islands in lakes. The lightning and the flashes of fire and the varied colours that you saw, Mac Roth', said Fergus, 'were the eyes of the warriors flashing in their heads like sparks of fire. The thunder and the din and the great uproar that you heard, that was the whistling of swords and ivory-hilted rapiers, the clatter of weapons the creaking of chariots, the hoof-beats of the horses, the might of the chariot-fighters the loud roaring of the warriors, the shouts of the soldiers, the ardour and anger and fierceness of the heroes as they rushed in fury to battle. So great is their anger and excitement that they think they will never arrive.'

'We shall await them,' said Ailill. 'We have warriors to encounter them.'

'You will need them,' said Fergus. 'For not in all Ireland nor in the western world from Greece and Scythia westwards to the Orkneys and the Pillars of Hercules and to Tor Breogain and the Islands of Gades,' will anyone be found who can withstand the men of Ulster when they are in their rage and anger.'

After that Mac Roth went once more to survey the march of the men of Ulster and came to their encampment in Slemain Mide. He came back to Ailill and Medb and Fergus, and gave them a detailed description, and describing them he spoke as follows:

'There came on to the hill at Slemain Mide,' said Mac Roth, 'a great company, fierce, powerful, proud. I think that it numbered three thousand. At once they cast off their garments and dug up a turfy mound as a seat for their leader. A warrior, fair, slender, tall, pleasant, led that company. Fairest in form among kings was he. He had yellow hair, curled, well-arranged, trimmed and wavy, which reached to the hollow between his shoulders. He wore a purple mantle wrapped about him with a beautful brooch of red gold in the mantle over his breast. He had shining, beautiful eyes. His countenance was crimson and comely, narrow below, broad above. He had a forked beard, very curly, golden-yellow. He wore a white hooded tunic with red insertion. Across his shoulders he had a gold-hilted sword, and he carried a white shield with animal designs in gold. In his hand he held a broad shining spear on a slender shaft. His array was the finest of all the princes of the world, alike as regards followers and fierceness and beauty, equipment and garments, as regards terror and battle and triumph, prowess and fearsomeness and dignity.'

'There came too another company,' said Mac Roth. 'They were almost the same as the other in numbers and arrangement and equipment, in dreadfulness and fearsomeness. A fair heroic warrior in the van of that company. A green cloak wrapped about him and a golden brooch on his shoulder. He had yellow curling hair. He carried an ivory-hilted sword at his left side. He wore a bordered (?) tunic reaching to his knee. He carried a smiting shield with scalloped rim. In his hand a spear like a palace torch with a silver band around it which runs now back from shaft to spearhead, now down again to the grip. That company took up position on the left hand of the leader of the first band. And the position they took was with knee to ground and shield-rim held to chin. It seemed to me that the tall haughty warrior who led that band stammered in his speech.

'There came yet another band,' said Mac Roth. 'It looked to be more than three thousand. A valiant man, handsome and broad headed, was in the van. He had brown curling hair and a long, forked, fine-haired beard. A dark-grey fringed cloak was wrapped about him, with a leaf-shaped brooch of white gold over his breast. He wore a white hooded tunic reaching to his knee. He carried a variegated shield with animal designs. A sword of bright silver with rounded hilt at his waist, and a five-pronged spear in his hand. He sat down in front of the leader of the first company.'

'Who were those, Fergus?' asked Ailill.

'We know those companies indeed,' said Fergus. 'It was Conchobar, the king of a province in Ireland, who sat down on the mound of turf. It was Sencha mac Ailella, the eloquent speaker of Ulster, who sat down in front of Conchobar. It was Cúscraid Menn Macha, Conchobar's son, who sat at his father's hand. That spear which Cúscraid has is wont to behave thus before victory; at no other time does the ring run (up and down). Those who came there were goodly men to inflict wounds in the attack of every conflict,' added Fergus.

'They will find men to answer them here,' said Medb.

'I swear by my people's god,' said Fergus, 'that until now there has not been born in Ireland an army which could ever check the Ulstermen.'

'There came still another company,' said Mac Roth, 'in number more than three thousand. In the van was a tall, valiant warrior, hideous, fearsome, swarthy and with fiery countenance. He had dark brown hair which lay smooth and fine over his forehead. He carried a curved shield with scalloped rim. In his hand he had a five-pronged spear and with it a pronged javelin. He bore across his back a bloodstained sword. Around him was wrapped a purple mantle with a golden brooch on his shoulder. He wore a white hooded tunic reaching to his knee.'

'Who was that, Fergus?' asked Ailill.

'He who came there is the starting of strife, a warrior for conflict, the doom of enemies, to wit, Eógan mac Durrthacht, King of Farney,' said Fergus.

'Another great, haughty band came on to the hill in Slemain Mide,' said Mac Roth. 'They cast off their garments. In truth they marched valiantly to the hill. Great the horror and vast the fear they brought with them. Terrible the clatter of arms they made as they marched. In the van of the company a man, big-headed, valiant, heroic, fierce and hideous. He had fine grizzled hair and great yellow eyes. A yellow mantle with a white border wrapped around him. Outside this he carried a smiting shield with scalloped rim. In his hand he held a spear, broad-bladed and long-headed with a drop of blood on its shaft, and a similar spear with the blood of enemies along its edge. A great smiting sword across his shoulders.'

'Who was that, Fergus?' asked Ailill.

'The warrior who came there shuns not battle nor conflict nor contest. It was Lóegaire Búadach mac Connaid meic Iliach from Immail in the north,' said Fergus.

'Another great company came to the hill in Slemain Mide,' said Mac Roth. 'A handsome warrior, thick-necked, corpulent, led that company. He had black curling hair and he was swarthy-faced with ruddy cheeks. Shining grey eyes in his head. He wore a dun-coloured mantle of curly wool in which was a brooch of white silver. He carried a black shield with boss of bronze, and in his hand he held a shimmering perforated (?) spear. He wore a plaited tunic with red insertion. Outside his garments he carried an ivory-hilted sword.'

'Who was that, Fergus?' asked Ailill.

'He who came is the stirring up of strife. He is the stormy wave which overwhelms streamlets. He is the man of three shouts. He is the threatening doom of enemies,' said Fergus. 'That was Munremur mac Gerrcind from Modorn in the north.'

'There came still another great company to the hill in Slemain Mide,' said Mac Roth. 'A company beautiful and splendid in numbers and arrangement and equipment. Proudly they made for the hill. The clatter of arms they made as they advanced shook the whole army. A handsome and noble warrior led that company. Most beautiful of men was his appearance, alike for hair and eyes and skin, alike for equipment and appearance, and voice and fairness, for dignity, size and honour, for arms and excellence and for garments and weapons and proportion, for worth and wisdom and lineage.'

'That is his (exact) description,' said Fergus. 'That handsome man Feidlimid who came there is the brilliance of fire, the proud hero, the stormy wave which engulfs, the force, which cannot be endured, with victories in other lands after he has slaughtered his enemies (at home). That was Feidlimid Cilair Cétaig.'

'There came still another band to the hill in Slemain Mide,' said Mac Roth, 'no fewer than three thousand in number. In the front of the band a tall, valiant warrior, of dusky complexion, well-proportioned ... He had black curling hair, round eyes, dull and haughty in his head. He was a strong, bull-like, rough man. He wore a grey mantle with a silver pin on his shoulder, and a white hooded tunic was wrapped around him. He carried a sword on his thigh and bore a red shield with a boss of hard silver. In his hand was a broad-bladed spear with three rivets.'

'Who was that, Fergus?' asked Ailill.

'He who came there is the fierce ardour of anger, the one who dares (?) every conflict, who wins every battle. That was Connad mac Mornai from Callann,' said Fergus.

'There came still another company to the hill in Slemain Mide,' said Mac Roth. 'In size it appears an army. Not often is found a hero finer in form and equipment and garments than the leader in the van of that company. He had trimmed auburn hair. His face was comely, ruddy, well-proportioned, a face narrow below and broad above. His lips were red and thin, his teeth shining and pearl-like, his voice loud and clear. His was the most beautiful of the forms of men. He wore a purple mantle wrapped around him with a brooch inlaid with gold over his white breast. On his left side a curved shield with animal emblems in many colours and a boss of silver. In his hand a long spear with shining edge and a sharp, aggressive dagger. On his back a sword with golden hilt. A tunic, hooded and with red insertion, wrapped about him.'

'Who was that, Fergus?' asked Ailill.

'We know him indeed,' said Fergus. 'He who came there is indeed a worthy adversary, he is the dividing of a combat, he is the fierce ardour of a blood-hound. That was Rochaid mac Faithemain from Brig Dumae, your son-in-law, he who wedded your daughter Finnabair.'

'There came still another company to the hill in Slemain Mide,' said Mac Roth. 'A warrior brawny-legged, thick-thighed and tall in the forefront of that company. Each of his limbs was almost as thick as a man. In truth he was every inch a man,' said he. 'He had black hair and a ruddy, scarred countenance. A noble eye of many colours in his head. A splendid, eager man was he thus with fearsomeness and horror. He had wonderful equipment in clothes and weapons and raiment and splendour and attire . . . with the triumphant exploits of a warrior, with splendid deeds, with eager pride, avoiding equal combat to vanquish overwhelming numbers, with fierce anger towards enemies, attacking many enemy lands without protection (?). In truth the company came boldly to Slemain Mide.'

'He had (?) valour and prowess indeed,' said Fergus, 'he had (?) hot-bloodedness and violence, strength and diginity in the armies and troops. It was my own foster-brother, Fergus mac Leiti, King of Líne, the point of perfection in battle in the north of Ireland.'

'There came another great, haughty company to the hill in Slemain Mide,' said Mac Roth. 'They wore wonderful garments. A handsome, noble warrior in the van. He had every endowment of beauty in hair and eyes and fairness, in size and demeanour and proportion. He carried a shield made of five concentric circles of gold. He wore a green mantle wrapped about him with a golden brooch in the mantle above his shoulder, and a white hooded tunic. A spear like the turret of a royal palace in his hand, a gold-hilted sword across his shoulders.'

'Fierce is the anger of the victorious hero who came there,' said Fergus. 'That was Amorgene mac Eccetsalaig from Búas in the north.'

'There came another company on to the hill in Slemain Mide,' said Mac Roth, 'in size like the overwhelming sea, in brightness like fire, in fierceness like a lion, in numbers a battalion, in greatness like a cliff, in strength like a rock, in combativeness like doom, in violence like thunder. A coarse-visaged, fearsome warrior in the forefront of that company, big-bellied, thick-lipped, big-nosed, red-limbed, with coarse grizzled hair. He wore a striped cloak pinned with an iron stake, and carried a curved shield with scalloped rim. He wore a rough plaited tunic and in his hand he held a great grey spear with thirty rivets. Across his shoulders he carried a sword tempered seven times by fire. All the army rose up to meet him and the host was thrown into confusion as he went towards the hill.'

'He who came there is the leader of battle,' said Fergus. 'He is a worthy adversary. He is a hero in prowess. He is (like) a stormy wave which overwhelms. He is (like) the sea pouring across boundaries. That was Celtchair mac Cuithechair from Dún Lethglaise in the north.'

'There came still another company to the hill in Slemain Mide,' said Mac Roth. 'A warrior, altogether fair led them. Fair in all points was he, hair and eyebrows and beard and clothing. He carried a shield with golden boss and a sword with ivory hilt. In his hand he had a great perforated spear. Bravely did the troop advance.'

'Splendid indeed is the strong-smiting hero who came there,' said Fergus, 'the valiant warrior who performs great deeds against enemies and destroys men! That was Feradach Find Fechtnach from Nemed Sléibe Fúait in the north.'

'There came still another company to the hill in Slemain Mide,' said Mac Roth. 'A fearsome warrior in front of that company, big-bellied, thick-lipped. His lips were as thick as those of a horse. He had brown curling hair, bright cheeks too, and a broad head and long arms. A black swinging mantle around him with a round brooch of bronze over his shoulder. A grey shield across his left side. A great spear with neck-rings in his right hand, a long sword across his shoulders.'

'He who came is (like) a lion fiercely combative with bloodstained paws,' said Fergus. 'He is the warlike, valorous hero of heroic deeds. He is (like) a fiery, unendurable blast of heat across the land. That was Eirrge Echbél from Brí Eirrge in the north,' said Fergus.

'There came still another company to the hill in Slemain Mide,' said Mac Roth, 'led by two fair, youthful warriors, both alike. They had yellow hair. They carried two white shields with animal designs in silver. A slight difference of age between them. Together they raised and set down their feet; it is not their wont for one to lift his foot before the other.

'Who are those, Fergus?' asked Ailill.

'Those are two warriors, two bright flames, two points of perfection in battle, two heroes, two combative chiefs, two dragons, two fiery ones, two champions, two fighters, two scions, two bold ones, the two beloved by the Ulstermen around their king. They are Fiachna and Fiacha, two sons of Conchobar mac Nesa, the two loved ones of the north of Ireland.'

'There came still another company to the hill in Slemain Mide,' said Mac Roth. 'At their head three noble, fiery swarthy-faced warriors. They had three heads of long yellow hair. Three mantles of the same colour wrapped about them with three golden brooches above their shoulders. They wore three . . . tunics with red insertion. They carried three similar shields, with golden-hilted swords across their shoulders and broad shining spears in their right hands. There was a slight difference of age between them.'

'Those are the three great champions of Cuib, the three valorous ones of Midlúachair, the three chiefs of Roth, the three veterans of Airther Fúata,' said Fergus. 'Those are the three sons of Fiachna who have come in purusit of the Bull, to wit, Rus and Dáire and Imchad,' said Fergus.

'There came still another company to the hill in Slemain Mide,' said Mac Roth. 'A fine and fierce man in the forefront. Red eyes full of courage in his head. A vari-coloured mantle around him in which was a circular brooch of silver. He carried a grey shield on his left side, a sword with silver hilt on his thigh, and in his avenging right hand a splendid spear with sharp points (?). He wore a white hooded tunic reaching to his knee. Around him was a company bloodstained and wounded, and he too was covered with blood and wounds.'

'That,' said Fergus, 'is the bold and ruthless one. He is the daring one (?) who rends. He is the boar (?) of battle. He is the mad bull. He is the victorious one from Baile, the valorous one from Bernas, the champion of Colptha, the protector of the north of Ireland, namely, Menn mac Sálchada from Coranna. It is to take vengeance on you for their wounds that that man has come.'

'There came still another company to the hill in Slemain Mide,' said Mac Roth, 'and they were heroic and eager. At their head a tall, sallow-faced, long-cheeked warrior. He had brown, bushy hair. He wore a red mantle of fine wool and a golden brooch in the mantle over his shoulder. He wore a fine tunic. On his left side he had a splendid sword with bright silver hilt. He carried a red shield and in his hand he held a broad shining spear on a beautiful shaft (?) of ash.

'It was the man of three stout blows who came there,' said Fergus, 'the man of three roads, the man of three paths, the man of three highways, the man of three triumphs, the man of three battle-cries who is victorious over foes in other lands. That was Fergna mac Findchoíme from Coronn.'

'There came still another company to the hill in Slemain Mide,' said Mac Roth. 'It appeared greater than three thousand in number. A handsome, fair-breasted warrior in the van of that company. He was like Ailill yonder in size and dignity, in dress and equipment. He wore a golden diadem on his head. A beautiful cloak was wrapped around him with a golden brooch in the cloak over his breast. He wore a tunic with red insertion. He carried a smiting shield with golden rims and in his hand a spear like the turret of a palace. Across his shoulders he had a gold-hilted sword.'

The man who came there is (like) the sea inundating rivers,' said Fergus. 'It is the fierce ardour of a warrior. His rage against his foes cannot be borne. That was Furbaide Fer Benn.'

'There came still another company to the hill in Slemain Mide, heroic, countless in number,' said Mac Roth. 'They wore strange garments unlike those of the other companies. Glorious were their weapons and their equipment and their raiment as they came. In this company was a great, proud army led by a little freckled lad. His form was the most beautiful of all men's forms. In his hand a white-bossed, gold-studded shield with rim of gold. He held a light sharp spear which shimmered. He was wrapped in a purple, fringed mantle, with a silver brooch in the mantle over his breast. He wore a white hooded tunic with red insertion and carried outside his garments a golden-hilted sword.'

Thereupon Fergus fell silent.

'Indeed I know not,' said Fergus, 'anyone like that little lad among the Ulstermen, but in fact I should think it likely that those might be the men of Tara with the fine, noble lad who is Erc, the son of Cairpre Nia Fer and of Conchobar's daughter ... Without asking permission of his father, that boy has come to the assistance of his grandfather. It is because of that lad that you will be defeated in battle. He will experience neither dread nor fear as he makes for you in the middle of your own army. Bravely will the warriors of Ulster roar as they hew down the army before them, rushing to rescue their beloved lad. They will all feel the ties of kinship when they see the boy in that great conflict. Like the baying of a blood-hound will be heard the sound of Conchobar's sword as he comes to the boy's rescue. Cú Chulainn will cast up three ramparts of (dead) men around the battle as he rushes towards that little lad. Mindful of their kinship with the boy, the warriors of Ulster will attack the vast (enemy) host.'

'I find it tedious,' said Mac Roth, 'to recount all that I saw, but I have come at any rate to bring you tidings.'

'You have (indeed) brought (tidings),' said Fergus.

'Conall Cernach, however, did not come with his great company,' said Mac Roth, 'nor did the three sons of Conchobar with their three divisions. Nor did Cú Chulainn come for he has been wounded fighting against odds. Except only that a single chariot-warrior who came there is probably he.

'The chariot was drawn by two strong-haunched steeds, with flowing tail and broad hoofs, broad in back and thin in flank, with head held high and arched neck, with thin mouth and flaring nostrils. Two black, firm (?) wheels, smooth easily-running rims, framework high and creaking and a green ornamented awning. There was a warrior, broad, ruddy-faced, in that chariot. He had a curly jet-black head of hair reaching to the hollow between his shoulders. He wore a red girded mantle. In each hand he carried four daggers and at his left side a gold-hilted sword. He had both shield and spear. He wore twenty-four shirts tied wth cords and ropes. In front of him was a charioteer whose back was turned to the horses and who held the reins between his fingers in front of him. A chess-board spread between the two, half the chessmen of yellow gold, the other half of white gold. His thighs rested on another boardgame, a *búanbach*. He cast nine feats aloft (?).'

'Who were those, Fergus?' asked Ailill.

'Easy to tell,' said Fergus. 'Those were Cú Chulainn the son of Súaltaim from the fairy mounds and Lóeg mac Riangabra, Cú Chulainn's charioteer.'

'Many hundreds indeed and many thousands,' said Mac Roth, 'came to this encampment of the Ulstermen. Many heroes and champions and warriors raced their horses to the assembly. Many more companies who had not arrived at the encampment when I (first) came were coming there now. But indeed wherever my eye fell on hill or height in all the space visible to me between Áth Fir Diad and Slemain Mide, I saw nothing save men and horses.'

'It was indeed a brave (?) company that you saw,' said Fergus.

Then Conchobar and his army went and made camp beside the others. He asked Ailill for a truce until sunrise on the morrow, and Ailill guaranteed it on behalf of the men of Ireland and the exiled Ulstermen while Conchobar guaranteed it for the men of Ulster. The [1]men of Ireland's[1] tents were pitched, and before sunset there was scarcely a bare patch of earth between them and [1]the encampment of the Ulstermen.[1]

Then the Mórrígan spoke in the dusk between the two encampments, saying:

1-1 translating conjectural emendation

'Ravens gnaw the necks of men. Blood flows. Battle is fought ... Hail to the men of Ulster! Woe to the Érainn! Woe to the men of Ulster! Hail to the Érainn!' These were the words she whispered to the Érainn: 'Woe to the men of Ulster for they have not won (?) the battle.'

Cú Chulainn was beside them in Fedain Collna. Food was brought to him from the hospitallers that night. They used to go and converse with him by day. He killed no one north of Áth Fhir Diad.

'See a little flock coming from the western encampment to the encampment in the east,' said the charioteer to Cú Chulainn, 'and see a band of youths come to meet them.'

'Those youths will meet and the flock will go across the plain. He who will not accept quarter will go to help the youths.'

It happened afterwards as Cú Chulainn had said.

'How do the youth of Ulster fight the battle?'

'Bravely,' said the charioteer.

'It were right that they should fall in rescuing their flock,' said Cú Chulainn. 'And now?'

'The beardless young warriors are fighting now,' said the charioteer.

'Has a bright cloud come across the sun yet?' asked Cú Chulainn.

'No indeed,' said the charioteer.

'Alas that I have not the strength to go to them!' said Cú Chulainn.

'There is fighting here already today,' said the charioteer at sunrise. 'It is proud folk who are now fighting the battle, but there are no leaders for they are still asleep.'

It was at sunrise that Fachtna spoke. —Or (according to another account) Conchobar chanted these words in his trance:

'Arise, O valiant kings of Macha, generous people! Sharpen your swords. Fight the battle. Dig a trench. Strike your shields. Men's hands are weary. Their flocks are loud voiced ... They all fight with one another ... Sorrow will fill the heart of their queen so that the grassy sod on which they might strike, and on which they might go should be covered with blood. Arise, kings of Macha.'

'Who has chanted these words?' asked they all.

'Conchobar mac Nesa,' they answered. 'Or Fachtna chanted them. —Sleep on, sleep on but set your sentinels.'

Láegaire Búadach was heard speaking:

'Arise, kings of Macha. Strike your kine with the sword. Protect your booty ... He will smite all the world on the plain of Gáirech.'

'Who has chanted that?' they all asked.

'Láegaire Búadach mac Connaid Buidi meic Iliach. Sleep on, sleep on but set your sentinels.'

'Wait on a while,' said Conchobar, 'until the sun has risen well above the glens and mounds of Ireland.'

When Cú Chulainn saw the chiefs from the east putting on their diadems and coming to the rescue of the troops, he told his charioteer to arouse the men of Ulster.

The charioteer spoke. —Or else it was the poet Amargin mac Eicit who spoke:

'Arise, valiant kings of Macha! A generous people. The war-goddess desires the kine of Immail. The blood from men's hearts spreads around . . . None like Cú Chulainn was found. Arise!'

'I have aroused them,' said the charioteer. 'They have come into battle stark-naked except for their weapons. He whose tent-opening faces east, has (in his eagerness) come out westwards through the tent.

'That is speedy help in time of need,' said Cú Chulainn.

The doings of the men of Ulster are not described for a while.

But as for the men of Ireland, Badb and Bé Néit and Némain shrieked above them that night in Gáirech and Irgáirech so that a hundred of their warriors died of terror. That was not the most peaceful night for them.

The Muster of the Men of Ireland

That night before the battle Ailill mac Máta chanted these words:

'Arise, O Traigthrén! I send you to the three Conaires from Slíab Mis, the three Lesfinds from Lúachair, the three Meid Corpthe Loste, the three called Bodar from the river Búas, the three called Bodb from the river Búaidnech, the three called Búageltach from the river Barrow, the three Muiredachs from Mairge, the three Láegaires from Lec Derg, the three Suibnes from the river Suir, the three Échtachs from Áine, the three Doíl Eirrig, the three called Damach from Loch Derg, the three Bratrúaid from Lough Ree, the three Mielleths from Lough Erne, the three called Bresal Bodgna, the three Amalgaids from Mag nAí, the three Fiachras from Fid Némain, the three Nechtans from Mag Muirisce, the three Mac Amras from Es Rúaid, the three Ruirechs from Crúacha Aigle, the three called Bruchar from Glais Febrat, the three Conalls from Collamair, the three called Fiac from Finnabair, the three Cairbres of Clíu, the three called Mane Milscoth, the three Descertachs of Dromm Fornochta, the three Fintans from Femen, the three Rathachs from Mag Raigne, the three Eterscéls of Etarbán, the three Guaires of Fid Gaible, the three Aeds from Mag nAidne, the three Mongachs of Mitain, the three Dúadaid Áine, the three Gairb Glunnaidi, the three Deiscirt Uaga, the three Lethluind Linti, the three Coinchind Shile, the three Dauich of Líamain, the three Celtchair of Umall, the three Coscrachs of Clothra, the three Barrchais from Eille, the three Dáires from Tipra Find, the three Arts from Ard Ladrann, the three Muiredachs from Mag Femin, the three Congbaidi of Clíu, the three Morda Mosad, the three Roir of Ros Buite, the three Ánrad of Tráig Thuirbe, the three Eterscéls of Tara, the three Galgaidi Goain, the three Feradaig Foltchais, the three Feidmnig Rotail, the three Scáil Sobail, the three Ailill Uaiti, the three Gortaig Granaisc, the three Mesaig Maethla, the three Uilleith of Ard Airthir, the three called Corb from Clár, the three called Art from Ard, the three called Foimdech from Irrus, the three Illands of Ireland, the three Sochaide from Shannon, the three Brónachs from Bethra, the three Mongachs from Mag Mucruma, the three Moch- maidne from Mag nAí, the three called Tigernmas from Túath Ambrais, the three Échtachs from Finnabair, the three Cormacs of Uiscre, the three called Odar from Buaile, the three Ruis Ruscae, the three Ferad Find, the three Athchuirp Tulcha, the three Túathail Tanni, the three Maccáech Femrag, the three Láegaires from Berramain, the three Fidaig Saigthi, the three called Cormac Cúanach, the three called Cairbre Luingi, the three called Odar Conchobair, the three Glais meic Cathbad, the three Duib Drúad, the three Airrig Cluichiur, the three Laitne Luiged, the three called Conchobar Collsen, the three Elair Deiuais, the three Fiadail Duinergin (?), the three Airig Inse Uan, the three Níths from Áth Craíbe, the three called Óengus Uisce, the three Fiach Ferna nImbais, the three called Dorn, the three Bailcbroindi from Móenmag, the three Cais Cuile, the three called Trén from Mag Éle, the three called Sruthmar from Mag nOchtair, the three called Glonnmar from Mag Lethan, the three called Dornmar from Mag nUisci, the three Glaisderg from Tethba, the three Tigirn Taince from Tiprait Talindi.'

These triads made up what was called the *Ferchuitred* of the men of Ireland, not counting those of them whom Cú Chulainn had previously killed.

Tidings of Cú Chulainn are now told:

'Look for us, my friend Láeg, and see how are the men of Ulster fighting now.'

'Bravely (they fight),' answered the charioteer, 'If I were to go today in my chariot and Óen, the charioteer of Conall Cernach, in his chariot and if we were to travel from one wing (of the army) to the other, no hoof of horse or wheel of chariot would go through (to the ground).'

'The makings of a great fight are there,' said Cú Chulainn. 'Let nothing be done in the battle,' said he to his charioteer, 'that I shall not hear an account of from you.'

'That will be so insofar as I can do it,' said the charioteer. 'Now as for the warriors from the west, they make a breach eastwards through the battle-line. The same number of warriors from the east breach the battle-line westwards.'

'Alas that I am not healed,' said Cú Chulainn, 'or my breach too would be clearly seen there like that of all the others.'

Then came the *ferchuitred,* the triads of that second mustering. When the warriors came afterwards to the battle at Gáirech and Irgáirech, there also arrived the nine chariots of the warriors from Irúath. In front of them were three men on foot who travelled no more slowly than the chariots. Medb allowed them into battle only to drag Ailill out of the conflict if the enemy defeated him, or to kill Conchobar if it were he who was overcome.

Then his charioteer told Cú Chulainn that Ailill and Medb were begging Fergus to go into battle. They said that it was not wrong of him to do so for they had shown him great generosity in his exile.

'If I had my own sword,' said Fergus, 'men's heads cut off by me would be as numerous on their shields as hailstones in a swamp to which the king's horses come when they have travelled swiftly into the land.'

Then Fergus swore this oath:

'I swear my people's oath that I would strike men's jawbones from their necks, men's necks from shoulders, men's shoulders from elbows, men's elbows from forearms, men's forearms and their fists, men's fists and their fingers, men's fingers and their nails, men's nails and the crowns of their heads, men's crowns and their trunks, men's trunks and their thighs, men's thighs and their knees, men's knees and their calves, men's calves and their feet, men's feet and their toes, men's toes and their nails. Their headless necks would sound in the air (?) like a bee flying to and fro on a day of fine weather.'

Then said Ailill to his charioteer:

'Bring me the sword that cuts (men's) flesh. I swear the oath of my people that, if its condition be worse with you today than on

17

the day I gave it to you on the hillside in the territory of Ulster, even though the men of Ireland were protecting you against me, they would not save you.'

Then his sword was given to Fergus and Ailill said:

'Take your sword. Though you may smite Ireland, a great warrior of her sons will fight at Gáirech ... For honour's sake do not wreak your fierce anger on us in the presence of the chariot-fighters of Ulster ...'

'Welcome, O hard blade, the sword of Leite! ... My sword shall not inflict slaughter on you. I am a proud leader as I stand before the men of Ireland.'

'A pity that you should fall on a crowded (?) field of battle!' said Fergus to Ailill.

That night Badb and Bé Néit and Némain shrieked above them at Gáirech and Irgáirech so that a hundred of their warriors fell dead of fright. That was not the most peaceful night for them.

Then Fergus seized his weapons and turned towards the fighting, and holding his sword in both hands he cleared a passage for a hundred through the line of battle. Medb too, took up her weapons and rushed into battle. Thrice she was victorious until a phalanx of spears turned her back.

'I wonder,' said Conchobar to his people, 'who is it who is victorious in the fight against us in the north. Do ye stay here in the battle until I go against him.'

'We shall hold the spot where we now stand,' said the warriors, 'but unless the ground quakes beneath us or the heavens fall down on us, we shall not flee from here.'

Then Conchobar went to meet Fergus. He raised against him his shield, the Óchaín, which had four golden points and four coverings of gold. Fergus struck three blows on it but not even the rim of the shield above his head touched Conchobar.

'Who of the men of Ulster raises the shield (against me)?' asked Fergus.

'One who is better (than you),' said Conchobar. 'One who drove you into exile to dwell with wolves and foxes, one who today will hold you at bay in the presence of the men of Ireland by dint of his own prowess.'

Thereupon Fergus, holding the sword in both hands, aimed a vengeful blow at Conchobar, and the point of the sword touched the ground behind him (as he swung it back). Cormac Con Loinges laid hands on him and grasped him by the arm.

'That is harsh yet not harsh, friend Fergus,' said Cormac. 'That is cautious yet not over-cautious, friend Fergus. Friendship proves hostile. Behold your enemies, your friends have been destroyed. Wicked are these blows that you strike, friend Fergus.'

'Tell me,' said Fergus, 'whom shall I strike?'

'Strike the three hills above them. Turn your hand and strike on all sides of you. Heed them not (?). Remember the honour of the Ulstermen which has not been lost. It will not be lost unless it be through your fault today.'

'Go in some other direction, Conchobar,' said Cormac to his father. 'This man will no longer wreak his fierce anger here on the men of Ulster.'

Fergus turned away. With his sword he slew a hundred warriors among the Ulstermen in his first onslaught, until he came face to face with Conall Cernach.

'Too great is that force which you exert against (your own) people and race, following a wanton woman as you do,' said Conall Cernach.

'What shall I do, O warrior?' asked Fergus.

'Strike the hills beyond them and the trees about them,' said Conall Cernach.

Then Fergus smote the hills and with three blows struck off the (tops of the) three hills in Meath (now called) Máela Midi, the flat-topped hills of Meath. Cú Chulainn heard the blows which Fergus had struck on the hills, or (those he had struck) on the shield of Conchobar.

'Who strikes those great strong blows in the distance?' asked Cú Chulainn. 'Blood seals up the heart. Anger destroys the world. Quickly it loosens the dressings of my wounds.'

Láeg answered saying:

'The finest of men strikes them, Fergus mac Róig, the dauntless. The (coming of the) hero Fergus mac Róig means wounds and increase of slaughter. The sword was hidden in the chariot-pole so that the cavalcade of my master Conchobar did not arrive at the great battle.'

Then said Cú Chulainn:

'Quickly unfasten the hoops over my wounds. Men are covered in blood. Swords will be wielded. Men's lives will be ended.'

Thereupon the dry wisps which plugged his wounds sprang out of him (and rose up) as high as a lark soars in the air, and the wooden hoops (túaga) sprang from him as far as Mag Túag in Connacht. They flew out of him in all directions. His wounds took violent effect on him and he struck the heads of the two hand-maidens one against the other so that each of them was grey with the brains of the other. —These handmaidens had been sent by Medb to pretend to lament over him so that his wounds might break out afresh and to tell him that the Ulstermen had been defeated and that Fergus had fallen opposing them because Cú Chulainn had been unable to join the battle. —Then Cú Chulainn was distorted (with rage). The twenty-seven shirts which he used to wear going into battle, tied to him with ropes and cords, were now brought to him, and he took on his back his chariot with its frame-work and two wheels and went round the battle towards Fergus.

'Turn hither, master Fergus!' cried Cú Chulainn, but (though he said this) three times Fergus did not answer.

'I swear by the god by whom Ulstermen swear,' said Cú Chulainn, 'that I shall drub you as flax-heads (?) are beaten in a pool. I shall go over you as a tail goes over a cat. I shall smite you as a fond woman smites her son.'

'Who among the men of Ireland speaks to me thus?' said Fergus.

'Cú Chulainn mac Súaltaim, the son of Conchobar's sister,' said Cú Chulainn, 'and hold back from me now.'

'I have promised to do that,' said Fergus.

'Begone then,' said Cú Chulainn.

'I agree,' said Fergus, 'for you refused to encounter me when you were pierced with wounds.'

So at that juncture Fergus and his division of three thousand went away. The men of Leinster and the men of Munster went away too, and nine divisions, those of Medb and of Ailill and of their seven sons, were left in the battle. It was midday when Cú Chulainn came to the battle. When the sun was sinking behind the trees in the wood, he overcame the last of the bands, and of the chariot there remained only a handful of the ribs of the framework and a handful of the shafts round the wheel.

Then Cú Chulainn overtook Medb going from the battle-field.

'Spare me!' cried Medb.

'If I were to kill you, it would be only right for me,' said Cú Chulainn. But he spared her life then because he used not to kill women. He convoyed them west to Áth Lúain and across the ford too. He struck three blows of his sword upon the flagstone in Áth Lúain. They (i.e. the hills) are called Máelana Átha Lúain.

Now when they were finally routed Medb said to Fergus:

'Men and lesser men (?) meet here today, Fergus.'

'That is what usually happens,' said Fergus, 'to a herd of horses led by a mare. Their substance is taken and carried off and guarded as they follow a women who has misled them.'

In the morning after the battle the bull was taken away, and he met the bull Finnbennach in combat in the place now called Tarbga in Mag nAí.—Tarbga means Bull-sorrow or Bull-battle. — Roí Dedond was the former name of that hill. Everyone who had survived the battle now did nothing except to watch the two bulls fighting.

Bricriu Nemthenga had been in the west convalescing after Fergus had fractured his skull with the chessmen. He came now with all the rest to watch the bulls' fight. In their violent struggle the two bulls trampled on Bricriu and so he died. That is the tragical death of Bricriu.

The Donn Cúailnge's foot was impaled on the horn of the other bull. For a day and a night he did not draw his foot away, until Fergus urged him on and struck his hide with a rod.

'It was bad luck,' said Fergus, 'that the belligerent old calf that was brought here and because of whom many now lie dead should dishonour his clan and lineage.'

Thereupon Donn Cúailnge drew back his foot. His leg broke and his opponent's horn sprang out on to the mountain beside him. So Slíab nAdarca was afterwards the name of that place.

He carried off the Finnbennach then for a day and a night's journey and plunged into the lake beside Crúachu, and he came out of it with the loin and shoulder blade and liver of his opponent on his horns. The hosts advanced then with intent to kill him, but Fergus did not allow it and insisted that he should go wherever he pleased. So then the bull made for his own land. As he came he drank a draught in Finnleithe and left there the shoulder-blade of his opponent. That land was afterwards called Finnleithe. He drank another draught at Áth Lúain and left the other bull's loin there. Hence the name Áth Lúain. At Iraird Cuillinn he bellowed so loudly that he was heard throughout the province. He drank again in Troma. There the liver of his opponent fell from his horns. Hence the name Troma. He went then to the place called Étan Tairb and rested his forehead against the hill at Áth Da Fherta. Hence the name Étan Tairb in Mag Muirthemne. Thereafter he travelled along Slige Midlúachra to Cuib—it was in Cuib he used to abide with the dry cows of Dáire—and there he pawed up the earth. Hence the place-name Gort mBúraig. Then he went on and died in Druim Tairb between Ulster and Uí Echach. That place is called Druim Tairb.

Ailill and Medb made peace with the Ulstermen and Cú Chulainn. For seven years after that no one was killed between them in Ireland. Finnabair remained with Cú Chulainn and the men of Connacht returned to their own land, while the Ulstermen went in triumph to Emain Macha.

Finit.   Amen.

NOTES TO TEXT

4 *co hAilill* Thurneysen noted the anomaly of Ailill's sending messengers to himself. But the Ailill here referred to is no doubt Ailill Ardágach mac Mágach. He is mentioned with his brother Cet mac Mágach in Bruiden Da Chocae (his death is recorded there, Stokes's edition §61). The LL-compiler seems to have shared Thurneysen's opinion; for Ailill he substitutes Scannall mac Mágach. Anachronistically Ailill Ardágach is said in Cath Airtig (Best's edition §15) to have been killed by Conall Cernach and Scannall together with him: *Dorochair Ailill Ardagach ⁊ Scandal da mac Magach la Conall Cernach.*

5 *tricha cét la cach n-áe* Lit. thirty hundred, but often used to denote merely a great number of fighting men. See F. J. Byrne, 'Tribes and Tribalism in Early Ireland', Ériu xxii 159ff. where it is noted that the term was a conventional estimate of a *tuath's* whole population, but was applied secondarily to the *slúagad* or 'rising out'. Note, however, that some scribes of early texts took the term literally and further defined it as *deich cét ar fichit cét* (Táin 4244–5, 4259). In general I have translated it as 'a division' (of fighting men).

6 *co Cormac Cond Longas* Despite the soubriquet Cormac does not play a dominant rôle as leader of the exiled Ulstermen. Rather it is Fergus who is the important figure. In the LL-version messengers are sent to both Cormac and Fergus (Táin 155–6); in the Stowe version, which was influenced no doubt by Recension I, only Cormac and the *dubloinges* are summoned (162–3). Fergus, Cormac and Dubthach, the three who had guaranteed the safety of Meic Uisnig, were the three leaders of the exiled Ulstermen.

cona thríb cétaib One would expect *cona thríchait cét* here, but W has also 'three hundred'. In two later passages in this text Fergus is said to have had 3,000 followers (infra 58, 175). In this passage in Recension II the exiles under Cormac and Fergus are said to number 3,000 (*deich cét ar fichit cét a llín* Tain 156). In TBFlid. II in some verses enumerating the chiefs of Medb's army we get the lines *Fuil ann Cormac Conloinges | Tri deich cet ar n-a cóimes* (Celt. Rev. iii 120). Cf. also *Tricha cet rop e lín na llongsi* LL 34477 (Longes mac nUsnig); similarly in Aided Fergusa maic Róich (Death-Tales 32 §1).

8 *hi Crúachnaib Ai* T. F. O'Rahilly suggested that *Cruachain* may have been in origin a plural tribal name, as the dative *Cruachnaib* suggests. From a gen. pl. *Cruachan* (as in *Ráth Cruachan*) a new nominative *Cruachu* gen. *Cruachan* and *Cruachna* and dat. *Cruachain* was formed (EIHM 26 n. 2).

9 *Trí luirg* ... In Bruiden Da Chocae Cormac Cond Longas draws up his men as here in three bands (*Diroine Cormac tri luirg de oc techt a Cruachain* §8), and they number three hundred (*tri cét laech i lin* ib.). Stokes asserted that the triple division and the description of the bands (which is close in wording to the description here) were 'obviously imitated from Táin Bó Cualngi LL 55ᵃ–55ᵇ', and Thurneysen agrees with Stokes (Heldensage 588).

Bruiden Da Chocae is preserved only in late MSS., but Thurneysen who attributes the extant version to the 13th century postulates a 9th-century version of the tale. Its title is found in saga-lists A and B, and it is referred to by Cinaed Ó hArtacáin. So one might well take the opposite view and suggest that this passage in LU-TBC was influenced by an old version of Bruiden Da Chocae in the number 300 and in the wording of the descriptions.

For a triple division of troops with a detailed description of their appearance and equipment compare the opening passage of Tochmarc Ferbe. The beginning of that tale is lost owing to a lacuna in the MS., but part of the second band's description and the whole of the third are given. Note that it is the hero of the tale, Maine Mórgor, who leads the third band as Cormac does here and in Bruiden Da Chocae (in tres buiden dana .i. in buiden i mbai Mani fodéin LL 33459).

11 *fo thairinniuth* This would seem to be the old vn. of *do-airindi*, but one would expect it to read *oc tairinniuth*, 'descending, falling', but *fo th.* here = 'fold, drape'. It has been generally taken as a scribal error for the common *fo dercintliud* (as in ll. 13, 18) but it is strange that both Eg. 1782 and LL should have the same misreading. (LL reads *ba tórniud*). See Táin 158n.

27 *co n-imparrá* This form has generally been taken as 1 sg. pres. subj. of *imm-soí*, trans. See note by Sommerfelt, Ériu viii 126, who compares the form *ara tintarrad* Thes. II 314. I suggest that it may be 3 sg. pres. subj. intrans. here used without a reflexive pronoun. Cf. 3 sg. *ar nachn-imparrae* Corm. Y 756, 'so that he may not turn round', with reflexive pronoun. There are many instances of *imm-soí*, intrans., without reflexive pronoun. See Contributions.

deisel The right-hand course, the direction of the sun, was believed to be auspicious.

29 *dosoí forsin carpat* *Do-soí* is generally transitive. But cf. *Toí forsna heochu* infra 1338. I suggest that *do-soí for* means 'turns back'. In the Recension II equivalent of l. 1338 *for cúlu* is inserted: *Impá dún in carpat, a gillai, arís for cúlu* Táin 1629–30, ... *ar ccul* Stowe 1672.

34 *di partaing* *Partaing* is generally taken to be from Parthica, 'Parthian leather dyed scarlet'. See TBFr[2] 92n.

37 *claideb corthaire* A weaver's beam. Generally *claideb garmnae* as in LU 7700 (TBDD). More explicitly in Recension II she is said to be weaving a fringe: *Is amlaid boi ind ingen ic figi chorrthairi ⁊ claideb findruine ina láim deiss* Táin 185–6, that is, weaving threads in a magical manner to enable her to prophesy the coming battle. See Stowe TBC 199n. and Addendum.

39 *Gaisced lasin n-ingin* This is not in Recension II. One would not expect Feidelm to carry arms if she was also carrying a weaver's beam. Possibly this was an addition by some scribe who misunderstood *claideb corthaire*.

43 *A hAlbain* Following Dr. Knott (Irish Classical Poetry, p. 8) I have taken *Alba* here as = 'Albion' i.e. Britain, rather than in the later sense of 'Scotland'.

iar foglaim filidechta The word *filidecht* is here used with its original meaning, the art of the *fili*, the seer or diviner.

44 *imbass forosna* 'divination which illuminates'. A detailed description of the practice of this rite is given by Cormac in his Glossary. See further EIHM 339f.

51 *atá Conchobor ina chess* The *cess Ulad*, also called *cess noínden* or *noínden Ulad* (later *cess noíden*), was a mysterious incapacity or torpor which at times afflicted the Ulstermen. There are two accounts of the origin of the *cess*, one found only in a single MS (Harl. 5280) and which does not really give any clear explanation, the other in LL and later MSS. (A critical edition of the second from four late MSS. was published by V. Hull, Celtica viii 28–29). According to the second tale the *cess* was due to the curse of Macha. forced when pregnant to race against the king's horses. She prophesied that when the province was in its greatest danger the Ulster warriors would have only the strength of a woman in childbirth (*nert mná siúil ba hed no bíd la cach fer di Ultaib fri saegal nónbair isind noe[n]den* LL 14578–9). On the basis of this tale some scholars have suggested that the *cess* was a survival of the practice known as couvade. Recently Tomás Ó Broin has dealt at length with *cess noénden Ulad* in Éigse x, xii, xiii, and has suggested that it is the remains of a seasonal fertility myth, here representing the death of winter decay and the spring rebirth (Éigse x 288). This theory would fit in well with the implication in Recension II TBC that the *cess* lasted from Samain until the beginning of Spring (Feb. 1). Recension I agrees with this when in the Breslech Maige Murthemni section we are told that Cú Chulainn had fought single-handed *ón lúan iar Samain cosin cétain iar n-imolg* (infra 2138). Again in Sírrabad Súaltaim (3434) he is said to have defended the province *tri misa gaimrid*. There is also however in Recension I a suggestion that the attack of *cess* was intermittent. In a long passage denoted by the scribe as *córugud aile* containing many *roscada* and obviously belonging to the oldest stratum of TBC we are told that Cú Chulainn goes to Conchobor to warn him of the enemy's attacks, but Conchobor tells him that the warning is useless and comes too late: *Indiu tonánic ar tinorcuin in chétnae* (1219–20), 'Today we have been smitten (by the *cess*) as before'. The H-interpolator later takes up the same point and borrows the word *tinnorcain* when he tries to explain how the Ulsterman Munremar can come to fight with Cú Roí. 'At this point the *noénden Ulad* came to an end. According as they awoke (from their *cess*) a band of them kept attacking the (enemy) host until they were once more smitten (by their *cess*)' infra 1629–30.

It is mainly in TBC that we find reference to *cess Ulad*. But in the account of the death of Cú Chulainn, both the fragmentary LL- version and the modern tale Breisleach Mór Muighe Muirtheimhne tell us that Cú Chulainn was killed while the Ulstermen lay prostrate in their *cess*, unable to defend him (cf. LL 14096–7, Compert Con C. pp. 78, 87, 125).

The word *noínden* which Stokes connected with Lat. nundinae (ACL ii 426) is generally taken to mean a nine-fold period. Cf. *noínden Ulad quasi novem dies, ar is i re laithe nobitis isin cess* O'Mulc. 835. The later *cess noíden* (which may perhaps have originated in a scribe's omission of the *n-* stroke, as e.g. LL 14579) may have helped to reinforce the couvade theory, *noíden* being taken as gen. of *noídiu*, 'infant'. (For rejection of this point see Tomás Ó Broin, Éigse xiii 165ff.). For *-nd- > -d-* see my note Éigse xvi 252.

The *cess noínden* has generally been translated by 'debility' or 'affliction'. Thurneysen renders it 'der Schwachezustand der Ulter' (Heldensage 359).

O'Curry (M & C II 319) talks of the Ulstermen rising 'from their enchanted sleep' (a rendering which I find appealing). Elsewhere he calls it 'torpor', 'lethargy'. Tomás Ó Broin who translates it 'prostration' notes (Éigse xii 110) that the verbs used in connection with *cess* denote an awakening or rising from a somnolent condition. (Note, however, that in *is hé Conchobar rochan trena chodlad* infra 3903-4 the reference is not to the *cess* but to a trance in which Conchobar chants a prophetic *rosc*). For the meaning of 'torpor, sleep', cf. *cess ⁊ suan* (Teanga Bithnua) Ériu ii 112.

In poetry in the later language *ces naiden* occurs with the meaning 'torpor', 'state of inactivity'. *Beid san crichse i gceas naoidhean* TD 20.27; *Créad í an time nó an bhuige nó an mhéirtne | ... | nó an ceas naoin do bhíos dá dtráocha?* Five Pol. Poems I 139. In a 17th-century poem by Fear Flatha Ó Gním the poet unrewarded by his patron is compared to the cuckoo which does not sing in the harsh winter weather. (No ornithologists, these poets! They seem to think that the migratory cuckoo hibernates in this country). Thus: *Ní thógaibh ceann is ni chan ceól | ó dhubhas dreach an aiéór,* and he speaks of *ceas naoidhean an eóin annaimh | san aimsir fhuair iodh-lannaigh* (L.Cl.A.B. 164). The silence of the cuckoo is referred to again in a love-poem describing the beauty of a woman's hair (Dánta Gr.[2] 13.6): *Atá ar do chéibh chleachtsholais | ealta chuach i gceas naoidhean.* This has been elegantly translated by Robin Flower as 'Your golden locks close clinging | like bird-flocks of strange seeming | silent with no sweet singing.' The comparison of locks of hair with flocks of birds may sound bizarre. But it is of course impossible to bring out in English the play on the words *cuach*, 'a cuckoo' and *cuach*, 'a curling lock of hair, a ringlet'.

54　*Fedelm*, nominative = vocative. Again 58, 63. Contrast the first occurrence 48, *A Feidelm*. Similarly in Recension II: *a Feidelm* (Táin 204, 208, 213), but *Feidelm* when Medb's question and Feidelm s answer form a couplet. Thus:

> *'Feidelm banfáid, cia facci ar slúag?'*
> *'Atchiu forderg forro, atchíu rúad.'*
>
> (Táin 209–10, 214–5, 224–5, 230–31)

This usage has been called 'the omission of the vocative particle'. But it is really nominative used for vocative. It is occasionally found in Mid.-Ir. in verse (metri gratiâ) or in a *rosc* passage. An Old-Irish example occurs in the Irish Gospel of Thomas where we get *Ioseph* §13c for *a Ioseph*. See Dr. Dillon, Serglige Con Culainn 337n. and Thurneysen's note in ScM[2] p. 27. Thurneysen implies the use of nominative for vocative when he takes *at comsa mac Finchaíme frim* §15.11 as meaning 'thou art a match for me, son of F.' and expands m̄c of the MS as *mac* not *meic*. In the same *rosc* on which he comments we get *Fochen Conall* §15.9 and again *Fochen Cet | Cet mac Mágach* §15.13–14, which I take to mean 'Hail, Conall', 'Hail, Cet, Cet mac Mágach'. In Serglige Con Culaind cf. also *Fochen Labraid Lúathlám ar claideb* (178, 192, 205, 213) and *Fochen Cú Chulainn* (646). Contrast with these *Fochen a Chonaill chain Chuirc,* the opening words of a *rosc* LL 37009. At the end of the present text a *rosc* begins *Comérgid, ríg Macha* (3905, 3911), 'Arise, kings of M.', but in Breslech Muige Muirtheme in LL we get *Comergid, a firu Herend* (13925).

For the use of nominative for vocative, but with the vocative particle, see note by Bergin, Ériu ix 92–4.

It seems probable that there was an omission here in LU's exemplar. In Recension II Conchobor, Celtchar and Eógan mac Durthacht are named here. Note that in the passage preceding the Macgnímrada these three are named in both recensions.

67–112 Thurneysen suggested that this H- interpolated poem may have been written in the space afforded by the erasure of a *roscad* which is what one would expect from Fedelm Banfáith. This poem is the only H- interpolation of LU which is also found in LL. Thurneysen noted that the LL- poem was closer in wording to the LU-version than to that of W (ZCP ix 431).

73 *fil fuidrech fora glinni* I have taken the LL- reading and tentatively translated 'His spear-points are unsheathed'. O'Clery glosses *fuidhreach* as *fodhérach .i. nochtadh*. In the RIA Dictionary the W- reading is translated 'his jaw is stripped, laid bare (?).' This may be a reference to Cú Chulainn's distortion, but if so the first line of the next quatrain contradicts the idea. In the H 3.18 Glossary five lines of this poem are quoted, this being the first of them and *fuidre* not *fuidrech* is the form given: *Fuidhre .i. ainm do lic oidhre, ut est Fil oidhre for a nglaine* etc. (Ériu xiii 71 §123). This makes even less sense in the context.

84 Here W inserts a repetition of Medb's question *Co accai ar sluagh?* and Fedelm's answer, thus dividing the poem in two (ZCP ix 123).

89 *Dá gáe bolga immosbeir* The meaning given to the verb *immbeir* here in Contribb. is 'carries around', with this the only example. (I note that Faraday translates 'Two *gáe bolga* he carries them'). But I suggest that *imm-beir* here is used with the reflexive pronoun, 'he attacks'. In Mid. Ir. the infixed pronoun -*s*- has spread and is often used for 3 s.m., particularly as a reflexive. Cf. *dosléci Cú Chulaind riam* (infra 869–70), *nos dítin* (infra 1946). In a prose equivalent of this line one would expect *immosbeir forro*. Cf. for the meaning of *imm-beir* + reflexive: *rodn-imbeir forru amal fóelaid etir chaírcha* TTr² 1433, and (with independent pronoun as reflexive) *Ro imbretar iat for[s]na sluagaib* ib. 946.

Thurneysen seemed to take the line as meaning that Cú Chulainn possessed two *gáe bolga*, reading *dá*, 'two', but there is no reference in the saga to more than one. Note how carefully is described in the Fer Diad episode of Recension II the procedure by which the one and only *gáe bolga* had to be retrieved from the victim's body. In Recension II the line reads *A gáe bulga mar domber* (Táin 256). *Dá < dia* is infrequent in this text. But in the BMMM episode we get *is cumma imthescad dá scíath ⁊ dá sleig ⁊ dá chlaideb* (infra 2237). It is perhaps worth noting that in that part of LL-TBC corresponding to the LU portion *dia* and *dá* occur in about equal proportion. In the remainder of the LL-version *dá* predominates.

94 I have given the translation of LL here.

100 *mani airlestar* A modal use of preterite according to E. G. Quin (Hermathena cxvii 54).

114 For the marginal *.r.* before the list of place-names see my note Celtica x 146–8 and compare a similar use infra 2320 before a list of leaders slain by Cú Chulainn.

116 *for Cúil Sibrinne* Better *Cúil Silinne* as in LL and in the alternative reading in W. Again infra 137 read *hi Cúil Silinne*. See Gwynn's note on *Turloch Silinde* MD III p. 547. In the prose dindshenchus of Loch mBlonac it is called *Cúil Silinde a Maigh Ai* (ib. 546). This was in Co. Roscommon (now Kilcooley) and is to be distinguished from *Cúil Sibrinni* 121, *Cúil Sibrille* 309, which is glossed by hand M as an old name for Cennannas or Kells, Co. Meath. The two places have been confused in Hogan's Onomasticon.

120–1 *for Slechtai selgatar* For the place and the derivation of its name see the later passage infra ll. 305–8. The meaning is clearer here in Recension II: *for Slechta conselgatar claidib ria Meidb ⁊ Ailill* Táin 287, 'by Slechta which was cleared by swords for Medb's and Ailill's passage'. Conrelative + *selgatar* 3 pl. pret. of *sligid*. Cf. BDD² 912.

132–3 *Ár ... Findabair* This sentence is not in W and reads like a scribal comment.

143 Note the inclusion of Conall Cernach among the exiles. According to Cóir Anmann §281 Fiacha was son of Conall Cernach: *Feabh inghen Chonchobair maic Nessa bá ben do Chonall Cernach i ⁊ rug mac dó .i. Fiacha ⁊ is eissidhe Fiacha mac Fir Feba.* According to FB Conall's wife was *Lendabair ingen Eógain meic Durthacht* (LU 8234).

145ᵉ *Flidais* It is impossible to tell whether this interpolation means that H had knowledge of a version like Recension II (which here was influenced by TBFlid. II), or whether Recension II drew on another version known to H. The first explanation seems more likely. See supra n. 67–112.

148 *in trícha cét Galión* The Galióin were a Laginian tribe. See EIHM 92–95, 99. T. F. O'Rahilly always spells the name *Gálioin*. He notes that a few verse example show the vowel of the first syllable as long. But in LU-TBC (and in LL-TBC) it is never marked long. T. F. O'Rahilly suggests that *Ga-* and *Gá* were probably both in use. See also op. cit. 459–61. I note, also, in Recension II in a poem not represented in Recension I *giall: Galian* (gp.): *grian: Galian* (gp.) Táin 414–5, 422–3.

158 *Ficfit fornd* In RIA Dictionary this instance and one other (doubtful) are given under *feccaid (for)* with the meaning 'turns (on or against)'. I take the meaning to be 'attacks'. Cf. *imm-soí fo* = 'attacks' and *do-ella for* id. Thus *amsoí fóthu* Táin 804 = *doella-som forsin macraid* infra 450. (In a later passage we get *feccais forro aithirrach* 3407, 'he attacked them again'). The W- reading is *fichfit for*, 'they will prevail against, conquer.'

164 *Ní maith a n-asbir* This sentence has generally been taken by translators as spoken by Ailill. I attribute it to Fergus.

La sanais ón presents a difficulty if we take it as the beginning of Fergus's remarks. It was probably parenthetical. I am inclined to put it after *ol Fergus* and translate '(that was said) in a low voice', though the usual phrase is *a sanais*. Cf. *sanais .i. cogar* O'Cl. On the other hand if we read *.i. la sanais ón* where it stands in both MSS., we might take *sanais* in the meaning of 'bad advice, instigation'. Thus: 'What you say is wrong, it is meant as instigation. Faraday mistranslates 'With this folk, said F. it shall not happen.' W. Krause discusses the phrase ZCP xxii 134–5, but does not offer any helpful solution. The suggested reading *lasin n-ois ón ní 'maricfe* will hardly do. The preposition with *imm-ric* is *do* not *la*. Cf. BDD² 703 n.

190 Here we find marginal .r. before verses in a syllabic metre. But the poem, obscure in part, is a prophecy of evil to come, which is what we should expect in a *rosc*. For a short discussion of this poem see Táin Introd. pp. xxxiii-xxxiv.

193 *fri Findbend* Called *Findbennach* in the introductory section of Recension II, but not mentioned by name again in Recension I until the final battle between *Finnbennach* (4126) and *Dond Cúailnge*. In these two bulls were re-incarnated the two swineherds of the *sid* referred to ll. 196–7. *Finnbend Ai ⁊ in Dond Cualṅgi a n-anmand in tan batar da tharb* LL 32996–7.

196 *lugbairt lacht* Lit. 'the milk of the garden', here metaphorically used for 'the blood of the battle-field'.

198 *Crann fóitech* In RIA Dictionary the adjective is derived from *fót*, 'a sod', and translated 'containing sods, earthy, turfy,' a meaning which does not seem appropriate here. I take the adjective to be from *fót*, 'watchfulness'. Cf. *fatchius ⁊ fót* Táin 400. The quatrain is repeated (infra 1160) where the reading is *Gaibid Crón cóidech friu*, which I take to be for *Cronn coidech*, 'the river C. lamenting'. Cf. *caiteach* 'a mourner' Eg. Gl. 185 = *caithech*, *caidech* < *cai*. In the later passage C reads *Crann faoitioch*, (*-faoitheach*?), the adj. probably from *faid*, 'outcry', hence 'lamenting', or 'loud-voiced'. Or perhaps a misreading of *Crann faitech* which would mean 'the watchful river C.' i.e. watchful on behalf of the Ulstermen. O'Clery glosses *fót* as *faiteach*.

198 *friithu* There are a few instances of this form of 3 pl. prep. with suffixed pronoun. See Thurn. Gramm. p. 515.

210 *Dosfóbair thrá ind Némain* Again in the BMMM passage: *cordas mesc ind Némain forsin tslóg* (2084–5). The same expression occurs three times again in the later part of the tale in YBL, twice after a *rosc* (as it occurs here after verses the equivalent of a *rosc*), once where it seems out of place (3942–4). *Némain* or *Nemain* (the length of the first vowel varies but is always long in the LU- text) was the war-goddess, wife of Néid who was *dia catha la geinti Goidel* (Corm. §965). The phrase seems to be a figurative way of saying that the army was roused to battle-fury. It is generally followed by a description of forces thrown into confusion and a number of them dying of fright. It has usually been translated literally as 'the Némain (war-goddess) attacked them'. It might perhaps be rendered better by 'war-frenzy seized them.' As a common noun *nemain* (*némain*) means 'battle-fury, frenzy'. Cf. *rofhéch Suibhne suas iarum co ro lion nemain ⁊ dobhar ⁊ dásacht* Buile S. (Med. and Mod. Series) §11.194, which in O'Clery's MS reads *⁊ rolion némain ⁊ dásacht é.*

211 *la buadris ind athig triana chotlud* Meyer (Contribb.) gives the meaning 'disturbance' for *buadris* in this passage, but in his Addenda he quotes from a poem in *bérla na filed: doráis buadhris um thuil .i. do chonnac aisling am chodladh* (ZCP v 448 §6) and gives the meaning 'vision'. *Aisling* and *buadris* (and *brinna*) are used meaning the mystic trance in which a poet or seer prophesies. In the latter part of the text in Recension II the words *Búadris Celtchair and so innossa* (Táin 4127) are prefixed to a *rosc*. In a similar context in the YBL version *aisling* is the word used.

211–2 *foscerdat inna buidne* Meaning doubtful. The RIA Dictionary s.v. *fo-ceird* II(b) gives the meaning of this sentence as 'form ranks' (no doubt taking the Y reading). But that does not seem appropriate here as they certainly break ranks in the next sentence.

228–9 *co fórsed do Ultaib terchomrac slóig* In RIA Dictionary it is suggested that this is past subj. of *fo-reith*. But the Y- reading *co foirsed* = *co toirsed* seems to be the correct one. Here we have a confusion of *fo-ricc*, *ro-icc* and *do-airic*. Compounds of -*icc* are often confused in Mid. Ir. Cf. for example *co tairnic dō raind na muici* Anecd. v 15 = *co rránic dó raind na mmucci* LL 13216.

231 *is andam* Gwynn (Hermathena 1933 p. 145) suggests the rendering 'Tis an empty country this way—what sort of road are we marching?', taking *andam* as sb. = 'an unfrequented place.'

256–7 *Eirr ⁊ Indell, Foich ⁊ Fochlam* The marginal note in hand M suggests that the compiler had a version like that of LL (*l*?) before him. This note is lacking in both Y and W. For a full discussion of these four men see Táin n. 604–627.

261 *Lelgatár .i. lomraiset* 'They licked, that is, they stripped bare'. Note the later form of the verb in the gloss in W.

284 *ferg i ndá* I can make no sense of this. E. G. Quin suggests reading *ferg i tá* (nasalized *t* spelt *d*, Gramm. 147). The LL- reading of the couplet is *Costud ruirech, fer co ndáil | ras cuir óenfer dá óenláim* (Táin 492–3), 'the containment of chiefs, with their followers (*fer co ndáil* = *co ndáil fer*), one man cast it with one hand'.

294–7 In a note entitled 'The magic withe in Táin Bó Cúailnge' (Ériu ix 159) Bergin corrects previous translators of this passage. I have of course rendered the sentence in LU according to Bergin's interpretation. The LL-version gives a similar meaning. Of the withe Bergin says: 'I leave to folklorists the discussion of the magic writing, which cannot be held, but will escape and warn the writer if it be disregarded'. The Stowe paraphrase of the passage seems to give better sense ... *da rabsabair fo talmain no i ttig fo dunad, doghena guin duine dioph ría ttrath erghi do lo imbarach* (522–3). To get such a meaning LU would require too drastic an emendation: *cia beithe i lláim dune ... ricfe inbar ndiaid in fer ro scríb in n-ogum* etc. But the reading of LU and Y may be due to an early scribal error and the meaning may originally have been as in Stowe, that the writer of the *ogam* would find and kill them even if they were imprisoned or locked up. Cf. a later passage where Cú Chulainn threatens the Connacht physicians: ⁊ *asbert nosmairfed-som uile cid fo thalmain no betis isin dúnad* (3178–9 and similarly C 2284–5) = direct speech in Recension II: *gid fo thalmain beit nó i tig fo iadad, is missi conáirgeba bás ⁊ éc ⁊ aided forro* Táin 3637–8.

307 *Is ar blas ón* UY It is difficult to make sense of this. I have adopted the helpful emendation of E. G. Quin, *Is ar[a]bia són*.

315 *Ní má lodmar ... ná mertamar* The syntax of *ná mertamar* is difficult to explain. Are we to understand it as = *ní ma mertamar*. Stokes (Addenda to Subj. Mood p. 132) confesses himself unsure of the construction.

327[a] The long marginal note in hand M has been taken over by the Stowe compiler, but is not in the LL- version.

352-3 *co ndercaiss* One would expect *co ndercastar*, but the sentence is confused with and anticipates l. 355. In U there is a full stop after *ass*, but punctuation in this MS is not always reliable.

362 ff. Recension II adds a fourth question (after the reference to Conchobor): *Dóig innar tísed Cúscraid Mend Macha mac Conchobair ó Inis Cúscraid* Táin 701-2.

382 ff. *Ní fairgéba-su* etc. A similar passage is found in a eulogy of Cú Chulainn by Emer in Fled Bricrend (LU 8445-54) where it is preceded by the list of Cú Chulainn's 'feats', and the whole passage marked by a marginal *.r.* See note Celtica x 146-7.

396 *Ní ar ní són.* All three MSS. have the same reading. I can only suggest that some such word as *áirmide, áirmithi,* part. of necess. of *ad-rími,* is to be understood after *Ní.* Cf. *ni áirmithi ar ni* Wb. 8[c]13, 'it is not to be accounted as anything'. The equivalents in Recension II are *Ní focclam-ne ón, ar Fergus* (Táin 736); *Ní fíor son, ar Fergus* (Stowe 761). Or simply take the U- reading to be the equivalent of *Ní ni dom é,* 'It is of no concern to me' ?

400 *ocond Airgdig* Pokorny suggested this reading (ZCP x 453) taking the name to be from *arg,* 'hero' + *tech,* i.e. 'hero-house'. LL has *icon Airdig* (Táin 739) but Stowe reads *icon Airgthic* (765). In Compert Conchobair (RC vi 177) the stone on which Conchobar was born is said to have been *fri hAirgdhigh aniar.* Cf. also *Aircthech* glossed *nomen regionis,* (the usual gloss on a place-name in the poem) Voyage of Bran p. 9, §12a.

403 *oc imbirt fidchille* Fidchell, a board-game, which for convenience' sake I have translated 'chess' elsewhere. Taken in RIA Dictionary to be *fid* + *ciall,* 'wood-intelligence' (= W. *gwyddbwyll*). Meid has an interesting suggestion (TBFr.[2] p. 29) that *ciall* here is O.Ir. *ciall,* 'trickery'. Cf. infra 1809 *acht má dorónaid céill occai.* For a discussion of *fidchell* see D. Greene, Ériu xvii 7; E. Mac White, Éigse v 26ff.

414 *Dobér indass fair* Here LL reads *Dobér-sa ardmes furri amne* Táin 757 (*furri* referring of course to *Emain*). *Indass* would seem to be for *indmus* vn. of *ind-midethar.* For the disappearance of aspirated *-m-* cf. loss of *-b-* in *atbiur* > *atiur, nírbo* > *níro* etc., and see Zimmer KZ xxviii 327-8.

422 *Arguntis do* All three MSS are corrupt here. For a suggested emendation see Stories from Táin[3] Glossary.

428-34 There is no reference to a distortion at this point in Recension II. Zimmer believed that these lines were quite superfluous here and an obvious interpolation (KZ xxviii 485). The sentence *Benaid fona maccu* 435 follows naturally on from l. 422. Note, however, that in the fight with Nad Crantail Cú Chulainn was distorted *amal dorigni frisna maccu i nEmain* (infra 1478-9). Again the description of Cú Chulainn's distortion in the H-interpolation (infra 1651-7) seems completely out of place and may have been built by the interpolator on the sentence in Aided Nad Crantail.

The tradition seems to have been that whenever Cú Chulainn got angry he was distorted. Cf. a passage in Scéla Chonchobuir LL 12537-42.

431–2 *combo móir beólu midchúaich* The reading is ... *fidchóich*, 'of a wooden bowl', in Y W. This would seem to be the stock phrase. Cf. in the description of the gigantic Goll mac Carbad: *Samla beolo fidchuaich indara súil dó fria chind dianechtair* LL 12636.

432 *do-érig*, synonymous with *do-rig*, 'lays bare'.

433 *coa inairddriuch* Cf. 2 *airdrech* Contribb.? Some part of face? Or the word *inairddriuch* may show the same formation as *inchróes* and mean 'that which is contained between the ribs'. O'Davoren 176 gives *airdriu .i. esna ut est asoilg a beoil go airdriuch* translated by Stokes 'his lips open as far as (his) rib'. In the Glossary in TCD H 3.18 we find *ardrach .i. esnach ut est i Táin: a beóil co hardrach*. *Ardrach* and *esnach* are collectives. In other passages referring to Cú Chulainn's distortion and in particular to the distortion of his lips we find an adverb *co urtrachta: Ríastarda a bél co urthrachda* Táin 2276; *Ríastartha a bél co úrtrachta* infra 2259. Again in Fled Bricrend: *Sia[ba]rthar co urtrachta im Choin Culaind* LU 8880. Windisch would connect this word with *airdrech*, 'an apparition', hence *co urtrachta*, 'spectrally, fearsomely'. Thus the reading *coa inairddriuch* in LU and YBL, may be a scribal error for *co urtrachda* in their exemplar, or conversely *co urtrachda* which, it must be noted, occurs only in connection with distortion, may be a scribal misreading of *coa airdriuch* or *coa inairddriuch*.

433 *a inchróes* Generally translated 'gullet', but see note Celtica x 140–142, where I suggest the meaning 'inward parts'.

457–539 These episodes are not in Recension II. See Táin Introd. xxxiv–xxxv where I suggest that the passage has been added by some compiler. It will be noted how different in tone this passage is from the rest of the *macgnímrada*. In particular the style of Cath Eógain meic Derthacht with its short abrupt sentences is in sharp contrast to the description, for example, of Cú Chulainn taking up arms and riding in a chariot for the first time. In the short tale Do Fallsigud Tána Bó Cuailṅge in LL 32879–32909, in an enumeration of the *remscéla* of the Táin, we get the following: *Atberat dano is di remscelaib De Thecht Con Culaind do thaig Culaind Cherdda, De Gabail gascid do Choin Chulaind & dia dul i carpat, Dia luid Cú Chulaind do Emain Macha cosna maccu. Acht is i curp na Tána adfiadtar na tri sceóil dedencha-sa* (32905–9). These are the three episodes of Recension II, though they do not occur there in exactly that order.

457–8 *ni chotlad ... co matain* See note by E. G. Quin, Hermathena xcix 51 who suggests that *co matain* may be compared with *co aidchi > caidchi*, with negative '(n)ever'. He compares *co fescor* infra 735 = *coidchi*.

470 *Aided na Maccraide* This occurs three times as a title to an episode in this Recension; here and in an H-interpolation 1631, and finally in Breslech Mór Maige Murthemne 2153 which would seem to be its original place.

476 *Conérget Ulaid imbi* Against all MSS. readings I should like to suggest that the passage originally read *Co n-éiget Ulaid imbi. Conérgim-se ⁊ Conchobar lais-seom*, 'The Ulstermen raised a cry of alarm against him, but I and Conchobar stood by him.' It is easy to see how *co n-éiget* would be contaminated by the verb *con-érig* in the following two sentences. In a passage of

Tochmarc Étaíne occurs the sentence *Conérget in tslúaig imón ríg iar mélacht forro* LU 10911 which may well have been for *Co-n-éiget* ... For the meaning 'stand by' in the second sentence cf. a passage in TBFr. After Fráech has skilfully cast back Ailill's spear and pierced his garments with it we get the sentence *La ssin cotéirget ind óic la Ailill* (TBFr[2] 216–7), which I take to mean that the warriors rose up to defend him (against further attacks).

482 *Eógan mac Durthacht* Eógan is often represented as in a feud with Conchobar and the rest of the Ulstermen. Cf. LL 34455.

486 *Hi fiadnaise Bricriu ucut* This implies of course that Bricriu is actually present among the exiled Ulstermen as Fergus is speaking. Here the name is not declined. In the final part of TBC in YBL the gen. is *Bricrend*.

489 *Fuit!* Originally 'cold!', expressing a shiver, as in the well-known poem on Winter, but sometimes a blank interjection which like *amae!* takes its colour from the context. Here it seems no more than an addition to the greeting *Dia do betha*.

Dia do bethu! Mod. Ir. *Dé do bheatha!* or *Sé do bheatha!* 'Welcome'. See Éigse x 96–102 where Professor R. A. Breathnach suggests that the phrase is *dia* = 'enough' followed by the partitive, a common usage in chevilles in poetry. Cf. a similar use of *lór*. *Betha* then would be the shortened form of the dative. One would have expected an occasional instance of the dative form *bethaid* to occur. (*Bethaid* is the dative form which is used throughout TBC). One might also have expected to find the addition of *duit* or *duib* occurring sometimes. The meaning 'Enough of life' i.e. 'Long life' would fit in well with the answer always given in current Irish *Go mairir i bhfad!* But this answer would equally well suit the meaning 'May God be your life!' i.e. 'God preserve you!' or 'May God give you life!' Thus the phrase would be a juxtaposed subject and predicate with the verb (optative subjunctive) omitted, (*corop*) *Dia do betha*. Cf. the opening line of a poem *Narab Dia do betha, a bháis!* (Ériu viii 92). In Echtra Nerai the king of the *síd* says to Nera: *Fo dia do betho assin galur hir-rabo!* translated by Meyer 'Welcome alive from the sickness in which thou wert!' (RC x 222). Here we might take *fo* as the preposition rather than the adjective *fó*, 'good'. (But cf. *Fiadha .i. fo Dhia .i. Dia maith* O'Cl.). Thus the meaning would be 'May your life be under (the protection of) God!' i.e. predicate + subject with the verb *corop* omitted. An alternative explanation, if not too far-fetched, would be that the formula here was influenced by the common *Fo chen!* Cf. a shortened form of the Echtra Nerai phrase which occurs in the tale Erchoitmed Ingine Gulidi. Gulide's daughter goes out to welcome Feidilmid mac Crimthainn and the men of Munster. *Luid [ind ingen] co riacht na slógu ⁊ atbert: Fo dia, a Feidilmid cot slogaib archena,'* translated by Meyer 'Hail, O F., with thy hosts as well' (Hib. Min. 66 §6). Here *Fo dia* could well be replaced by *Fo chen*. (In a text from Rawl. B. 502 Meyer takes the sentence *Dia ar a bethaid* as = 'God preserve her life', and from it assumes *Dia ar do bethaid* as an alternative to *Dia do betha*. But in a footnote (ZCP ii 135) he acknowledges that he may have punctuated wrongly and that the sentence should read *Is bennachda dún Dia ar a bethaid* i.e. 'God be praised that she is still alive!'.)

In the later language at any rate *dia* in the phrase was definitely felt to be *Dia*, 'God'. Note the plural *Dia bar mbetha, a daltada inmaine* (RC xxxv 205) where the force of 'Hail!' or 'Welcome' alone remains for the sentence

18

is spoken by Maelsuthain to the spirits of three of his dead pupils who have appeared to him. Similarly of course in the sentence quoted above *Nárab Dia do betha, a bháis*! 'No welcome to you, O Death'.

That a Christian greeting should occur in the early pagan tale of TBC need cause no surprise. A monkish scribe might well inadvertently substitute it for some such phrase as *Mo chen, Fo chen* in his exemplar. So a 14th-century poet, Gofraidh Fionn Ó Dálaigh, writing of an episode in the mythical Second Battle of Moytura makes the doorkeeper of Tara invite Lugh to enter with the words: *Tair san dúnadh. Dia do betha*! 'Enter the fortress. Welcome!' (Irish Bardic poetry 17 §45).

501   *La sodain fónérig* Y reads *faneraig*. Possibly the U- reading is a scribal error (with *fó-*for *fa-*) for *fanópair*. Cf. infra *fanópair-som* 518 and *fónópair* 575. It is suggested (Stories from Táin[3] Glossary) that *fo-érig* means 'rises to attack'. See RIA Dictionary s.v.

525   *Ní bí nóenden* . . . This would seem to be a direct quotation from the tale Noínden Ulad: *Ní bíid trá in ces-sa for mnáib ⁊ macaib, ⁊ for Coin Culand ar nirbo do Ultaib dó, nach for cach óen no-bíid frisin crích anechtair* Celtica viii 29.65–6.

528–9   *⁊ ane . . . garséle* This sentence which is not in Y reads like a scribal addition.

532   Here U alone reads *doíagat*. Again infra 1017. In both instances Y reads *dothíagad*. One would expect the verb *do-tét* here. Cf. *Tancaisiu fon egim* IT i 101.24; *Éighthi in muccid co tánic túath in dá Maine fae* BDD[2] 210. T. F. O'Rahilly, quoting from a conversation with Bergin, says that the form *doíagat* is due to the influence of *tíagat* which owing to its original *t-* looked as if it were a compound of *do-* (Hermathena 1926 164). Might the U-spelling indicate that *-th-* had become *-h-* and was omitted? Thus in the present text we find *dorissi* 661, *arisi* 2511, i.e. *-th- > h* is omitted. Cf. *dothoet ina frithlurg afrihisi* Trip.[2] 412. In the present text we also find *afrithisi* 1341, *aridisi* 685, this spelling where *-d-* alternates with *-th-* showing that *-th-* was not always pronounced *-h-*.

559   *co mbítis tornochta* The use of the substantive verb here is remarkable. See Bergin, Ériu xii 226. I note that in Stories from Táin[3] the phrase is altered to *comtis tornocht*.

561–2   *Asbert-side in [n]-etarbíad a gnímu acht tísed dó co áes ferdatad* In Stories from Táin[3] the readings taken are . . . *a ngnímau* . . . *dóib*, and in the Glossary s.v. '*etar-bí* (or *etar-ben*?)' the translation given is 'whether there would be a distinction between their deeds provided they reached manhood'. In the context this does not make very good sense; Conchobor is amazed at the little boy's prowess in games and must be referring to him rather than to his playmates. The compiler of Recension II certainly took Conchobor's words to refer to Cú Chulainn: *Amae a ócu, bar Conchobor, mo chin tír asa tánic in mac bec atchid dá mbetis na gnímu óclachais aice feib atát na macgníma. Ní comdas a rád, ar Fergus. Feib atré in mac bec atrésat a gnímu óclachais leis* Táin 843–6, 'Ah my warriors, said Conchobor, happy is the land from which came the little boy ye see if his manly deeds were to be like his boyish exploits. It is not right to speak thus, said Fergus, for as the little boy grows, so also will his deeds of manhood increase with him'. Stowe has a similar passage (876–9). I should therefore read . . . *a gnímu* . . . *dó*. See note by M. A. O'Brien, Ériu xi 161–2, who reads as I do and translates 'He asked would there be something corresponding to his present deeds when he reached manhood.'

573   *a hEspáin dosfucad*   This has been taken as a scribal interpolation here. It may well have been a footnote copied into the text. Here *-s-* (if not Mid. Ir. eztension of *-s-* to all genders), has a relative function, but no relative would be required in such a sentence in early Mid. Ir.

578   *bunsaid*   the reading of LU here is noteworthy. Again infra *mullaid* 1360 for *mullaig*. Confusion between *-d* slender and *-g* slender begins in the 12th century. See Hermathena xx 192.

585–6   *Mad iar n-arailiu* [*slicht*] . . .   *Mad iar n-arailib* supra 303 and *Mád iar n-araili slicht* infra 873. See Zimmer, KZ xxviii 489 and note by E. G. Quin, Studia Celtica ii 95. Note that for this passage Recension II combines both versions of the killing. The boy cast the ball into the hound's gaping jaws and then seized him and dashed him to pieces against a standing-stone (Táin 881–5).

594[a]   The marginal note in hand M does not agree with the account of the three hounds in Conganchnes's brain given in Aided Cheltchair (Death Tales p. 28 §11). There is also a discrepancy in the age attributed to Cú Chulainn in this note, *hi cind a secht mbliadna*. Cf. 605 *amdar lána a sé bliadna*. So too in Recension II: *i cind sé mbliadan arna brith* Táin 916.

602   For *ass* here Vendryes suggests reading *acht* and translates 'unless I do not consider them visible i.e. worthy of being seen' Ériu xvi 21f.

618   *Cia dorinchoisc sén duit*   *Do-inchoisc* trans. means 'instructs, teaches', often 'instructs in druidic art.' Cf. note on *tecosc* Éigse xi 214–5. But *do-inchoisc sén*, (*ainsén*) *do x* = 'prophesies good fortune (ill fortune) for x'. In the tale Longes Chonaill Chuirc, Corc is banished to Scotland by Crimthan mac Fidaig with a secret ogam writing on his shield asking that he be put to death. His friend Gruibne changes the instructions on the shield and says: *Cia rot lessaigestar, or se, cossind ogumsa fil it scíath? Nip sén dorinchossig* (LL 37024–5), translated by V. Hull 'It was not good fortune that it indicated', with footnote 'lit. that it has instructed' (PMLA 56.1941). 'It boded you ill' might perhaps give a closer rendering, lit. 'It was not good fortune that it foretold'.

624   *Falloing-side immorro éseom*   In Stories from Táin[3] (p. 11) this is emended to *F-a-lloing-som side immurgu*. Similar emendations for ll. 651–2.

631   *Nách tussu ém donarchossaig* . . .   In Stowe TBC this passage reads *Nach tusa do t[h]eagaisc sén dó?* (986–7) and Cú Chulainn says *Is é do t[h]egaisc sén dam-sa* (990).

633   *Cid dochana duit in bréc do imbirt form*   Note the W-reading *in mbréig*. This older syntactical construction, with the accusative governed by the main verb + dative of verbal noun preceded by *do*, is not uncommon in Mid. Ir., as e.g. *Ro triall-som dano in n-áes ndána do marbad* SC 836. See Celtica viii 164.

639 *animgnaid* In Stories from Táin[3] it is suggested this is a corruption of *anetargnaid*. In RIA Contributions the meaning given for *ainetargnaid* is 'unrecognized, unknown, strange', but like *ingnad* it may be a eulogistic term 'wonderful, remarkable', with *an-* an intensive prefix, not a negative. The ⁊ for *et* with stroke overhead for *-ar-* might easily be read as *-im-*.

655–6 *It cóema na heich* Taken by translators as said by Cú Chulainn. Obviously it is Ibor who implies that now that the boy has seen how fine the horses are, he should alight. But see infra note on *cáem* 1754. Could 'small' rather than *cáem* 'fine' possibly be the meaning intended here?

663 *indaig brot forsin n-echraid* The same use of *ind-aig brot*, 'ply the goad' occurs again infra 776. The commoner phrase is *aigid brot*, or *saigid brot*. Cf. *Saig brot dún forsin n-echraid* Táin 1152; *Saigis Láeg brot forin n-echraid* LL 12585 (Aided Guill ⁊ Gairb) and *aig brot forin n-echraid* ib. 12742, 12807. In the Fer Diad episode we get *ic indsaidi brot forsin n-echraid* 2971 = *ic indsaige broit* . . .

727–8 *tollem écraite fris* 'to show yourself unfriendly to him'. In Stories from Táin[3] Strachan in the Glossary s.v. *tuillem* translates this 'to incur enmity (i.e. from the Ulstermen by slaying Cú Chulainn).' But as the W- reading shows the idiom here is *tuillem écraite fri nech* = 'to incur someone's enmity'. The word *fris* is essential to give the meaning. Cf. *Nirb áil don rig ⁊ don rigain cosa tancaibair tullem ecraiti frib* LU 8978–80 (FB), 'to show themselves unfriendly to you.' The genitive is sometimes used instead of *fri* in such sentences, so it is possible that the U- reading was originally *tollem a écraite*. Cf. *chum gan a dhiomdha do thuilleadh* Stapleton 119. (*diomdha* = *di* + *buide*, so this is the opposite of *tuillem buide*, for which see ZCP xviii 206–12).

738 *lám deóraid* See note by Vernam Hull (ZCP xvii 70–71) who takes *lám deóraid* to be a proverbial expression meaning 'death, destruction'.

779 *Slaittius . . . dammainti* Strachan (ZCP ii 485) takes the affixed pronoun of *slaittius* to refer to the horses and that of *dammainti* to refer to the deer. I have followed his translation. I suggest, however, that there may be some doubt. The scribe may have misread *Slaitti sethnón* . . . or we may have here an early instance of confusion of affixed pronouns. Cú Chulainn is not in the chariot. He has dismounted to catch the deer, and lashing the horses to a gallop would not tame the deer. If we take the sentence *cumrigis* . . . as preceding this one it would make sense of Strachan's rendering.

787 *Tria tháithbémmend* . . . In Aided Aenfir Aífe the boy Conla brings birds down alive with stones from his sling: *dosleged tathbem forsna heonu congebead na airberthe dib it e beoa, conda leiged uad isinn aer doridisi* Ériu i 114 §2. Again in Seirgligi Con Culaind, Cú Chulainn brings down birds, but in this instance not with slingstones but with his sword: *ataig táithbéim dia chlaidiub dóib* (SC 49). Then he distributes the birds among the women-folk. One may conclude that the birds were alive and that the women coveted them as pets. Cf. Medb's *petta eóin*.

804 *ardáilfe fuil laiss cach dune* Again 809 *ardáilfe fuil lim cach áein* where only C has the reading *lium*. (The editors of YBL- TBC do not take

the verb as impersonal and suggest reading *ardáliub* in the second occurrence). Here *ardáili* is used impersonally with *fuil* accusative and the preposition *la* denoting the agent who sheds the blood. In the equivalent passage in Recension III the verb *feraid* is used impersonally and the preposition *oc* denotes the agent: *ferfaidh cru dar cuiged Conchobuir anocht aigi* ZCP viii 538.14. Cf supra 309 *ferais snechta mór forru*, lit. 'it poured great snow on them', *snechta* accusative, i.e. 'it snowed heavily on them.' Other instances of a transitive verb used impersonally with *la* for agent occur again in *no tróistfed lais in cloich fria cend* (970), 'he would throw the stone at her head'; *Is and romemaid lais forin mbuidin* (4111–2). With these examples cf. *nimirchói nach géin* (= *céin*) *libsi* Wb. 7^a 11, translated 'I shall not be delayed with you for any long time' (but I take *libsi* to mean 'by you'). For a discussion of the usage see Vendryes, Sur l'emploi impersonnel du verbe, Celtica iii 193–4. See also Pedersen VG ii 310–11.

806 *clár clé* Here a *geis*, but sometimes a challenge to battle. See infra 1341.

808 The form *toingthe* in U is a corruption of *toingte* the regular 3 pl. relative form, which we find supra 794–5.

815 *focherdat i ndabaig n-úarusci* Cf. similar passages in Seirglige Con Culaind LU 3793–5 and in Brislech Mór Maige Murthemni LL 13763–8.

823 *nipo machdad* . . . See Prof. E. G. Quin's article on the Irish Modal Preterite, Hermathena cxvii 45–62. *cia chonbósad-saide* I have adopted Strachan's emendation. Should we perhaps read *cia chonbósa[d]-ide*?

I have taken *notragad* (U Y) *nodragad* (W) as an early instance of substitution of conditional with infixed pronoun for imperfect subjunctive. *Téit for* = 'attacks' (Contribb.) but perhaps = 'overcomes'. Cf. *érgid for hUltu!* ZCP x 318 z. If we omitted *cia* before *notragad*, the use of conditional might be explained. Thurneysen quotes an instance of subj. with *cia* co-ordinated with an indicative without *cia*. *Cia beid* (subj.) *Crist indib-si et is* (indic) *béo ind anim tri sodin* Wb. 4^{a}6.

Strachan suggested 'an idiomatic use of *trágid*, exhausts, ebbs' (reading *no trágad*), but no other instance of *trágid for* is recorded.

831 One would expect the sentence *Lingid Fergus darsin n-omnai ina charput* to come here. In all versions of Recension I it comes after the interpolated Aided Fraích. I take it that the sentence was delayed by the interpolation of that episode. There would be no point in Medb's request *Discart dín in n-écin fil fornd* etc. unless they were in difficulty about leaping across the felled tree. On the other hand the interpolation is clumsy, for their predicament is the felled tree which prevents the advance of the army, but killing Cú Chulainn which is what Fráech is asked to do and attempts to do is not the help needed. For a full discussion of the Aided Fraích episode see Professor James Carney, Studies in Ir. Lit. and History pp. 66–76. Cf. also Táin Introd. pp. xxix–xxxi.

856 *for colaind Fraich meic Idaid* In the three other MSS. . . . *maic Fidaid*. See note on the name TBFr^2 2.

864 *cuitbiud*, 'mockery' > cause for mockery or derision, hence 'disgrace, shame'. Used in this sense by the H-interpolator here and again 1549, 1971. Again in hand H in TBFlid. LU 1604. In hand M in the present

text the word is used with the usual meaning 'mockery' (infra 1899–1900,). In FM iv 934.11 we get *fo mhéla ⁊ cuitbhedh.*

868 *Aided Órláim* Órlám mac Ailella is loved by Dartaid daughter of Eochu Bec, and brings her cows to help in the cattle-raid of Cúailnge (TBDartada IT ii² 194).

869–70 *Dosléci Cú Chulaind ríam* The translation suggested in the Contributions is 'lets them go before him (?)' which hardly suits the context. The equivalent sentence in Recension II is the exact opposite in meaning. *Luid Cú Chulaind ríam remáin rempu* Táin 1219. Zimmer translates the LU sentence as 'C.C. macht sich vorher'. I take -*s*- here to be 3 s.m. reflexive pronoun, a Mid. Ir. usage, and the meaning to be 'he goes forward.' Compare in a later passage *fosfóbair ina charpat remi* 3323 = *táinic reme trí lár fer ṅHérend* Táin 3805. In Tochmarc Emere when Cú Chulainn is angered by Bricriu: *Nos bertaigend co ráemid in cholcid boí foí* LU 10478 [H]. Contrast in Recension II the description of Dáire's gratification: *Ra mbertaig co raimdetar úammand a cholcthech faí* Táin 98.

906 *brisfed* = *no brisfed.* Note *do* replacing *no* in Y.

910 For the reading *an trí n-araid* see note by Bergin, Ériu xi 147.

911 *dá macdalta ind ríg* This refers to Eirr and Inell (supra 256–7). Note that no reference is made to their charioteers who were killed with them. Similarly in Recension II only the two sons of Nera are mentioned here.

913 *Bentatar . . .* Again 927. An analogical formation based on *bertatar.* Thus *berim: bertatar; benim; bentatar.*

918–9 *ní fír trá . . . cen chinaid* Omitted in W. It is hard to see any reason for killing the charioteer at this point. Possibly it was because he had dropped Órlám's head from his back as he neared the fort (902), but this seems inadequate. Note that Cú Chulainn also killed the three charioteers of meic Gárach, probably because he had been attacked by six men at once. Again when he kills Cuillius, the charioteer of Ailill, it was probably because he had taken Fergus's sword.

932 *Ní ma lodsaid dó* This is the reading of C only; the other MSS. read *Ba mad lodsaid.* Cf. infra 981 *Ní ma lodsaid dó.* It is of course possible that *Ba mad lodsaid* used ironically is here the correct reading.

938 *toingthe* See supra n. 808. Here one might have expected the singular form with *túath* as supra 736: *Tongu do dia toinges mo thúath.*

939 *Tait ass . . . dúnd* 'Come on . . . I beg you' *Dúnd* ethical dative as often used courteously with imperative. Cf. *Airisiu sein innocht dún* infra 2178. I take the spelling *táet* to be a mere scribal slip. I note that in a later passage where U Y W all read *Tait ass* (infra 1210) C again spells as *Taot.* This passage is quoted in Contribb. as an impersonal construction 3 s. ipv. with *do* of person, and translated 'let us set out'.

947 *Dagéini .i. tic* In Scél Baili Binnbérlaig where the 16c. MS. H 3.18 reads *Tainic in fer atuaigh dia torrachtain* (MS. Mat. p. 472), Harl. 5280 has *Dogene an uir* [Latin loanword] *atuaid dia torrachtain* (RC xiii 221.10). The

Harleian text contains besides loanwords borrowings from Bérla na Filed. In LU 10996 *Ethe [.i. dognither* M] *lasin óclaic[h], etha* = itum est, translated by Meyer, Voyage of Bran. I 52, 'They went with the warrior'. Cf. the later use of *do-gni* = 'goes'.

947–8 *Anais cadessin* ... Faraday translated 'He waited himself to meet C.C.' *Cadesin* here is an intensive or emphatic word, re-inforcing both subject and verb. Ailill has just ordered the army to travel in haste on to Cúailnge in order to avoid further bloodshed. But Lethan disregards the order. The full force of *Anais cadessin* ... here is 'He actually stood his ground and waited to encounter C.C.' In other instances of *cadessin* in the present text the English rendering might be 'moreover, too', or colloquially 'into the bargain'. See infra 1733, 3787.

Another instance *Bai bráthair laiss, Long mac Ebonis cadessin* (infra 1878) = *Bai bráthair laiss .i. Long mac E.* Cf. semi-archaic English 'even' = 'to wit, namely'. In current Irish *féin* might replace *cadessin* in such a sentence. *L. mac E. féin*, 'none other than L. mac E.'

Cadessin is generally equated with *fadessin*. Pedersen (VG ii 153) analysed as *cid* + pronoun + demonstrative. But Professor David Greene points out the objections to this analysis in his note on *fa-dessin* Ériu xxi 93–4. He adds, however, that 'the otherwise inexplicable *ca-* may have arisen from the influence of *cid eseom*, "even he".' *Cadessin* sometimes seems to retain the force of such a phrase. The sentence *Anais cadessin* ... might have been *Cid éseom* (or *Cid Lethan*) *anais ara chend*. There seems no doubt that *cadessin, cadéin, céin* are analogical formations based on *fadessin, fadéin, féin*.

(*Sin* enclitic with personal pronouns is, as Professor Greene pointed out, never found in O.Ir. But late instances of *cid esen, cid isen* occur in Stowe TBC 3971, 3990 = *cid hiside* in the older LL- version, Táin 4007, 4030).

Cadessin, emphatic, is always postfixed or parenthetical; *cid éseom, cit iat-side* etc. generally prefixed or parenthetical. But cf. *Ragat-sa ara chind cid me* LL 33066.

Is it possible that *cadessin* comes from *cid fessin*? Cf. *ni comalnatsom cid feissne recht* gl. neque enim qui circumciduntur legem custodiunt Wb. 20ᶜ 22. This is translated 'even they themselves fulfil not the law'. I should omit 'themselves'; *cid feissne* is adequately rendered by 'even'. In the 1827 edition of the Pauline epistles the reading is *Óir an dream sin féin atá timchill-ghearrtha ni choimhéuduid siad an reacht*, where *féin* = 'even'. Again *torand hi frecndairc indib cadesin* Sg. 150ᵇ2 is translated 'a signification in the present in them themselves'. I suggest omitting 'themselves' and adding 'too'. *Ataat tuisil indib cadésin* Sg. 188ᵃ2 I should render 'there are cases in them also'. In Immram Curaig Maíle Dúin, the voyagers come to an island whose inhabitants cease not from weeping. One of the crew lands ⁊ *gabais coi leó*. Two more go to bring him back and *fecsit cadesne for coi*, 'they too fell to weeping' (LU 1773).

954 *forrumai* for *fosruma*, the Y reading.

955 *Allechtu* = the Fury Allecto Thurneysen thought that identification of the Mórrígan with Allecto showed a direct acquaintance with Aeneid vii 323f. But Gerard Murphy noted (Éigse viii 157 n.4) that Allecto is also mentioned in a Mid. Ir. gloss on Amra Choluim Chille and that in an eleventh-century Anglo-Saxon glossary she is identified with the Valkyrie. He suggests

that such identification was probably a mere commonplace in the Irish and Anglo-Saxon schools and in no way denoted direct borrowing.

in Mórrigan (*Mórrigan* MS.) In LL the form is *Mórrigu*; Stowe agrees with Recension I and both forms are found in Recension III. The oldest instance is in the Vatican MS. Regina 215 where *lamia monstrum in feminae figura* is glossed *morigain* (with one -*r*- as later in this text l. 1845). The first element *mor*- is said to be cognate with OHG *mara* and AS. *maere* (the second element in Eng. nightmare, Fr. cauchemar). See KZ xxxviii 468. Folk-etymology changed *mor*- to *mór*-.

957–62 Wolfgang Krause has given a tentative German translation of this passage in ZCP xxiii. In Y *l*. (i.e. *laíd*) is prefixed to this *rosc*. In Recension III it is called *roscad* and is said to be a prophecy of his death to Donn Cúailnge: *Da ghabh aga faisneis ⁊ aga innisinn dó go muirfidhe é ar tanaidh ⁊ do rinne in rosgadh sa ann* (ZCP viii 541.7–8).

976 *Sraithus di c[h]loich* Lit. 'He pelted her with a stone', i.e. 'He threw a stone at her'. For the form *sraí* beside the regular *s*-preterite *sréis* see Ériu xviii 92. Like *do-bidci sréid* (*sreíd*) is used in the sense of 'casts, hurls' as in *Srethait cethri goi deac i n-óenfecht fair* infra 1945–6 as well as with the meaning 'pelts, shoots at', with object of the person or thing cast at and *de, di* for the missile: *sraíthe dín chertgai* 1504. It may be noted that in this text when *sréid* is used with the meaning 'casts, flings' it sometimes has an anticipatory infixed pronoun: *sréthi in n-id . . . isin n-abaind* (711), 'he cast (it) the withe into the river'.

1000 *Conéracht Glaiss Chruind friu* Thurneysen has compared this rising of the river to impede the army to a passage in the Iliad where the Scamander rises against Achilles (Heldensage 96, ZCP x 207–8). This might be taken as an incident common to early heroic literature, but, as Professor W. B. Stanford acutely notes (PRIA 70 c 3, p. 32 n. 68), such sudden flooding of rivers is not known in Ireland but was common in Mediterranean rivers. On the other hand, may not such river-floods have been common in Ireland at a very early period and the memory of them preserved in tradition? Recension II makes no definite mention of these floods, merely noting that the army tried to cross Glais Chruind and failed, and that the river swept a hundred chariots off to sea (Táin 1349–52).

1003 *gabais liic móir Lía* is generally masculine. But cf. *oc Líac Mór* supra 945 and *ic Líic Móir* Táin 1270. This may merely be an instance of a feminine adjective used with accusative of a masculine noun, for which see M. A. O'Brien, Celtica ii 346; iv 102.

1011–2 *⁊ ro fer fuire n-imnaise* Meaning obscure. RIA Dictionary quotes a gloss *fuire .i. brón* (KZ xxxiii 83). W. Krause suggested reading *fúiri* acc. of *fúire* 'furia' (ZCP xxii 142). Possibly we have here another instance of a scribe's deliberate choice of archaic obsolete words. Cf. supra 947.

1012 *Atbath cét n-ánrod friss rind ríg* Meaning of *rind ríg* is obscure. Recension III here reads *⁊ marbhais cet fer n-armach n-innrigtha díb im Raen ⁊ im Ri (⁊) im dha hsenchaidh na tana, gurab ed sin ruc tain amugha ⁊ ar iaradh in fad ro boi* (ZCP viii 543.19–21). A possible emendation of the Recension I reading might be *Atbath cét n-ánrod n-inríge friss*.

1030–1234 This *córugud aile* is something more than what the scribe denotes elsewhere as *slicht sain*. It gives a long series of *roscada* which obviously date from the oldest tradition of the Táin. But the framework in which these *roscada* are set has obviously been devised by some compiler. In part it is a re-telling of incidents which occur elsewhere in the tale. But it also contains matter not found in the other recensions.

1033–4 In the division of the cattle-prey there is an echo of a passage in Táin Bó Regamain (or may it be that TBReg. echoes this passage of TBC?). Maine Mórgor, driving off the cattle of Regamon to the help of Ailill and Medb, says: *Randtar in almu sa i ndé . . . ᛐ in slog, is romor for aenchae uile iad* IT II² 229. That is the YBL- reading; that of Eg. 1782 is closer in wording to TBC: ᛐ *rantar in cetra, ar ni rucfiter ar oenchoe* (ib.). There is here a repetition of the derivation of the place-name *Bernas Bó nUlad* (= the earlier and more lucidly explained *Bernas Bó Cúailnge* 1007–10).

1039 ff. This account of the stealing of Fergus's sword shows some discrepancy. Cf. the references to the same incident in Aided Etarcomail and Comrac Fergusa where it is implied that Ailill, not his charioteer, had taken the sword. See Táin Introd. pp. l-li.

1069–73 In Indo-Celtica, Gedächtnisschrift für Alf Sommerfelt pp. 35–6 Dr. Binchy has given for this passage a text based on the four MSS. of TBC I, marking the separate rhythms and giving an annotated translation. He has very kindly given me permission to use his translation of this *rosc*. For the rest of the passage 1075ff. I have given my own inadequate and tentative rendering.

1160–3 This is a repetition of a quatrain chanted by Dubthach in an earlier passage (198–201), or Dubthach's quatrain is a repetition of this passage. Thurneysen, who attributes the whole section called *córugud aile* to B, says that this quatrain has been taken over from an earlier A-passage (Heldensage 150 n.2).

1170–4 Cú Chulainn's welcome to Lugaid is couched in the same terms as his welcome to Fergus in a later passage (which Thurneysen assigns to A). This greeting was a set formula; we find it twice more, 1312–6 and in Comrac Fir Diad 2728–31.

In translating *alailiu, arailiu* as 'or else' I have adopted the brilliant suggestion of E. Gordon Quin (Studia Celtica ii 93–5). Quin would render it as 'You shall have a goose and a half. Alternatively if fish swim' etc. For this usage see Gramm. p. 239 and Bergin's note Ériu xiv 29. The punctuation of LU with full stop after both *alailiu* and *arailiu* may be disregarded; it merely indicates that the scribe no longer understood the meaning of the dat. sg. *arailiu*. One might have expected an early copyist to substitute *nó* for *arailiu*; against this would be the fact that the form occurred in a stock phrase. In the later language the usage was certainly not understood. Thus in the late version of the Comrac Fir Diad tale in Franciscan MS. 16 (Thurneysen's Version IV), the passage reads: *da ttaighle liath léna an magh rodbiasa caghan go leth ᛐ da ttaighle iasg an inmhear rodbhiasa eigne go leth ᛐ biaidh aroile dorn bioluir* etc. (ZCP x 280.10–12). Best edited to . . . *eigne go leth aroile ᛐ dorn* etc. but the misplacement of *aroile* shows the scribe's uncertainty and his attempt to emend the phrase as it probably stood in his original.

1171–4 *gass fochluchta* Again infra 1314. *Fochlacht* is the edible sea-weed known as laver. Plunkett gives the form *fochlach* s.v. laver. The so-called 'laver-bread', a delicacy peculiar as far as I know to the South Wales sea-ports, is made from this plant. *Fochlacht* occurs several times in Buile Šuibne, always in association with *biorar*, 'watercress'. In Fealsúnacht Aodha Mhic Dhomhnaill we get *falacht* 'water-parsley'. *Falacht is maith an luibh í so lena bruith air uisge ⁊ a sú de eol* 1303 § 38.

1187–90 Cf. another passage 1550–1 in an interpolation where reference is also made to Cú Chulainn's being provisioned by the enemy. In Recension II there is no mention of food supplied to Cú Chulainn, but in Recension III one of the terms of peace offered him is *A biathad ⁊ a eided in fad bheas ar tánaidh* (ZCP viii 547). Peculiar to this passage in Recension I is the limitation of the truce to Fergus's force, to the physicians and to Ailill's men when joined to those of Fergus.

1210 *Tait ass do Chúil Airthir* I take *tait* as 2 pl. imperative of *do-tét*, and these words to be part of Fergus's speech. Other translators read as *Téit ass* . . . ('He goes thence to C.A.' Faraday). The following episode *Ecmaic . . . Áth Duirn* (1211–27) interrupts the narrative and is inserted before we are told that they reached Cúil Airthir (1228).

1214–5 This is the same warning as that which Súaltaim takes to Conchobor in the later part of the tale.

1219–20 These words of Conchobor seem to imply that the *cess* was an intermittent affliction.

1227–8 The C- reading *níro ansatar* gives better sense. At some period a scribe must have read the *n*- stroke as being over -*s*-, and taken it as -*acht*-.

1256 *oc escaid* For etymology of *escaid* see note by M. A. O'Brien, Celtica iii 171–2.

1266 *Doéth* (again 1272). As noted in the Diplomatic Edition the aspiration mark over the -*t* is faint. Zimmer (KZ xxx.23) read as *doét* and took it to be for *do-thét*. But note that the verb in the next sentence is passive in both instances. *Doeth* is here the preterite passive. Cf. *Do-eth o Ailill ⁊ o Meidb do chungid in chon* Sc. M.² §1.3 where the variant readings for *do-eth* are *Tancas* . . ., *Do-thoet techta* . . ., *Do-tiagait techta* . . . In the present text it is obviously Mac Roth who goes on the mission. We might translate 'He was visited once more (by Mac Roth)'.

1284 *assa cessaib* The use of the plural is noteworthy.

1297 *ní tharda a rád fri diardain* In Stories from Táin³ taken as *ní tardae arad fri díardain*, *arad* 'ladder' used in a figurative sense. It is translated there 'provided thou dost not provoke a quarrel'. Note that the Stowe paraphrase agrees with this translation: *acht nat cuinge fen ugra no imreasain* 1618). See note on passage by editor of C.

1315 *má thecra* Strachan (Stories from Táin³ p 103) suggests that this may be a scribal error for *má thecma*, 3 s. pres. subj. of *do-ecmaing*. But see note by M. A. O'Brien, Ériu x 160, who takes the verb to be **to-ess-gair*, 'call forth, challenge'.

1337 *fiad Fergus* These words are in contradiction to the stipulation made by Fergus when he consented to let Etarcomal accompany him. In Y *fiad* is followed by the genitive, *fiad Fergais*.

1341 *dorala clár clé frinn* This was a challenge to fight. In Recension II Cú Chulainn comments on this sentence of Láeg: *Etarcumul sain, a gillai, condaig comrac cucum-sa* Táin 1637.

1348 *glanad mo lám inniut* Lit. 'to wash my hands in you', i.e. 'in your blood'. In the Rawl. B 512 version of Scéla Mucce Meic Da Thó the same idiom occurs. Cet says to Munremur: *Mé ro glan mo lám fá deóid innat* (Sc. M.². p. 11 §12a), 'I have dipped my hand in your blood at last'. Other translaters render: 'I am loath to cleanse my hands in you' (Faraday). 'I don't want to have to clean my hands on your account' (Greene). The idiom I use seems to give the essential meaning.

1360 *mullaid* in LU. Cf. supra n. 578.

1363 *Is garit mo lorg latt.* I have translated this literally, taking the meaning to be 'You do not expect me to chastise you'. For a suggestion of another meaning for the phrase see note by M. A. O'Brien, Études Celt. iii 169–71.

1383–4 *Ní tocrád dam . . . coin móir* Tocrád 'act of annoying, torment'. In this sense the word occurs twice in Stowe TBC (703, 829). In both Stowe and Táin it is a synonym of *confére*. Thus *Niba dóig mo chonpére sund* 445 = *Ní lat-su fo dóig lim-sa mo chrád d'fagbáil samlaid* Táin 797 (. . . *tocrad* Stowe).

In the Contributions this sentence is quoted s.v. *do-cuirethar* (without *do* before *glieid*) from YBL, *ni tocrad dam int aitheach gleid frisin coin moir*, and translated 'should not have engaged in fight with' (*dam* left untranslated).

In LL the equivalent passage reads *Ciarso dúal don athiuchmatud saigid forsin n-árchoin* Táin 1691, 'what right had the mongrel to attack the bloodhound?' In Stowe and Recension III *do gleo* is the reading: *Cid fa badh dual don aithechmadadh anuasal techt do gleo no d'esorccain frisin arcoin iorgaile* Stowe 1730–1; *Carsa dúal don aithechmhadudh tocht do ghleo ⁊ d'imrísin risin árchoin irghaile* ZCP viii 553.

1388 ff The Nad Crantail episode is the one which varies most in the three recensions. (See Zimmer, KZ xxviii 500–505; Thurneysen ZCP ix 434 and Táin n.1696ff.). The Recension I version contains some motifs found in other episodes, e.g. Lugaid warns Cú Chulainn of Nad Crantail's attack (= Fer Báeth episode). Nad Crantail refuses to fight with a beardless boy (= Lóch mac Mo Femis episode).

Nad Crantail is the first man to ask for and be promised Finnabair as a reward for encountering Cú Chulainn. Cúr is merely told that it would be a valiant deed to fight Cú Chulainn. (We may discount the H- interpolation which describes how Ailill tries to pacify Cú Chulainn by offering him Finnabair). Then Fer Báeth is promised the maid. So is Láiríne mac Nóis, and again she is named among the inducements offered to Lóch and Long.

1438–9 *cid moch donté* For *do-n-d-té*, with the usual infixed neuter pronoun.

1444 *Cáte* MS. Again 1473. Strachan suggested (Ériu i 10) that the *cáte* of LU was apparently associated with *áit*. Cf. later *cáit*.

1446 *domarfás* For the accent on the final *a* rather than the first see Glossary BDD² s.v. *do-adbat*.

1474 *do mmo maccaib* For this reduplication of *-m-* see KZ xxxviii pp. 468–9.

1478–9 This account of the distortion might well be omitted here. In Recension II (LL but not Stowe) Cú Chulainn's distortion occurs when he wraps his mantle around the pillar-stone. This would explain why Nad Crantail failed to recognize him on the second day.

1491 *Bude mac Báin* In Recensions II and III he is called *Buide mac Báin Blai.* Cf. a passage in Fled Bricrend where Sencha sends the three Ulster warriors for a decision about the *curadmir* to a *Buide mac Báin* (LU 8996–7). In the dindshenchas of Sliab Callann (MD iv 170) Buide mac Báin is said to have owned Callann, one of the three hounds from the brain of Conganchness. See supra footnote to l. 594. Buide's hound was killed by Donn Cúailnge. Slíab Callann = Slieve Gallion, Co. Derry, but in this passage of TBC Buide comes as we should expect from Slieve Gullion, in Armagh. Though near at hand in Armagh Buide is one of the Connacht warriors. In LL he is called *Buide mac Báin Blai do chrích Ailella ⁊ Medba* Táin 1772.

1498 *Atá amal fondráncamair* I take *amal* here to mean 'where'. To translate 'as we found him' would not answer the question. Again infra 1892 *Dotháet íarum dochum ind átha amal bui*, which I translate '. . . to the ford where he was'. This instance occurs in a passage which is not in Y. In C it reads '. . . *amal mbui* (950–1), with *am̄* deleted by a later hand and *a* added with a caret mark so as to give the reading . . . *a mbui*. To the emendator, at any rate, *amal* here meant 'where'. *Amal,* temporary conjunction, 'when', could come to mean 'where'. Cf. Fr. où meaning 'where' and 'when', la maison où je suis né, le jour où je suis parti. Again *áit i, airm i, port i* could mean 'where' or 'when'. *Ait i n-accai [.i. in tarb] in búachail tofábair cucai* supra 990–1, 'where (or when) the bull caught sight of the herdsman, he made for him'. In Comrac Fir Diad: *Demin leo baili i comrecdais dá úaitne chomlaind in tsaegail co mbad comthoitini dóib* (2818–9), 'when they would meet'. Other instances in Recension II Táin 1272, 3922.

In Recension III the answer to Cú Chulainn's question 'Where is the herdsmen?' is *Ait a fuil gu n-arlaither ris*, 'Where he is, speak to him' (RC xiv 257 §14).

1508 Perhaps we should insert *chách* after *ansu*. LL reads *nábud chalmu chách Cú Chulaind menibeth in clessin ingantach bai aice, clettin Con Culaind* (Táin 1805–6).

1511 The C-reading *a comairliu Ailella* seems the better one here. In RIA Contributions *a comarli* is quoted from this passage as meaning 'with intent, designedly'. But such a meaning does not seem to occur elsewhere; *a comairli x*, 'on the advice of x', is the usual expression.

1522 *Humarrith = Umaśruth.* Cf. O'Clery, *umharradh .i. umha śruth .i. śruth an umha.*

1537–8 *⁊ in fiallach timtacht in tarbh* *Timtacht* for *timmacht = do-immacht*, 'that drove away the bull'. Cf. the readings of C and LL and *conid timachtatár* in the next line.

1541 *Atá and . . . = Atá amlaid . . . = Is amlaid atá . . .*

1543 *adchota* *adcotad* Y and C. The U- reading is for O. Ir. *adcotae*, pass. subj.

1558 *ar galaib óenfer* is the reading of U here and 1736, 2493. Again in TBDD *ar galaib óenfer* LU 7283.

1572 ff. *Téit Mani* etc. This is a repetition of the earlier passage where Mac Roth goes to parley with Cú Chulainn (1246 ff.)

1577 *la sóud úad* A verbal noun phrase with *la* is common in the H- interpolations in LU. Thus in an H-passage in Fled Bricrend there occur five instances: *la eirgi súas co opund* 8381 and again 8522, 8536, 8545-6. However, there are two instances of the usage in hand M in Immram Curaig Maíle Dúin (1798, 1805).

1586 *ara n-airlathar dó in n-ingin* Something omitted after *ara n-airlathar* (read *ara n-arlathar* as in W). Some such words as ⁊ *ara tairgea* or ⁊ *ara naiscea* may have been dropped after the first verb. Alternatively we might simply omit *dó*.

1594 ⁊ *fasisidar di chéin Coin Culaind arnach n-aithgné* Strachan (Deponent Verb p. 62) gives *fasisidar* as 3 s. subj. (= ipv.), 'he shall stop'. I take it that he assumed a change of preverb and took the form to stand for *arsisidar*, in which case we should read *di chéin ó Choin Culaind*. The idiom *di chéin ó* does not seem to occur except in C. The efforts of the C-scribe to get the sense here are remarkable. A better reading for the whole sentence would be ⁊ *ara n-arlathar di chéin Coin Culaind*. Cf. a few lines later *ba di chéin arlastar Coin Culaind* (1598-9).

1600 I believe that the death of Finnabair was really intended here (cf. *Atát a ndi chorthi and* 1603), but the interpolator shirked it and softened the details of Cú Chulainn's attack on the girl. The cutting off of hair as an insult is a common motif. Cf. in Recension II Aided Etarcumuil where Cú Chulainn, having shorn off Etarcumul's hair, says: *Dó duit ifechtsa ar dobiurt gén fort* Táin 1653-4. 'Begone now for I have made a laughing-stock of you.' In Aided Con Roí Cú Roí cuts off Cú Chulainn's hair: *co roben mail fair cosin chlodiub* Ériu ii 22 §3. The same expression is used to describe how the boy Conla cuts off Cú Chulainn's hair Ériu i 118 §10 (Aided Ainfir Aífe).

1602-3 *sádid corthe tria medón in drúith* I have met no other instance of *coirthe* used as a weapon, like *cloch* or *lia*. In ll. 1603-4 *coirthe* = 'memorial stone'. Note, however, that in Recension II *coirthe* is taken to be a missile. Iliach's chariot is filled *do chlochaib* ⁊ *chorthib* ⁊ *táthleccaib* Táin 3909; again 3920, 3941.

1608 *Ni bai trá carti dóib* Note the inconsistency of the interpolator. After the next three episodes he writes *Guitter dano cairdi chlaidib dún for Coin Culaind* (1686-7).

1625 *co comrac Fir Diad* This is the only reference to Fer Diad in the LU portion of TBC. But in the versions of Cú Chulainn's fight with Fer Diad which survive there is no mention at all of Cú Roí. He appears later in an episode preceding Sírrabad Súaltaim in YBL and Recension II, and there he fights with Amargin not Munremar (3394 ff.).

1648 *imófor lécud* Cf. *tabrid for n-étaige immó bar sróna ⁊ immó bar mbeola* LU 1775-6 (Máel Dúin). Note that Ailill's advice is completely ignored. The whole passage 1648-57 seems superfluous. See supra n.428-34.

1654 *Nach findae bíd fair* An instance of relative imperfect without *no*. Again infra *bítis* 2217, 2282. The C- compiler changed *bíd* to *pui*, but this is unnecessary. The whole passage is in the imperfect. Cf. in a similar description of Cú Chulainn's distortion: *Nach finna no bid fair ba athidir delg sciach ⁊ no bíd banne fola for cach finna* LL 12538-9 (Scéla Chonchobuir).

1662 *in gilla* Here *gilla = ara*. In the LU text *gilla* generally means 'boy, lad', but in this H-interpolation and again in a sentence which seems to be an interpolation (2332-4) *gilla* refers to Láeg. In the late Fer Diad episode *gilla* is used throughout for *ara*.

1671ff. The unusual feature of this episode is the suggestion by Fergus that Rochad the Ulsterman should be tricked and seized. This is completely out of character for Fergus.

1673 *marcach* Possibly like *echlach* to be taken as meaning 'messenger'. Again infra 2467. See note Celtica vii 32. Another instance in Betha Colaim Chille: *ní fada go bfhaicfi-se dís marcach ag techt ar mo cenn-sa on righ* (312.18), where in the following sentence they are called *techta an(d) righ* (312.20).

1680 *nos gabar* A Mid. Ir. use of *-s-* for 3 s.m. infixed pronoun.

1684 *Bánchath Rochada* This has been taken as *Banchath R.* and translated 'The woman-fight of Rochad'. But see infra n.2517-8. In the later part of the tale this episode in Recension II is called *Bángleó Rochada* and the name is explained: *Is and sain ra ráidsetar fir Hérend : Is bán in gleó sa, bar iat-som, do Reochaid mac Fathemain, ocht cét láech lánchalma do thuttim trina accais ⁊ a dul féin cen fuligud gen fordergad fair* Táin 3889-3892.

1694 *Aided Cáuir* With this spelling of gen. of *Cúr* cf. *Cauland cerdd* 545, 546 beside *Culand* 572, and the phrase *másu Cháuland Cú* at the end of a *rosc* 1896-7.

1697 *Mad dia ngona* See infra note 2139.

1702 *Ní gó ém Ní có ém* MS. Not in Y, and a leaf lost here in W. The C- reading is obviously a mere guess. Cf. *Ní có ám* LU 1758 (hand M) Máel Dúin; *Ní gó ém* infra 3284. The phrase *Ní gó ám* is particularly common in LL-TBC (Táin 4377, 4411, 4415, 4436). In YBL *angó* is more usual. Thus *Ní gó ám is fer co talmain* Táin 4436, *Angó is fer co talmain* 3707.

is cert in bríg doberid dún I take *cert* to be O'Davoren's and O'Clery's *cert .i. beg.* Cf. *Nírbo sain mo bríg leu* Ml. 88ᵇ 4, 'I was of no account in their eyes'.

1703 *nim foglúasfind féin Féin, feissin* not generally added to the infixed reflexive pronoun in this text. But note an instance where it emphasises the affixed pronoun in Ml. 30ᵇ 20 *gníthi-sium fadessin*, 'he makes himself.'

1707 *imthésid-si* 'ye shall go forth', 2 pl. pres. subj. of *immtéit*, here used as imperative.

1714-9 The list of Cú Chulainn's warlike feats is enumerated also in Siaburcharpat Con Culaind LU 9288-93 and in Tochmarc Emere ib. 10340-5; in Scéla Chonchobuir LL 12543-8.

1720 *hi túamaim a scéith* For *túaimm*, originally meaning 'bend, arch' > 'mound, boss of shield', see note by D. Greene, Celtica iv 44.

1733 *Dointáth* The same spelling in Y W. Can it be intended for pret. pass.? C has *doinntaid* (819), possibly influenced by the later simple verb *tintáid*. Contrast *Tintai* 1729. Or does the spelling -*áth* suggest that broad -*th* was silent? Note infra 2503 *ro mesca* = *ro mescad*. In LL- TBC we get *fó leis gid no rissed* (= *gia no rissed*) Táin 1901; in LL-Togail Troí *re ndeo lai* = *re ndeod lai* LL 31080, 31138. In these instances broad -*d* was obviously silent.

1745 *mallacht a gascid fair* As I have suggested in Celtica x 145–6 this sentence may have originally been a marginal imprecation made by some scribe, but taken by later scribes as part of Lugaid's speech.

1748 *Sóid Láeg* etc. This sentence which is here written in rasura is in C but is omitted in Y W.

1751 ⁊ *a tabairt dó* ... The sense would be clearer and better if we read ⁊ *a tabairt dó ar chomrac fri C.C. ar ba sí a thogu.* C reads *ar ba si a toghae* and omits the words ⁊ *a tabairt dó.*

1753 Fer Báeth learned the arts of war with Cú Chulainn when he went to Scáthach (Tochm. Emere LU 10432).

1754 *bá cáem leó-som a llind sin* In the Glossary from H 3.18 this sentence is quoted: *Caem .i. beg, ut est ba caem leósom in linn* (Ériu xiii 67 §79). One must take this gloss with reserve; in this particular glossary other glosses show misunderstanding. In the Contributions s.v. *caem* I (a) the H 3.18 gloss is said to be a mistake, and the sentence is translated 'they considered that wine precious'. This was the meaning I took for it in translating LL-TBC. But curiously enough I find Plunkett giving *caomh* s.v. exiguus (*beag, mion, baoideach, caomh*); and s.v. exilis he gives *caomh, fineálta, beag*, s.v. exilitas *caomhhacht*. The meaning of the sentence is not much altered even if we take *cáem* to mean 'little'. If they have but little of the liquor, they will prize it, consider it precious. O'Davoren (6484) also gives *caem .i. terc*; O'Clery, *coemh no caomh .i. beag.*

1755-6 *ba hí ind ingen no gebed láim fora c[h]uit-seom de* In pagan times the acceptance by the bridegroom of a drink offered to him by the bride was supposed to denote mutual consent to the marriage (T. F. O'Rahilly, Ériu xiv 15). No doubt this passage is a relic of old beliefs.

1758-9 *co topachtur* This strange form seems to be intended for 1 sg. pres. subj. of *do-boing*. It is found in all MSS. For an ingenious explanation of its origin see Strachan, ZCP ii 480 n.1. Or possibly it was a misreading of *co topasar*, pres. subj. pass.

1765 *Nícon beó-sa i mbethaid* Subjunctive form used for future.

1767 *Co comairsem* I cannot explain this use of the subjunctive unless we take it with *celeboir dam.* 'Leave me now, Lugaid, until we meet', (or 'so that we may meet'), but even then, the order of words is strange. Possibly the meaning is *acht co comairsem*, 'if only we meet.'

1775 *Doṡelba do chotach* Thurneysen would read *Do ṡelba do chotach* and translate 'deines Besitzes ist nun dein Bund', taking *selba* as predicative genitive. It is suggested in RIA Contributions s.v. *selb* III that *doṡelba* is 2 s. pres. subj. of *do-selba*, used as imperative. This is borne out by the Recension III reading: *Sealbaighim-sea do chadad ⁊ do charadrad it leith badeṡin* (RC xiv 260 §36), 'I renounce, hand back (into your possession)'. See *selbaigid* (c) Contribb. = 'assigns to, gives into possession of'. Cf. *Do-ṡelbi fein tra do praind* Mon. Tall. 48.26, 'Keep thy meal for thyself.'

1785 *Nó iss é Fiacha* ... This is the version given in Recension II. In Recension III it is Cormac Con Loinges who praises Cú Chulainn's cast (RC xiv 261 §40).

1790 *Co cloth ni* ... This formula usually introduces a *roscad*.

1806 The C- reading is the correct one here, Mid. Ir. *tiat* 3 s. ipv. The reference is to the later meeting of Lugaid and Cú Chulainn in Glenn Fir Baíth. Cf. the reading of Recension III where Lugaid is speaking to Láeg; ⁊ *raidh-siu ré Coin Culainn taidhecht go gleand Fhir Baith go n-agaillium a chele ann* (RC xiv 263 §49).

1834 *ar dáig co forgénmais* A corrupt form of *do-gni*. Cf. supra 545 *Dia forgéni Cauland cerdd óegidecht do Conchobar*. See RIA Dict. s.v. *for-gni*. *cé no slaiss* for *cé na slaiss*.

1837 *Danethat Cú Chulaind* This has been translated 'C.C. attacks him'. We might read *Danetha*, 'he approaches him'. C. reads *Donetha Cú lais cen armb* (903) for which the editor of C suggests reading *Danetha Cú cen arm lais*. The Y-reading *donetat* (= *da-n-autat*) would mean 'attacks him.'

1838 C gives the correct reading *Tallaid-side* (901), the simple verb *tallaid < do-alla*.

1845 The title is found only in LU. For this passage see Táin Introd. xxxi–xxxii.

1848 *Cé tai-siu?* The substantive verb is commonly found with interrogative *cia*. Again infra 2108 *Cia tai-siu eter?*

1860 *t'asnai* In the passage *Slánugud na Mórrigna* it is her head which is healed, not her ribs.

1862 *Timorc-sa* Thurneysen (Gramm. 373) suggests that this is likely to be an error for *timorr*. His suggestion is supported by the future tense of the other threats: *Dorag-sa, Not géb-sa* etc. The mistake must go back to an early exemplar; all three MSS. have *timorc*.

1867 *nim aircecha-sa* Reduplicated future of *ad-cí* with *ro*.

1872–3 *Combad sechtmain* etc. This is omitted in Y. It refers to a variant version, and in fact it is on these sentences that H or H's predecessor has built part of the long interpolation beginning l. 1904. In the interpolation, however, more than one man a night is killed by Cú Chulainn. It is probable that the mention here of a week spent in Áth nGrencha suggested Lóch's postponement of his fight for a week, and *that* despite the fact that Cú Chulainn now appears to be bearded and the womenfolk urge Lóch to fight him. Logically, if the H- interpolation was from another version, these sentences *Combad sechtmain* etc. should come after l. 1883.

Áth Darteisc = Áth Tarteisc. Again 1981. Nazalised *t* written *d*.

1883 *no mairfed-som hé* The object pronoun suggests that this passage is of later date, and probably a scribal addition.

1884–98 Omitted in Y, but in C. This passage is obviously a doublet of a later passage. See Táin Introd. xxxv.

1902 *conid gnid-som* MS. The same spelling for 3 s. pres. ind. of *do-gní* occurs in Mon. Tall. 129.6. Or possibly here intended as an imperfect— it was his custom to do so when fighting with a grown man ?

1904–5 Here there is a clumsy repetition of the making of the false beard, already told l. 1902. An interesting point about this passage is that it echoes one in Immacallam in Dá Thúarad in LL. Bricriu tells Néide that he cannot be *ollam* in Emain Macha because he is young and beardless: *Gabais Neide lán a duirn dond [f]eór ⁊ focheirt brict fair conid ed dommuned cach ba ulcha bai fair* (24238–40).

1923 Both *techt* and *techta* occur as singular. See Táin 2095. For *Ludi in techtairi* 1926 C has *Luith an techtae* (979).

arco tiasad Again *bad amlaid tiasad* (= *no théised*). The vocalism of the radical syllable is irregular. Again l. 2157 in the Breslech Muige Murthemne passage which is later in language than the rest of the text. Such forms are common in LL-TBC.

'na coinni T. F. O'Rahilly notes that this is the earliest instance of *coinne*, 'meeting', which he has found. It does not occur elsewhere in LU (Celtica i 371).

1924 *⁊ sé anarma* For *anarmda*. Again in another H-interpolation *⁊ mé anarma* 2530. Recension III here reads *⁊ gomadh amlaidh thisadh sé anarmdha*, RC xv 64 §73. Cf. *dodhealba = dodelbda* Fianaig 58.12, *somesga = somescda* ib. 58.18, and the common *bodba = bodbda*.

1932 A similar remark in Bruiden Da Chocae: *At mora glonda Medbae. Ní cóir dia namait a cor i n-eslis* (RC xxi 312.§30).

1943–4 *Drúcht ⁊ Delt ⁊ Dathen* The same three names occur as those of *dáilemain* in Bruiden Da Derga (BDD² 1154–5) and as those of *deogbairi* in 'The Second Battle of Moytura' (RC xii 78 §65). In these contexts the names (Dew, Moisture, Glistening) are more appropriate than here where they are given to Cú Chulainn's opponents. Obviously, here as elsewhere, the interpolator drew on his recollections of other tales. In Cath M. Tuired there are nine names in all, two of the remaining six being *Taei* and *Glesi*.

1974 *is óenmummi forcetail conrotacht dán dúib* *Conrotacht* for *conrotaig*. In the Diplomatic Edition this is printed *is o énmummi . . .* the editors taking the verb as passive. There are sporadic instances in Middle Irish of passive forms used for active. For instances see Zimmer KZ xxviii 363. In the present text it occurs only occasionally e.g. *dobretha, dobreth* 2297–98, *ro chress* 2242. Other instances from LU are: *Is de asbreth Fergus for Tána inso* 1457 (MU); *Is disi ro chet in senchaid na runna sa* 3062 *Alt Deichtine in mac* 10590 (Comp. CC). We may also note that the spelling *én-* for *óen-* never occurs in the LU text.

1975–95 This continuation of the passage overlaps in the H- interpolation that of Y. It is interesting to note the difference between the two accounts, the H- written one being more detailed and altogether more verbose. Y has probably the original version here as elsewhere, but H wished to fill in the space at his disposal.

1979 *ó thánic íarom* . . . one would expect *in Mórrígan* after the verb. *bibsat* is preterite formed on the future of *bongid*. Cf. ⁊ *comboing in cethri darsna slúaga sair* 1997. Possibly the C-reading is the better one here, *bidcaid* used transitively. Cf. *do-bidci*; 'pelts at, strikes'.

2003 *Is and asbert-som*: '*Ní airciu a n-átha la linni.*' In C these words are followed by ⁊*rla* which suggests that they may have been the opening line of a *rosc*.

2025 ⁊ *fichid Lóch* . . . *cosin gai bolga Eichid* here used with personal object. If the meaning was 'fights with' one would have expected *fichid fri* (or *for*) *Lóch.* Cf. *Fessa in mílid* LU 10921, 'I shall overcome the warrior'.

2026 *Gaibthi dó* See note by Strachan, ZCP ii 486. The meaning 'he takes it to him' must = 'he attacks him with it'.

2031–5 This fight is not mentioned in Recensions II and III. It is repeated again later. The names *dá Chrúaid, dá Chalad* would appear to have been taken from the list of the leaders killed by Cú Chulainn at Breslech Mór (infra 2320–1). See n.2320 ff.

2036–7 *de duniu ná cethir* For this generic use of *de* with singular noun see note by Professor Mac Cana Ériu xx 212–4. (A similar use of the preposition *o* in Welsh, . . Professor Mac Cana points out). The equivalent passage in LL- TBC reads . . . *barémid nech díb a aged do soud fodess in lá sin do choin nó ech nó duine* Táin 2101–2; . . . *do choin no d'ech na do dhuine* Stowe TBC 2140.

2043 *I n-íam* (*iniam* MS.) The *n*-stroke and the *m*-stroke are easily confused in LU. At first glance I read this passage in the manuscript as *Dobert-si blegon sini dó i n-ian. Bid slán doduc.* (There is of course no punctuation in the manuscript here). *I n-ian*, 'in a drinking-vessel', makes good sense in the context. I would suggest that it is at least possible that an early scribe copied *inian* as *iniam* and that the m̄ ̄e was repeated by subsequent copyists. In fact the *m*-stroke is given fṳ ṳⸯ ᴣ *n*-stroke elsewhere in this text in LU. Thus supra 1828–9 *Conrecat im Glend Fir Baith*, where C reads *i nGlend F.B.* and infra 2506 where U has *com glinni* against *co nglinni* in Y and C.

The spelling *iniam* is found only in U and Y in Recension I. C omits the words. But the later compilers of Recensions II and III clearly took *iniam* to be for *i n-éim*, 'quickly, forthwith', which is the reading they give in this passage.

bid slán For *bad slán*? Imperative rather than future. Cf. the Recension II sentence: *I n-éim rop slán* (Táin 2110).

2057   Zimmer (KZ xxx 77), taking the reading as *etha Cú*, (which is also the reading of the Diplomatic Edition), would explain *etha as* a passive form used as 3 sg. pret. active (like *dobretha*). But Strachan disagrees (ZCP ii 483 n.2) and dismisses the passage as 'not clear' to him. I take the verb as passive and *cú* as intended for an unfinished *cuici* (which is the Y- reading). C substitutes *ara c[h]enn* for *cuici*.

2058 ff.   There is obviously an omission here in LU before *cóicer*. Some such words as *Táncatar ara chend* are needed.   Y reads *Is and iarum etha ar galaib óenfir cuici* 2057 after which there is a long omission in the MS.   C has *Is and sin ethai ar galaibh aoinfir ara cenn co ngeogoin coiccer Cind Coiris no Duin Cind Coris* etc. (1154–5).   The Recension III reading is of interest here: *And sin tvgadh cuigiur chuigi siun arnamharach d'[f]erthain chomlaind ris ⁊ geoghain C.C. iad condrochradar les, gurab cuigiur Chind Chuirsighi iderar ríu. Iss edh seo anmanna in chuigir sin .i. Dá Chrúaidh ⁊ da Chaladh ⁊ Derothor* RC xv 71 §§96–8.   So obviously this passage 2057ff. is merely a repetition of the earlier passage 2031–5 where Cú Chulainn is said to have killed five at Cóicsius Focherda.   Possibly the names given here in the second passage should be five not six.   Omit *Fer Toithle*?   He seems to be the same as the *Fer Tedil* already killed (supra 936).   The main difference between the two passages is that in the first all five attack him together, in the second they meet him in single combat.

2072 ff.   *In Carpat Serda ⁊ in Breslech Mór*.   This long descriptive passage is, as Thurneysen noted, later in language and style than the rest of the tale in Recension I.   It has become a more or less self-contained episode. The whole passage 2073–2332 is practically identical in all three recensions. (There is a long omission in YBL, and Eg. 1782 does not go beyond l. 1811). The title of the piece Breslech Maige Muirthemne has been taken over for the late version of the tale Oided Chon Culainn.

2074   *isin Breslig Móir*   The place-name anticipates the coming battle. In Recension III the men of Ireland encamp at *Áth Alad Fhind i Maig Murthemne* (§113).

2084   *re úathgráin na gáre dosbertatár*   Stowe TBC and Recension III have a better reading.   Note the *-s-* in relative verb *dosbertatár* which shows lateness of composition.

2084–5   *Cordas mesc ind Némain forsin tslóg   Mescaid for* with or without reflexive pronoun = 'attacks'. Cf. *ro mesc barin slúag é* LL 23026 (CRR); *do mesc sin co soinnib ar na sluagaib* Celtic Rev. iv. 114 y.

2090   *a Chúcán*   Again 2176.   This diminutive is found only in this section in the LU- text.   Here LL reads *a Chúcúcán* (Táin 2139).   In Comrac Fir Diad YBL has *a Chúcacán* (2702) occurring in a similar context when Láeg warns his master of an arrival.

2098   *feib nachas faiced nech hé*   A late use of pronoun object together with infixed pronoun.

2100   *dáig ar bíth*   Again 2211.   This double conjunction is common in LL- TBC. See Táin n.50.   It occurs only twice in this text, both instances in this late section.

2100–1 *foretatár-som in t-imned már inam ḟuil-sea*   For a tentative explanation of this use of the nominative see Celtica viii 164 n.2. Recension II and C have nominative also.   Recension III reads *foreadarson* (sic) *ind nith mor inarfuilim-sea* (§120).

2105–10 *Ferda sin . . . mo íc*   These lines are omitted in Recension II.

2106 *Ní mór side etir*   In C the answer given is *Ferdai eiccein* (1200) which recalls the wording of a passage in Echtra Nerai: *'Ferdoi sin, a Nero!' 'Feurdo ecin!' ol Nerai* RC x 214 §4.   See my note Éigse xvi 326.

Possibly the original reading here was *Ní móirithir*, 'not so great' i.e. a disclaimer, 'not really'.   The phrase *ní móirithir* in this sense occurs twice in LL 14405, 37264.   Both passages are cited by Bergin in a note on the equative form *móirithir* Ériu xiv 141.   He compares *lir* treated as a positive with the normal equative ending added to form a new equative *liridir* (Aisl. M.C.).   So *mór*: *móirithir*.

2111 ff.   In the LL- version the visitor from the *síd* (unnamed) tells Cú Chulainn to sleep for a short time.   Then Cú Chulainn sleeps for three days and three nights, and while he sleeps, the warrior from faery puts enchanted herbs of healing in his wounds so that he recovers *cen rathugud dó etir* (Táin 2153–66).

2114 *Canaid a chéle ferdord dó*   The form *fordord* of C (*for*- emphatic particle + *dord*, 'murmuring, chanting') is preferable, but I note that Zimmer (KZ xxviii 534) translates *ferdord* as 'männerbass'.   The original reading may have been *fodord*.   Cf. O'Clery's gloss on *fodhord*: *murmar no briathra nach abairthear go hard*.   Incidentally we should note that the *fordord* is not to be taken as referring to the *Éle Loga* which is chanted by Lug after Cú Chulainn has been completely healed and which calls on him to arise from sleep.

2114–5 *co n-accae nách crécht and rop ógslán* (*ropo glan* MS.) lit. 'until he saw every wound that he bore (that it) was completely healed'.   *Crécht* is accusative and *rop(a)* relative.   For this construction see Celtica ii 348–9; viii 162.   Cf. the example cited by M. A. O'Brien in Celtica ii: *Otchonneatar . . . in mboin deirg . . . corbo coland duine.*

2114 ff.   Obviously two versions of Cú Chulainn's healing have here been combined.   One version is that of Recension II: Lug puts healing herbs into Cú Chulainn's wounds and he is healed as he sleeps.   In the other version he is lulled to sleep by Lug and sleeps on until Lug sees that all his wounds are completely healed.   The telescoping of the two versions and the consequent misplacing of the *Éle Loga* here are more clearly seen in a comparison with the C- version.   In C after the words *Ba héim dam mo íc* comes the sentence *Canaid a cheliu fordord ndo contaili fris co medon lai ara barach con faca nach* [*crecht*] *ron both pa hoghslan* (1203–5), while the *Éle Loga* comes in the natural place after Cú Chulainn awakes from a sleep of three days and three nights (but a contradiction here with the sentence *contaili fris co medon lai ara barach*). The *Éle Loga* is meant of course to rouse Cú Chulainn to action.

2130–4   These five lines of *Éle Loga* in hand H are also found in Recension III (RC xv 74 §123).

2139 *acht mad mani chotlad* Similarly Recension III: *acht mádh mini chotladh.* *Acht mad* is omitted in C. Recension II is *acht mani chotlad* (Táin 2160). We might compare with *mad mani* the *mad dia* which occurs commonly in LL- TBC, but is rarely found in LU except in H- interpolations. Cf. supra *Mád dia ngona* 1697 where Y has *Ma rongona* and C has *Ma rodgona.* Exceptionally in hand M *mád dia nderscaigther* LU 7476 (TBDD).

2157 *ba nert leiss a menma* 'his spirit was invigorated'. The same use of *nert* occurs in Serglige Con Culainn 232: *ba nertiti leis a menma na scéla,* 'his spirits were all the more invigorated, rose all the higher, for hearing the tidings'. Professor Dillon (Glossary SC s.v. *nertaid*) took *nertiti* to be formed from past participle *nertae* + *-de, -te.* In the construction of copula + *la,* the predicate may be a noun, as here in *ba nert leiss,* or an adjective. Occasionally the noun predicate is inflected like an adjective. Thus *is fuath liom,* 'I hate'; *ni thánag-sa riam a n-inad ba fúaithi lium-sa ná sé,* 'any spot I hated more', Comp. C.C. 87.24–25 (OCC); *ni fuathaide le neach againn a chéile é,* 'none of us hates the other more because of that' CF² 146–7. I take *nertiti* of SC to be a similar inflection of *nert.* Noteworthy here is the use of *ocus* before imperf. subj. = *amail* 'as if, as though'. In the later language we get *amail ocus.* See Contribb. s.v. *amail* II. For the form *tíasad* see supra n. 1923.

2166 *Ceist cia arránic?* This is the past tense of *cia-(r)ricc, ce-(r)ric* which glosses quid ergo, quid igitur etc. See Gramm. §458. In Recension II it has been altered to *Ceist cia rodas fópair?* (Táin 2185). One might of course take *cia arránic* literally, 'who has arrived?'

2173 *Apraind* See Vendryes, Lexique Étymologique s.v. *apraind.* Vendryes, quoting a suggestion by Dr. Binchy that *apraind* is a form of 1 sg. imperfect subjunctive of *asbiur.* comments 'L'hypothèse est très séduisante'.

2178 *arco ndíglom* The conjunction *arco* = *ara* is very common in the LL-Táin. In this recension it occurs only in this passage and in an H-interpolation *arco tiasad* supra 1923.

2181 *ni fair bías a nós* The relative verb after a periphrasis is late Mid.-Ir. It occurs elsewhere in interpolated passages of LU e.g. 2395 (H) Scéla Laí Brátha; 2740, 2742, 2745 (H) Scéla na Esérgi etc.

2185 The abrupt introduction of Láeg here suggests that the original of LU and LL had an omission. Contrast Recension III which before the words *Ocus in carpat serda* . . . tells of the departure of Lug (unlike LU and LL, there is in recension III no reference to Lug's having fought beside Cú Chulainn at Sesrech Breslige 'according to another version'). Then in Recension III Cú Chulainn addresses to Láeg almost the same words as he has spoken to Lug (which might account for an omission here): *Maith a m[o] phoba a Laigh, bhar C.C., tegum imall[e] do dhighail na macraidhi arna slúaghaibh. Rachaidse let on, bhar Láeg* (§132).

2194 *do Dáir do ríg Rómán* A confusion of Romans and Persians. The Recension III compiler replaces *Dáir* with *Ner* (Nero).

2195 *conda rairbert* = *conda tairbert* See Translators' Notes §197, Gramm. p. 686.

2208 *bricht comga* Recension III reads *celtair chomgha.* Cf. infra 2243 *celtar comga.*

2212 The exact nature of these feats of chariot-driving is obscure. One might translate: 'leaping across a chasm, straight driving, the carrying of a goad.'

2213 *ro gab* etc. Here Recension III offers a better reading *Is annsin ro eirigh in cur . . .* ⁊ *do ghabhasdair* etc. (RC xv 77 §138).

2223 *ro chiulaitis* The Recension III reading would suggest some compound of *clichid.* Possibly *ro-* is for *con-* or *fo-* here, *conclich,* 'dashes', *fochlich,* id. In this later passage interchange of verbal particle in what would be relative position in late Mid. Ir. would not be surprising. The meaning is clear in the Stowe reading: *daig as ionann consgincdis de* ⁊ *marbadh do cloich no congna de benfaidis* (2280–1).

2230 *ima arm dét* Recension II has *ima cholg ṅdét* (Táin 2247) and Recension III has *iman colg nded* (§158), perhaps a better reading.

2231 The marginal note ⁊ *a saigetbolg* added in hand H seems an anachronism. The use of arrows as weapons is rarely mentioned in the early sagas. Cf. *ic díchur gai* ⁊ *rend* ⁊ *err* ⁊ *sleg* ⁊ *saiget* supra 2221–2. Again in a description of Cú Chulainn's shield the same phrase is used LL 24895. *Saigetbolc* occurs in the Second Battle of Moytura (RCxii 98).

2234 *ina tul tárla* The meaning of *tárla* is obscure. See Táin n.2251. Or should we begin a new sentence *Tarla . . .* ?

2236 *Inbaid fogníth Fogníth = dogníth,* change of preverb, *fo-* for *do-,* in relative position. Stowe has *An tan do-ghni . . .* (2291).

2242 *Ro chress* A passive form used as active. Cf. 1974 *conrotacht,* and 2297, 2298 *dobretha, dobreth.*

2246 *a charíni* Meyer Contribb. takes this as diminutive of *cara,* 'shank, haunch'. O'Clery's gloss *cairin .i. feoil gan saill* would seem to be the correct meaning. Cf. Plunkett s.v. lardarium ('a larding stick where with cookes used to draw lard through flesh') *crann saille re thairrngeann cocaire saill thrid cairín.* Here the plural form = 'the flesh of his whole body'.

2251 *tulféthi Tul-* intensive prefix, like *tarb-.* Recension III here reads *tarbéthi* (= *tarbfhéthi*).

2259 *co úrtrachta* See supra n. 433.

2260 *comtar écnaig a ginchróes* For my suggested reading *inchróes* see supra n. 433. LL reads *comtar inécnaig a inchróes* Táin 2277; Stowe has *comba leir a inne* ⁊ *a inathar tara bhél* 2316.

2261–2 *béim n-ulgaib leóman* The word *ulgaib* is obscure. Cf. Bedell's *agus sméaróid dhearg iona láimh noch do bhean sé leis a niolghaibh don altóir* Isaiah 6.6, 'having a live coal in his hand which he had taken with the tongs from off the altar'; and in Stair an Bhíobla III 116.17: *do ghlac an iolgaib ann a laimh* ⁊ *do thóig smeuraid no athinne don teinidh.*

2265–6 *na klne* MS. In a footnote in the Diplomatic Edition of LU *coinnli* is given as the reading of Stowe, but in fact the words *na klne bodba* ⁊ are omitted in Stowe. LL has the same contracted form as LU. *Coindli* is the reading of Recension III (§150).

2272 ff. The Stowe reading *airtim* (= *airtem*) makes better sense here and is the word commonly used as a measure of length in such descriptions. Cf. in a similar but shorter description of Cú Chulainn's distortion: *No theiged indala súil ina chend ⁊ araile ass fot airthema* LL 12540 (Scéla Chonchobuir). The sentence from *corbo chomfota* to *slóg* might well be omitted here as it is in Recensions II and III. It is quite superfluous. It was probably part of a 'run' which the scribe inserted unthinkingly. Cú Chulainn has not yet begun his attack on the host, and in this section of TBC there is no reference to a sling (*oc taibleth* = 'shooting from a sling') in the description of Cú Chulainn's weapons.

2283–91 The description of Cú Chulainn's chariot and horses here is superfluous. It occurs only in LU. The *carpat serda* has already been described 2280–3. This description of chariot and horses is a set piece which occurs again in Comrac Fir Diad. It is found for the third time in an unlikely context at the end of the tale where Mac Roth says that Cú Chulainn has not joined the Ulstermen but proceeds to describe his chariot and horses (infra 3847–58).

2285–6 *clangdírig* seems to be a scribal error for the adjective *colgdirech* which is common in descriptions of a chariot.

2288 *biruich* pl. of *birach*, or *biruich* from *biróach*. Cf. *gabair . . . bircluasach* TTebe 2279, 'prick-eared'.

2289 *lugaid* epithet for a horse. The meaning is obscure.

2290 *fótmar* Dr. Knott (RIA Dictionary) suggests 'skittish' as the meaning (from 2 *fót*), but in his edition of the modern Breisleach Maighe Muirtheimne Van Hamel suggests *fódmhar*, 'spreading large sods'. In the description of horses galloping it was a commonplace to describe the sods cast up by their hooves as dark birds flying through the air.
fochorsid Given merely as 'epithet for a horse' in RIA Dictionary. It is spelt *focharsaid* infra 2954, *focharrsaigh* ZCP x 299.1.

2291 *airgdech* Another epithet for a horse the meaning of which is obscure.

2296 *d'insaigid a námat* Elision also in C and in Stowe but LL and Recension III have *do innsaigid a námat* (Táin 2304).

2297, 2299 *dobretha, dobreth* Passive form for active.

2299–2301 Omit either *dollotar . . . hi talmain* or the sentence *feib . . . hi talmain*? The first sentence is omitted in Recension III, the second in Stowe. But LL agrees with LU.

2320 ff. The names are in three columns and *.r.* is inserted between columns. The *.r.*-symbol here probably denotes a chanted list, learnt by rote. See note Celtica x 146–8.

2332–4 These lines are not in Y. Note the use of the word *gilla* = 'charioteer', in this text generally confined to interpolations in LU and common throughout Comrac Fir Diad and later passages in Y. After this sentence Recension III reads *Gorub e in carbad seardha conigi sin. Finid. Amen.* (RC xv 202 §171). This reinforces Thurneysen's suggestion that the long descriptive passage 2072–2334 may have been a separate piece later incorporated in the text.

2341 *in mac thánic*   Aspiration of relative is noteworthy.

2344 *teóra imsrotha   teorae himsrethae* C, *teóra sretha* Rec. III, either of which readings would give better sense.

2352 *co forgabáil ingne griúin*   Faraday translates 'griffin' probably taking as *gribin*, dimin. of *grib*. But such a form does not seem to be attested, nor do we get the spelling *u* = *bh* elsewhere in this text. O'Clery gives *griun .i. graineóg*, 'a hedgehog'.

2357 *nád chumgaitis súili doini déicsin*   Probably we should read *a déicsin* as in C. See Táin n.2360.

2361 *Claideb . . . co torceltaib óir   Torc-* used here as an intensive. (Cf. *tarb-* in *tarbféthi*). *Elta* is always used in the plural.

2365 *Conid comram aidchi sin   Comram*, 'successful exploit' or 'trophy'. I prefer the more concrete translation here. Altered to *fóbairt*, 'attack', in Y and C, possibly because the scribe realized that Cú Chulainn had killed more of the enemy than the heads he brandished. Recension II alters to *do chomartha a gascid*, and Recension III substitutes for the phrase *faidhbh fir ina brédibh etarru* (cf. l. 2382 in the poem which follows).

2368 *Follaig Medb a hainech . . .*   Contrast with the earlier passage (1889–98), an obvious interpolation though not in hand H, where Medb insists on seeing Cú Chulainn.

2371 *Conid de sin . . .*   There is here in Recensions II and III an explanatory passage (which has been taken over by C): Dubthach is filled with jealousy on seeing that his wife too tries to catch a glimpse of the wonderful Cú Chulainn. Dubthach is addressing the men of Ireland and speaks of *far mná* and *far rígan*.

2383 *deich cind ina rothēdaibh*, 'tied together', is the reading of Recension III.

2386 For this line, part of which is in rasura hand M, LL has *Adchíu-sa far rígain móir.*
After l.2389 a half-quatrain is missing. It is found in C and in Recensions II and III.

2388–91 Meyer has drawn attention to certain couplets in *deibide* metre where the usual order of rhyme-words is reversed (Misc. Hib. 15–16).

2393 *Ber ass Dubthach nDóeltengaid*   The first three quatrains of Fergus's verses are quoted in Mesca Ulad LU 1458–69.

2396 *ó geogain in n-ingenraith*   This refers to Dubthach's having killed the maidens of Ulster in revenge for the betrayal of Meic Usnig (ᄀ *ingenrad Ulad do marbad do Dubthach* LL 34474). Cf also Celtic Rev. I.216.

2398, 2400 *Fiacha mac Conchobuir, Coirpre mac Fedelmtheo*   According to the LL- version of Longes Mac nUsnig Dubthach killed Mane mac Conchobuir and Fiachna mac Feidilmi (LL 34469–70). The Coirpre here mentioned does not seem to occur elsewhere. Recension III here reads . . . *guin Fhiachaig mic Conchobhair . . . guin Dairi mic Fhedhlimtheo* (RC xv 205 §198) which agrees with the tradition of Oided Mac nUsnig in the Glenmasan MS. according to which Dubthach killed Fiacha mac Conchobair and Daire mac Fedlimthi

(Celtic Rev. I 212, 214; II 118). In the quatrain quoted in MU the names are *Fiacha mac Conchobair* and *Maine mac Fedelmtheo*, an obvious confusion of the two names in the LL- version of Longes Mac nUsnig.

2407 *costud Ulad má dobi* LL has *costud Ulad danfor tí* Táin 2420.

2409–10 It is difficult to make much sense of these lines. In C they have been added in a blank space by a late hand. Recension II reads: *Scérdait far n-óendili* (*.i. far nindili* marginal note) *i fat | re nUltaib acht co n-éirset* Táin 2423–4. I have read *sinfid* for *sirfid* here. Cf. the later lines *Regaid ind longas hi fat do Ultaib* (2421–2).

2418 *bi* in U. but *bid* Y and C. The U-spelling is probably a mere scribal error as *do lui* for *do luid* LU 10192.

2428–54 This passage is not in Recensions II and III.

2455 ff. The order of events is different in Recension II. The death of Óengus mac Óenláime comes immediately after the poem spoken by Fergus (supra 2393–2424).

2455–63 This is not an encounter between Connachtmen and Ulstermen aroused from their torpor, but a clash between men of the *dubloinges* and Connachtmen. Fiacha was accompanied by Dubthach Dóel Ulad. He does not seem to occur elsewhere, but was the son of one of Medb's sisters. Dócha casts a spear at Fiacha but hits Dubthach; Dubthach throws a spear at Maine but hits Dócha. Neither Mane nor Fiacha has been hit. So Thurneysen is wrong when he implies in a note on Mellgleó Iliach (Heldensage 196 n.2.) that Mane Andóe had been killed. In fact there is no mention of killing in this version of Imroll Belaig Eóin, merely of wounding.

2464–82 For this second version of Imroll Belaig Eóin see Táin Introduction p.xxxii.

2471 ⁊ *slán uile a ndorónad and* In RIA Contributions s.v. *slán* II (d) *slán* here is taken as a noun and the translation of this sentence is 'restitution for all that was done there'. I take *slán* to be an adjective with a preceding copula form (*ba* ?) omitted, *slán* being the legal term 'exempt from liability', and the meaning to be 'what has been done there will be completely free from liability' i.e. 'no compensation will be demanded for whatever depredations the Connacht army has committed in Ulster territory'. Note that this passage, an obvious interpolation in Recension I, is the only one in which the Ulstermen are represented as offering terms to Medb and Ailill.

2472 *úair robáge Medb* The C-scribe, given to the use of archaic terms, here reads *co comairset in bar cetfuid* (1503). Cf. *i cedfuid a fo .i. a fiadhnaisi a tiagerna*, gloss in a poem in Bérla na Filed ZCP v 483.

2488–94 According to Táin Bó Flidais II in the Glenmasan MS. Óengus mac Óenláime was with the *dubloinges* in Connacht (Ériu viii 134). (In this connection we may note that in the other versions of Táin Bó Flidais the three exiles who go to ask Ailill Find for cattle are Fergus mac Róig, Dubthach Dóeltenga and Fergus mac Óenláimi (LU 1579). I suggest that the third man was named as in the Glenmasan MS. version Óengus, not Fergus). Of this passage in TBC Thurneysen remarks that the Ulstermen are now recovering from their debility; he assumes that Óengus has come from Emain.

But we might perhaps take it that this was a move on the part of one of the exiled Ulstermen to hold up the progress of the Connacht forces. In the LL-list of Ulster warriors summoned to battle by Conchobor Óengus occurs, but he is not in the YBL-list. Such inconsistency means little, however. Conall Cernach, said in Recension I to be among the exiles, is one of those summoned in both LL and YBL. An even more glaring inconsistency appears in Cath Ruis na Ríg which is a sequel as it were to TBC. Despite the account of his death in TBC, in CRR Óengus mac Óenláma Gábae is one of the messengers sent by Conchobor to his foreign allies (LL 22755).

We might compare the role of Óengus here with the even more forceful intervention of another exile, Fiacha mac Fir Febe (infra 2550 ff.).

2496-7 *oc Áth Da Ḟerta* As the C-reading shows these words are spoken by Cú Chulainn. The editors of TBC² end Cú Chulainn's speech at *mo chend-sa*, and the passage is translated accordingly by Faraday.

2514 There is no mention of *Grellach Dolluid* in Recensions II and III.

2515 *Tairbling* In the other recensions we are told that Cú Chulainn fled in his chariot (Táin 2501; Rec. III §213).

2517-8 The order of sentences is better in C, and that is what has been translated.

The title *Bánchomrag Ferghusa* is given at the end of the episode and explained in Recension III; *Gurub e Banchomrag Ferghusa ar Tanaidh connigi sin ┐ is uimi aderar bánchomrag ris doigh ní bhí fuil for fáebhur dhe* (§215). This explanation would justify reading *Bánchath Rochada* in the H- interpolation supra 1658 ff. Rochad was set free unwounded.

2519-22 This episode is much expanded in Recensions II and III.

2523-46 This H- interpolation is found of course only in LU.

2527-9 *Fer dothengt[h]ach . . . amal Dubthach* ɛ̀c. These comparisons seem to echo a type of passage which occurs commonly in the Lives of the Saints where the saint in question is compared to various OT characters. Compare, for example, a passage in the Tripartite Life: *Fírailithir, amal Abráam. Cendais dílgadach ó chridiu, amal Moysi. Salmchetlaid molbthaide. amal Dabid. Etsúd n-ecnai, amal Solmoin* etc. (Trip.² 3063-5).

2529 *Triscod* In the fragment of MU in LU the name is *Triscoth, Driscoth*. In the LL-version of MU he is called *Trisgatal trénfher tigi Conchobair* LL 35046. He is described among the Ulstermen in the Stowe version of TBC (4537) where he is again called *Trioscatal trénfer tigi Conchobair*.

2548 *Fuiliarnn* In Recension II *Fuil Iairn* is given at the end of this passage as the name of the place where these men fought with Cú Chulainn: *Is aire atberar Fuil Iairn ris dáig báe fuil dar fáebor and* (Táin 2604). Cú Chulainn's opponents are named in Recension II as *Calatín Dána cona šecht maccaib fichet ┐ a úa Glas mac Delga* (2534-5).

2561 Here we are simply told that Cú Chulainn killed all twenty-nine of his opponents. In Recension II this episode is much expanded and includes a vividly described little incident in which Glas mac Delga escapes from the slaughter but is pursued right into the Connacht camp by Cú Chulainn who cuts off his head. The incident evidently appealed to the compiler of C; he inserts it clumsily into what is otherwise the Recension I version. After re-counting the killing of Glas he goes on to say *Gontais Cu Chulaind ierum a noi fira fichit* (1590), though of course only twenty-eight were still alive.

2561-2 ⁊ *dá mac Ḟicce lais occo* ... This passage, which is not in Recension II, seems to be a scribal addition. Nowhere else in TBC do Ulstermen fight by the side of Cú Chulainn. Throughout the narrative the emphasis is on his single-handed defence of Ulster. When the Ulstermen finally recover from the *cess* and come to Cú Chulainn's aid, they fight individually against the men of Ireland e.g. Cethern, Fintan, Rochad etc.

In LL but not in Recension I, these two warriors, called *dá mac Ḟeicge, Muridach* ⁊ *Cotreib*, are named in the list of Ulstermen summoned to Conchobar (Táin 4096). They are also mentioned as helping to bathe Cú Chulainn's wounds at the end of Comrac Fir Diad in both recensions: *dá mac Fice* infra 3145, *dá mac Gégge .i. Muridach* ⁊ *Cotreb* (Táin 3599).

2565 *Atá isin cloich* ... I take the whole sentence to refer to Cú Chulainn's opponents and have emended accordingly; *rolátha a nai coirthi fichit and sin* following immediately proves this. In Recension II, after the account of the killing of the twenty-nine we get: *Conid marthanach ar lár in átha fóss in chloch 'ma ndernsat a sróengal* ⁊ *a n-imresón. Inad elta a claideb inti* ⁊ *a ṅglúne* ⁊ *a n-ullend* ⁊ *erlanna a sleg* (Táin 2600-2), 'And there still remains on the bed of the ford the stone around which they fought and struggled, and on it the mark of their sword-hilts and of their knees and elbows and of the hafts of their spears.'

2567 ff. Comrac Fir Diad must originally have been an independent tale, later incorporated into TBC. It is the only episode in the Táin which is listed separately in the saga-list in LL. The motif of the tale, a duel with a foster-brother who had studied the arts of war along with Cú Chulainn, is found in earlier episodes, the fight with Fer Báeth and the fight with Lóch. Further-more Lóch has a horn-skin like Fer Diad, and like him too he is slain by the *ga bulga.*

Thurneysen, judging by language and metres, would date the composition of Comrac Fir Diad to the 11th century. But some form of the tale must already have existed in the 10th century. (See Stowe TBC xxiv n.3).

At a later date, possibly 15th century, the episode was again reconsti-tuted and elaborated as an independent tale. This version has been called Version IV by Thurneysen. In the following notes and in the variants quoted in footnotes to text I refer to it as F (taking as typical the 17c. Fran-ciscan MS. text edited by Best, ZCP x 276 ff.).

In all the later versions of the tale it is obvious that the compilers drew largely on other passages of TBC. Either they had MSS. of TBC before them (Thurneysen assumed, for instance, that the composer of F drew on four different manuscript versions of the Táin), or they knew these passages by heart. Thus in F a passage from Recension II TBC is quoted in the description of Fergus's arrival, exact in its account of the missing sword even to the opening words *Bliadain riasin scél so.* So too the Fer Diad episode in YBL frequently echoes earlier passages in TBC.

The account of the fight is unfinished in YBL. The scribe breaks off p. 39ᵇ6. The remainder of the column has been filled in by a different hand.

The whole of p. 40 had been left blank, presumably for the final part of the tale, not then available to the main scribe. On p. 40 the second hand has written fifteen lines in column a. The space filled in by this scribe 39ᵇ, 40ᵃ, contains a summary of the final part of the tale and some strange and confused verses which seem to be written from the memory of three poems in Recension II.

2571 *in Conganchnesach* ... Fer Diad is named here in Recension II: *Fer Diad mac Damáin meic Dáre, in milid mórchalma d'feraib Domnand* (Táin 2609–10).

2575 *dáig cnes congnaidhi imbi* Cf. *ar ba conganchnes oc comruc fri fer boi la Lóch* (supra 2027).

2577–78 *Dobretha* Passive with active meaning.

2583 *Tucad Findabair* ... This passage is not in Recension II here, but occurs there in the account of the fight with Fer Báeth. Similarly in the same episode in LU (supra 1755) there is a brief reference: *ba hi ind ingen no gebed láim fora c[h]uit-seom*.

2599 *deich fichit crosach* Crosach was a standard of weight for gold or silver. See note by Dr. Binchy, Ériu xx 56.

2600–1 ⁊ *comaid dom sliasaid-sea* The editors of TBC² punctuate differently. They end Medb's speech with the word *fogéba* (2601), and begin a new sentence which they print *Nadeiris, or cách*. (Inexplicably W. L. Faraday translated this as 'He does not need it, said every one', and her rendering has been adopted by T. Kinsella).

The YBL scribe is given to misplacing words. It seems likely that *air sin anuas* should come immediately after *comaid dom -sliasaid-sea*. In this passage in LL Fer Diad is offered not Medb's intimacy but *in t-eó óir báe i mbrut Medba fair anuas* (Táin 2634), ... *fair sin anuas* (Stowe). Moreover the words *dia rís a leas* do not seem applicable to Medb's offer of intimacy. Note that in the variant readings it is Medb who offers the gods as guarantee. I have punctuated and translated accordingly.

As mentioned above, in Recension II Medb offers Fer Diad not her friendship but merely her golden brooch (Táin 2634). But in the introductory section of TBC peculiar to Recension II Medb offers Dáire mac Fiachna, in payment for the loan of the bull, *cardes mo sliasta-sa fessin* (Táin 86–7). In TBFlidais II Medb sends to ask the leaders of the Gamanrad, including Fer Diad, for their help and offers in payment *ríghe na Gamanraidhi ... agus feis a Cruachain do gres, agus cairdes mo shliasda-sa fos* (Celtic Review iii 124).

2609 *a m'anom* Cf. *Maith ám a m'anam a Chathbaid* LL 22681, 23042 (CRR). This term of endearment is particularly common in the later texts Acallam na Senórach and Cath Finntrága.

2613 *corob misi cétfer* ... ... The *-b* is added later. Here *corob* is 3 s. future. See note Celtica vii 34–5.

2615 *Dotria búaid* ⁊ *bendachtain* In AS the phrase is *Ad-rae buaid* ⁊ *bennacht*. See note by Myles Dillon, Stories from Acallam Glossary s.v. *ad-rae*. As Dr. Dillon notes, the verb *ad-rae* is sometimes taken as if 2 s. = 'may you get' and the nouns are accusative as here. Thus *At-rae buaid* ⁊ *bennachtain* Grail 1690, 2981; *Atré buaidh* ⁊ *beannachtain* CF² 317.

2633 *bid húas dam a feidm* Here LL reads *bud tairpech in teidm* (Táin 2654). This reading and that of C suggest that here *húas* = *úais*, 'difficult'.

2637 There are two extra stanzas inserted here in C, LL and St.

2641 *doradsad* Perhaps a better reading *doragat* in LL and C.

2659 The line missing here, *Domroiched sról santbrecc*, Meyer (Misc. Hib. p. 40) would translate 'satin as variegated as one may desire'.

2662 *Geb brugaid geib oirgne* Windisch suggests *Brugaid* and *Airgne*, and compares the names *Brig Brugaid, Blai Brugaid*.

2686 *Ro bai láech amra . . .* This introduction of Fergus as a character not yet mentioned in the tale has given weight to the argument that Comrac Fir Diad was originally an independent tale later incorporated into TBC. The passage occurs only in Y.

2687–98 This passage is also in F. It does not occur here in Recension II, but it is found in the fight of Cú Chulainn with Calatín Dána and his sons (Táin 2546ff.). There Fergus's appeal is answered at once by Fíacha who, in both versions, goes to the aid of Cú Chulainn. The passage fits better where it occurs in Recension II. The answer given here by Fergus's followers (2697–8) does not ring true but it occurs also in F.

2688 *in gnim dognither isin maidin sea imbárach* Present tense = future also in the passage of Recension II mentioned in preceding note. In a passage of Oided Chloinne Uisnig, Glenmasan MS., Lebarcham says to meic Uisnig: *Is fata lim fós an gnim doniter anocht a nEmain* Celtic Review i 122, referring to what will happen later that night.

2698 *conici* One would expect *conici sin*, but *connice* = 'to him' occurs Táin 207, 1241.

2703 *7 a druim fria thigerna* This would be the normal seating of charioteer and warrior. Cf. *ara ara bélaib* common in such descriptions. The two sentences which follow I take to be parenthetical remarks which might be compared to such a sentence as *Is é timchellas Hérind i n-óenló* (supra 1246–7) said of Mac Roth when he is first mentioned. (In F, however, Láeg is definitely stated to be playing a board-game with his back to Cú Chulainn).
The reference to draughts and chess (I give these translations of *buanfach* and *fidchell* for convenience) in this passage is perhaps an echo of an earlier description of a visit made by Fergus to Cú Chulainn, in which Láeg, playing chess, is said to be facing Fergus while Cú Chulainn has his back to him (supra 1300).

2703–4 *dobered* (read *no bered?*) *leth brandaigechta 7 fidchillachta fora thigerna* This is explained by an earlier passage in Recension II: *7 no bered cach ra cluchi for Coin Culaind asin búanbaig* (Táin 1577). Windisch notes the gloss in Recension III: *doberedh a ara leth air .i. gach re cluichi air* (ZCP viii 549.23).

2706–23 There is no description of Fergus and his chariot here in Recension II. This was a stereotyped passage which flowed easily from the scribe's pen. It is more detailed than the description of Fergus in an earlier passage where he comes to bring terms to Cú Chulainn). Note the elaborate description of Fergus's sword here although Fergus had no sword in his scabbard.

In the earlier account Cú Chulainn interrupts Laeg's description to explain how Fergus had lost his sword (supra 1306–10). Cú Chulainn's offer of hospitality (2728–31) echoes the earlier passage 1312–6, and LL (Táin 1595–1600).

2710–1 *ma grindib állib a fén* See infra n.2592–3.

2711 *ba chumsclaig in charpait* lit. 'under the movement of the chariot'. I take *cumslaig* (*cumsclach*) to be from *cumscugud* (*con-od-scuich*) 'moving, motion', with intrusive *l*. O'Clery gives *cumhsgal .i. gluasachd nó corrughad*. Cf. the later Donegal form of *cumscuigim* with epenthetic *r*, *cosgraim cusgraim* (Gadelica I 70–71). A form *cumhscnaighidh* occurs CF[2] 439.

2714–5 Editors of TBC[2] read *cromsciathigel* but their second *i* is merely a stroke made by the scribe or some owner of the MS. to denote division of words. The C reading seems preferable here—*Cromsciath brec scabalgel*. The Y scribe often confuses the order of words.

2715 *co trí radhaib* The F reading seems the correct one here. Ornamentation of circles was common on shields. Cf. in the description of Cú Chulainn: *Dondsciath . . . co cóicroth óir . . . fair* (supra 2360) and *sciath co cóicroth óir fair* BDD[2] 674, 882.

rodénma gs. as adj., 'very beautiful'. Cf. the F reading *Geilsciath . . . go ttri rothaibh caoimhdhenmhtha* ZCP x 279.

2717 *tairrsceo* See BDD[2] Glossary s.v. *tairsciu*, where it is explained as 'part of a shield'. Here it does not seem to be part of a shield unless we read *inn óclaich* after *in scéith* and translate 'on the leather covering of the warrior's shield which is over its broad-based *tairisce*'. The meaning 'circumference' might perhaps suit.

2718–9 *úas chróebaib a chnis* It is difficult to decide the meaning of this phrase, which here takes the place of the usual *iarna imda* or *iarna chindruim*. Is *cróeb* used like *géc* = 'limb'? *Cnes* frequently means not 'skin' but 'body'.

2728–9 *liath léna* C's *elta én* (1752) would seem to be the correct reading. But curiously enough F reads *liath léna*, and so does Rec. III in a different context (ZCP viii 550.18). The meaning 'crane' is tentatively suggested for *liath léna* in Contributions, but a collective noun seems called for here.

2800 *Cid immo tánacais?* A repetition of the question supra 2739; better omitted here. But see C-reading.

2887 *corob* 3 s. pres. ind. Contrast *corob* 2613, 2750 where it is 3 s. fut.

2898 *feirtsi in charpait* 2907 *fertsi a charpait* Similarly in F. The reading in Recension II seems to make better sense: *Scar dom fortcha ⁊ forgemen mo charpait fóm and so* (Táin 2831), 'Spread the coverings and rugs of my chariot beneath me here'.

2941 ff. *Túarascbáil charpait Con Culaind* Omitted in C. Obviously quite irrelevant here. A mnemonic passage suggested to the scribe by the poem *Atcluiniur cul carpait*. Cf. the insertion of a superfluous description of Cú Chulainn's chariot and horses in the Breslech Maigi Murthemne passage which occurs in LU (and C), but not in Recensions II and III.

In LL and F a shorter description of chariot and horses (but not of Cú Chulainn and Láeg) comes immediately after the verses beginning *Is mithig in chabhair* (Táin 2914–25, ZCP x 284).

The end of this passage in Y (2965–73) seems corrupt. It contains some scribal misreadings, but I tentatively suggest that the compiler has also incorporated in the text overhead or marginal glosses or alternative readings. Only on such an assumption can I make any sense of some passages. What may seem drastic emendations are supported in the notes by quotations from other texts.

2941 *in tres primcharpat* Probably the three chariots were those of Cú Chulainn, of Lóegaire Búadach and of Conall Cernach. Cf. the description of these three by Finnabair in Fled Bricrend (LU 8590–8702).

2942 *for Tánaich = for Tánaidh*.

2944–5 *cuing dronórda* occurs in a similar description LU 8672 (FB) *Tarbchlár Tarb-* a mere intensive Cf. *tarblaích*, 'mighty warriors' CF[2] 282 and a similar use of *torc-* in *torcasnach* 'strong ribs' ib. 1269.

2946 *co lungetaib* Some parts of a chariot but the meaning is obscure. The word does not seem to occur elsewhere, and may be a scribal error. There is a mark ('acute accent' Edd. TBC[2]) over the *g*. We might take this as a deleting mark and read *lunetaib*, dp. of *loinit* (*loinid*), 'a churn-dash', here with some such meaning as 'pistons' or perhaps the front shafts (as opposed to *feirtse*, those at the back).

2948 *contacmaing* In RIA Contributions s.v. *do-acmaing*, this verb is taken as intransitive = 'traverses'. I take the meaning to be *tacmaing*, 'encompasses, includes' + relative *con-*, and translate 'which that chariot contains'.

2949 *co lúas . . . cliabaigi allaid Cliabach* m. and f. (*cliabag*?) is the name of some swiftly-running wild animal. O'Clery gives *cliabach .i. cú allaidh*, but this may be no more than a guess. In the LL description of Cú Chulainn's horses (Táin 2920–4) their swiftness is compared to that of *tétag allaid* 'a mighty stag'. See note on *tét-* 'mighty', by G. Murphy, Celtica iii 318–9. Cf. supra 2285–6 *co lúas faindle nó gaithe nó chliabaig*.

2950 *is é tricius ⁊ áithius* The commoner forms of these abstract nouns are *tricce, áithe*. In the modern version of Aided Con Culainn we get *is é sin gliccus ⁊ trice . . . cingit na heich* (Comp. Con C. 100.24) with a variant reading *tricas*. *Áithe* = 'swiftness' occurs MU[2] 566, 650, 666.

imoroget seems corrupt. One would expect some such verb as *immríadat*. In Contributions *imoroget* is taken as 3 pl. pres. ind. of *imm-roich*, 'reaches'.

is chucaind imthigit As the sense requires the verb here is *do-icc*. Cf. *is cucaind tic* infra 2994 *Im-* is prefixed to the verb which is taken as relative, a late usage after periphrasis. For another instance of relative *im-* cf. *Nicon berat a drúcht dind feór ar áthi ⁊ imétrummi im-tháncatar* MU[2] 566, with variant *. . . tancadar*.

Dafil here used = *fil*. But *Fil fer . . . Fil didiu imbi-sidi . . .* 2957–8.

2951 *coirrbega* Perhaps a misreading of *corrderga* which we get in LU 6910. Meyer, Contribb., gives *corr-bec*, 'small-snouted', taking *corr* as = 'point, peak, prow of a ship', hence a horse's nose.

2952   *bascind*   Read the common adj. *baslethna*?

2952–3   *fo grindib áillib a* [*f*]*én*   The same phrase supra 2289, 2710–1. The meaning is obscure. *Grinde*, 'faggot, bundle', will hardly suit here. The usual meaning of *fén* is 'wagon' (as supra l.1755). Here gpl. seems to refer to some parts of the chariot.

lugaid   Meaning uncertain. Faraday translates 'supple'.

2953   *fótmar focharrsid*   See supra n. 2290.

2955   The reading *dreich* must be wrong. Cf. *da ndroch duba tairchisi* LU 8595 (FB), 9260 (Siaburcharpat Con C.).

2956   *crúanatai*   From *crúan-data*?

2957   *i n-airinach in charpait sin*   The usual meaning of *airenach* is 'front, van'. Here, as it refers to Cú Chulainn, we must take it to mean 'chief position'. Contrast *Ara comsid círdub i n-airenuch in charpait* LL 24904, in a description of Láeg.

2962   *teóra imsrotha*   *Imm-* + *sruth*, 'an encircling stream' is suggested in RIA Contributions, but a form *imroth* occurs in an earlier passage 2344 where LU has *imsrotha*. Possibly *imsretha* is a better reading. In the description of Cú Chulainn in the BMMM episode in Recension III we read *Cain congairsi in fhuilt sin concuirther téora sretha im chlais a chúlaidh* RC xv 203 §174. In the same passage C reads *teorae himsrethae* (1373).

2966   Here the MS reads *Cem co fosaib* which I take as intended for *Céim comfossaid* (*cobsaid*), 'a firm, steady pace'.

2967   The editors of TBC² print *Cróib glec laích ina lámaib*. We might emend to *Cróeb glaici laich*, 'a branch to fit a hero's grasp', but for the following *ina lámaib*, which we should have to alter to *ina láim*. So I have suggested that we read *cróib* as a misplaced gloss on *crúithib*, and that the sentence *Glac laích ina lámaib* should come after *secht meóir ar cach láim*.

2969–72   Printed in TBC² *Cochall eitech imbe co fuaslucud. Dā duilend echlasc urchāin ōrda in*[*a*] *láim* ⅂ *brat findglas imbi* etc. *Fúaslucud* vn. of *fúaslaici*, 'loosens, opens', does not occur elsewhere in the concrete sense of the opening of a cloak or cape. But *airslocud* does occur with this meaning. In a description of Láeg beginning *Ara ara bélaib isin charpat* which occurs twice in LU we find the sentence *Coichline ettech immi co n-aurslocud ara dib n-ullennaib* 9277 (Siaburcharpat Con C.) 10235–6 (Tochm. Emere). Cf. also the Dagdae's cape: *Cochline co bac a da ullend* RC xii 86.

I note that in the RIA Contributions the punctuation of the TBC² editors has been accepted and *dā duilendechlasc urchāin ōrda* is translated (s.v. *duillend*) as 'two leaf-shaped riding whips'. But why two, especially as we also have *brot findaircit ina láim*? Furthermore one would expect ⅂ *brat findglas imbi* to come immediately after the mention of his *cochall*. In the description of Láeg's attire given in Breslech Maigi Murthemne, stress is laid on the necessity of leaving his arms free to drive the horses. Cf. supra 2190–2. I suggest that some scribe inserted *echlasc . . . ina láim* as an alternative reading to avoid the repetition of *brot* in *ic insaidi brot*. In the description of Laeg's equipment in the passages referred to above, viz., Siaburcharpat Con Culaind and Tochmarc Emere, we get the sentence *Bruitne di dergór ina láim dia taircellad a eochu* (LU 9278, 10236). Cf. also in a description of

Láeg in the mnemonic passage Cathcharpat Serda LL 189ª⁻ᵇ: *Flesc arggit gil i lláim ind arad ic sobrostugud na hechraide na tiagat céim forddail acht ammar as dess ⁊ as less ⁊ as licht [read líth] lassin óclach atchonnac* [i.e. Cú Chulainn] LL 24913-5.

2972-3 The editors of TBC[2] here print *c[h]arpat. Arsad a chaich.* They read *carp* in the right-hand margin; I can see only the letter *c* which I also read faintly on the left-hand margin before the following line. The scribe did not understand his original; he writes *Arpad* (as I read it) with a capital *A* and probably added *c* in the margin when he realized his blunder. The editors of TBC[2] have a note on the word they read as *chaich*: 'There has been an attempt to add *e* at the end'. I can distinctly read *chaicle* which I take as = *choicle*. A *choicle atacomnaic* = *a choicle é*, 'He is his friend (comrade)' which one might take to be a misplaced gloss on *in mílid mórglonnach*.

2973 Printed *is bec leis inn Eiriu* in TBC[2]. The use of the article with *Ériu* is unusual but not unknown. See Tochm. Étaíne, Ériu xii 12 §5; Death-Tales p. 38 §7. But I can make no sense at all of this sentence. Even emending to *is bec leis a n-eire*, 'Their burden is light to him', there is nothing to which 'their burden' could refer. I have not attempted to translate it.

2977 *Dá n-impóind* ... The exact force of this remark is obscure. The sentence occurs also in F where it reads: *Dia n-iompaidhinn m'aghaid don leth a tta mo chul, dar liom do rachdaois na hairm indíllte fuilid chugad triom* (ZCP x 285).

2979 *romór molaid-siu* = *romór molai-siu* supra 2975. The spelling *-(a)id* for the ending of 2 s. pres. ind. occurs fairly often in late Mid. Ir. texts, when slender *-d* had become silent. An instance occurs in W: *Indis dam, ol Conchobor friss, cedh na cotlaid* (ZCP ix 131.21) = *Cid ná cotlai* U Y. There are several instances in Life of S. Féchín (RC xii), Stair Nuadat Find Femin (ZCP xiii) etc. See CF[2] 819n.

2999 *Bec nár chonair chonais Conas*, 'contention, quarrel'. An adjective *conasach* occurs in Carswell's translation of Knox's Liturgy: *daoine conasacha* 180.19, 'contentious persons'. Plunkett gives *conaiseach* ... *triobloideach* s.v. afflagrans.

3082-3153 Written by a different hand.

3146 *for cúlaib ailli* This is quoted in Contributions s.v. *all*, 'cliff'. But the Recension II reading seems to justify the suggested emendation: *& rucsatar leó é go glassib ⁊ go aibnib crichi Conaille Murthemne do thúargain ⁊ do nige a chneda ⁊ a chréchta* etc. Táin 3659-61.
do icc ⁊ búalad a c[h]récht Again 3149 *dia búalad asna huscib. Búalad* in the sense of 'rubbing (vigorously)'. Cf. *melid* used similarly in TBFr[2] 232, and *túargain* in the LL- passage just quoted.

3151 *Dolluid Mac Roth ón tslóg fodes Fodes* must be wrong here. Read *fothúaid*. Or omit; probably *fodes* was copied carelessly from the preceding sentence.

3154-60 This list is not in Recension II. It interrupts the flow of the narrative very abruptly. Possibly its insertion here denotes a different source from that of the earlier part of TBC.

Airecor nArad, Aislingi nAimirgin, Tochestul nUlad. There is a tendency to prefix *n-* to proper names beginning with a vowel in titles. For
instance *Longus nUlad* Anecd. ii 43.16. In an H-interpolation we even find
n. pl. *Fir nÓl nEcmacht* (supra 1656) where the tendency extends to a proper
name not in a title.

3161   *Caladgleó Cethirn* This long passage may not have formed part
of the original tale. As *Comrac Fir Diad* is an elaboration of a duel fought
by Cú Chulainn and one of the men of Connacht, so this passage is an expansion of an attack on the enemy made by an Ulsterman in support of Cú
Chulainn. Some of Cethern's opponents are obvious e.g. Medb, Illann mac
Fergusa, the Maines and Ailill, but others do not appear elsewhere in the tale.
Note, however, that the names Bun and Mecon occur in TBDD and also
Bróen (and Bruitne of LL and Stowe). Thurneysen (Heldensage 192 n.2)
remarked that the composer of this passage, containing as it does several
invented names, cannot have been well acquainted with the warriors of
Connacht.

It is remarkable that though Fíngin Fáithliaig is expressly asked to come
and cure both Cethern and Cú Chulainn, there is no further reference here to
Cú Chulainn's injuries. Not until the episode *Aislingi Aimirgin* are Cú
Chulainn's wounds referred to again. Though in the final passage of Comrac
Fir Diad some of the Ulstermen are said to have taken Cú Chulainn to bathe
his wounds and heal him in the rivers of Conaille Muirthemne (*do icc ⁊ bualad
a crécht do uscib Conailli*), yet he is still unhealed in *Aislinge Aimirgin* and
Sírrobad Súaltaim.

3164   *is denn céttamun fil forsin carpat* In RIA Contributions this
is quoted s.v. *denn*, 'hue, colour'. Probably it is *dend*, 'smoke, mist'. O'Clery
quotes *deann céideamhain .i. li nó cheó bealtaine.* Cf. *Brat at-chondarc immi,
is coibés ⁊ ceó cétamain. Is sain dath ⁊ écosc cacha húaire tadbat fair. Áilliu
cach dath alailiu* BDD² 997–9. *Ceó cétamain*, 'mist of May', seems to denote
iridescence, the shimmering or change of colour as the wearer of the mantle
or the chariot moves. The sentence does not occur in Recension II.

3164–5   *is cuma congoin ...* I take this as an instance of relative
con-. Cf. the parallel passage in Recension II: *Is cumma congonand a araid
⁊ a eocho* Táin 3623–4.

3165   *Is ed hed lais* etc. This seems to be corrupt. There may be such
an idiom, but no other instance is attested. I suggest reading *is ed mod lais*.
Cf. O'Clery, obviously quoting this phrase from TBC, *is eadh modh lais .i. as
teann obair lais*. Vendryes (Vend. Lex. s.v. *mod*) would distinguish *mod*,
'manière, façon' from *mod*, 'labeur, peine'. (O'Clery has *modh .i. obair*). The
phrase *is ed mod má* (or *dá*) = 'scarcely' is common. Cf. supra 2256–7 *iss ed
mod dánas tairsed fiadchorr a tagraim do lár a grúade*. Similarly in LL, but
in Stowe *is contapairt go dtairsed fiadhcorr a toghraim do lár a grúaidi* (2312–3).
The meaning of both idioms is 'scarcely, almost'. But note *dá* with *is ed mod*
and *co* with *is contabairt*. But *is ed mod* occurs without *dá* or *má*. O'Davoren
§1258 reads *modh .i. contabairt, ut est asedh modh fortalla ind tri mer .i. is
inbechtain dia dtalla inn tri mer isin* [n]*eoch*. Wrongly expanded by Stokes
and mistranslated? He expands *ut est acht* for *ut est (a)sedh* and translates
'save a space whereon the ends of three fingers fit.' Correctly 'ut est the tops

of three fingers can scarcely fit'. A similar expansion occurs in Stokes's edition of Aided Guill ⁊ Gairb (RC xv 404,5), and is repeated in the Diplomatic Edition, LL 12637 *acht mod ma 'dresed corr in tsúil anaill do ind a grúade* which I would read [a]*sed mod* (*s̄* MS.).

In this passage of TBC I take *Is ed mod lais nicon tair in slóg i mbethaid* to mean 'he thinks he will scarcely reach the army (and find them) alive'. Compare the equivalent sentence in Recension II: *Acus indar leis ni hé rafársed na slúago 'na mbethaid itir* Táin 3616; *Dar leis ni beraidh i mbethaidh arna sluaghaibh* Stowe 3528.

I note that where the idiom occurs in Recension III TBC (in the Breslech Muige Murthemne passage) the wording is *is ed a mod*. Thus *is edh a mhodh nach tairseadh fiadchorr toghraim uirri* (RC xv 199 §145) (= 2256–7). *Iss edh a hodh dha croitea righabhall . . . nách roisedh ubhall dibh* etc. ib. §151 (= 2270). The spelling *a hodh* is to be noted.

Again in Ces Ulad from Harl. 5280 (ZCP viii 120) ⁊ *essé uhud de sen no gaipioth esse in c[h]arpait*. In his edition of the text (ZCP xxix. 311) Vernam Hull suggests the reading *iss é a mod . . .* and translates 'hardly on that account did he ever grasp the reins of the chariot'.

3166 *Mílchú alath ríam* This sentence is not in Recension II. It seems irrelevant here. One would not expect a hunting hound to accompany a warrior bent on hostilities. In general such hounds are represented as accompanying warriors whose equipment and entourage are elaborately described e.g. *secht milchoin i slabradaib argait* LL 33126 (TBFr.); *Sect milcoin imma charpat i slabradaib argit* ib. 33490–1 (Tochm. Ferbe).

3174 *arceisi de a guin* In RIA Contributions s.v. *ar-ceissi* (b) this is translated 'complains', a rendering based on O'Clery's *airchisi de a guin .i. éccaoinidh sé a guin*. But *éccaoinid*, trans., may mean 'mourns for, pities'. Cf. Stowe TBC 3006, 4389.

3177 *isind duibdúnad* C reads *isin dúnad* 2283. Possibly *duibdúnad* is a mere scribal error, *duib-* should have been deleted. The exiled Ulstermen are called *dubloinges* only in the late Stowe TBC: *tricha cet na dubloingsi* (357).

co Fiacha No mention of Fiacha here in LL or Stowe.

3178 *do chuindchid legi* Npl. for gpl. In Recension III, but not in Recensions I and II, one of the stipulations made by Fergus when offering conditions to Cú Chulainn is that Medb's physicians shall attend any of the Ulstermen wounded when fighting on Cú Chulainn's behalf (ZCP viii 547).

3179 *do c[h]omchisin Cethirn* See note on *cumcaisiu* Éigse xiv pt. I pp. 54–5.

3185 *co tuilid a inchind fora chlúasaib* C is illegible here. Recension II has imperfect indicative for the whole sentence: *da benad . . . béim dá durn . . . co tabrad a inchind dar senistrib a chlúas* Táin 3647–8. But we should hardly expect *bentai . . . co tuiled* here in Y. It is just possible that *inchind*, singular is here taken in plural sense with plural agreement of verb and that we should read *co tuilet* (*t* and *d* are easily confused in this MS.). In Aided Conchobuir (in LL 14300–2) we find verbs and conjugated prepositions in the plural referring to *inchind*. See note on *inchróes* Celtica x 142–4.

3185-6 *Marbaid cóecait leigi diib* As Thurneysen pointed out (Helden-sage 191) this is not a variant version but a scribal mistake corrected at once by *nó marbaid cóic fíru déac díb*. C shows confusion, referring to sixteen physicians in one passage, to fifty in another.

3187-8 *Anachtai-side la Coin Culainn íarom* Not in Recension II. Perhaps a scribal addition here, a vague remembrance of a sentence in the episode Fiacalgleó Fintain infra 3333, where Cú Chulainn is said to have rescued a son of Fintan.

3190 *do choimchisin* Recension II reads *do leiges Chethirn* here (Táin 3658).

3194 *adoféchad* The editors of TBC[2] suggest that this is for *ad-da-féchad*. Perhaps for *atdécad* from verb *ad-déci*.

3199 *ba di chén* Probably to be read *bad* (ipv.) *di chén*, rather than *ba* 3 s. pres. subj.

3205 *Dománic ben* In Recension II Illand Ilarchless comes first in the list of Cethern's attackers. Possibly this accounts for the description in C *domannicc laech . . .* and for the insertion of *osé amulach* and *is é rombi* in both Y and C. There certainly is some confusion here; possibly part of some other description has slipped in. Medb is fully armed in Recension I; in Recension II she carries only a spear.

Here there are three descriptions of attackers not found in Recension II, viz., *Trí truaill Banba, Trí Fruich Baiscne* and *trí rechtaire Ailella agus Medba.*

3205-6 *ben . . . chainmar* This is the only recorded instance of this adjective. Possibly we should read *ben . . . chain már*. Cf. the equivalent passage in LL: *Ben chain . . . mór* (Táin 3678), and that in Stowe: *Ben mor chaoin . . . tainic cucam* (3600-1).

3207-8 *Cóicdornn . . . ara druim* Cf. *cocdhurn .i. sgiath* O'Cl. A shield on her back seems excessive together with *claideb . . . iarna imdae*. This might account for C's alteration of *ara druim* to *ara durn*. We should expect some such sentence as *cóicroth . . . ara dóit* to follow the description of the mantle. *Cóicroth* means 'a brooch of five circles' as well as 'a shield'. Cf. *Fúan . . . n-imbi. Cóicroth óir airgdide* and LU 8601 (FB). See Stowe TBC Glossary s.v. In LL Medb has a golden brooch (*eó óir*) on her breast.

Fuillechta Part. of *fo-slig*, 'smears'. Here in sense of 'overlaid'.

3212 *Fingal . . .* This is glossed by the compiler of Stowe TBC as *cnedh tuc duine dot coirpfhine fort* (3588). Both Fergus and Fintan were of the Clann Rudraige. For the plural *Nít bérat* referring to *fingal* see note Celtica x 142.

3224-5 *Nicon tiagait a noindin itir . . .* See Táin n. 3691-2 for a different translation from mine suggested to me by Gordon Quin.

There must have been two meanings for *noinden*. Cf. *noenden .i. tinol, ut est ardnœndin sluaigh .i. tinol sluaigh mhoir* O'Dav. §1297. This is the meaning I have taken here.

3228 *Bun ⁊ Mecon* The same names are given for two of the king's guards in TBDD, LU 7672-3 (H).

3230 *Duba ind fhuil se* Plural adj. when *fuil* sing. = 'wounds'. Again plural verb and adj. in *It imfoicsi ém inn fuil ro fersat fort* 3268. See Celtica x. 141.

3231 *co ndernsat crois de* *De* must refer to *cride*. More usually the expression refers to the weapon as a *cros*, e.g. of a *sleg: corbo chross tall tarsna triana chliab iar tregdad a chride* LL 33654 (Tochm. Ferbae); of a *gai: co rabi 'na crois triit* TTr² 980. The LL reading here in TBC is *co nderna chrois dib trit chride* Táin 3699, *dib* referring to the two spears thrust into Cethern by Bun and Mecon.

3231 LL reads ⁊ *ni furchancaim-se a icc and so* Táin 3700. Better *a n-icc* as in Y C.

3233 *Dergrúathar dá mac rig Chailli* Meyer (Contribb.) suggested that *dá rigchailli* of Y was du. of *rigchaindel, caindel* used figuratively = 'famous warrior'. But such a spelling of *cainnle* does not seem to be attested. Meyer may have been influenced by *dá mac teóra soillse*. Should we read *dá mac rig chaille* = 'the two sons of an outlawed king'?

3235 *fidchúach* See note Celtica x 144–6.

3238 *Bróen* ⁊ *Láiréne* *Bróen* ⁊ *Brudni* Táin 3712. In TBDD one of Conaire's *dáilemain* is named *Broen* (LU 7545) and one of his two table-attendants is called *Bruthni* (ib. 7691).

3241 *rocrechta fo eill* ⁊ *luin* Similarly C. I cannot translate. The account of the *tri trúaill Banba* is very laconic. It does not occur in Recension II.

3252 I read *Imathcosan* here in Y. In the MS. all the words referring to an attack on Cethern, viz. *Galach, Dergrúathar, Congal, Búrach* etc. are written with a large capital reaching into the left margin. The *I* of *Imathcosan* in the margin is blurred, but quite legible. The editors of TBC² read *mathcosan*. *Athchomsán* is sometimes used = 'attack, onslaught'. Cf. *Roba thromm in t-indargain* ⁊ *rap amnas in t-immairc* ⁊ *rop aithgér in t-athchomsán darat cách da cheile dina sluagaib* TTr² 2003–5. See note on *achmasán* Echtra Uilliam 3013. For the spelling cf. *nirbat scelach athcossánach* LU 3496, where the meaning would seem to be 'aggressive' rather than 'reproachful'.

3254 *Tri broine liatha foraib* *Braine*, 'top, tip, prow (of a boat)', like *barr* came to mean 'a head of hair'. In *Folt fochas . . . fair co sniged co brainni a imda* LL 33486 it means 'top'. But in *ben . . . co mbraine barráin bith-ruaid* MD iii 278.30 it means 'hair'.

3269 *immosrocréchtatar* Y originally read *immosrocechatar* which, I suggest, may have originally been *immosrethatar*. The verb may be *imm-reith*, 'runs about, moves about'. Cf. supra 3250 *co n-imreith do chridi indit*. I note that in a later passage in LL- TBC the verb *imm-reith* is used with reflexive pronoun infixed: *Is bés don tsleg sin nachas imrethet impe riam ná hiaram na féthana . . . & is dóig gombad gar re coscar ros imreittis impe and so innossa* Táin 4351–3. See also TBC (C) n. 2377.

dait Better the reading of C, *indut*.

3283 *Cindas atomchii-sea* Here *ad-ci* is used with more or less the same meaning as *com-ad-ci*, of which the vn. occurs supra 3179 and again 3285. This perhaps explains the form *Cindas atcoimchi-si* in C (2389), a confusion of the two verbs.

286 TÁIN BÓ CÚAILNGE

3284 There seems to be an omission here in Y. C has taken the LL reading: *dáig ní tu ros méla* ⁊ *ní tharmnaigfet dait* (Táin 3762–3), 'it is not you who will enjoy them and they will bring you no profit'.

3286 Reading my suggested emendation of the C addition the meaning would be: 'You will show no mercy attacking a great army, for you are destined to die in any case'. See note by editor of C 2392–3 for alternative suggestions.

slicht slúaig I take *slicht* here to mean 'track', lit. 'when it is the wake of an army', i.e. the wounds left behind on Cethern's body by the attacks of many opponents. Thurneysen (Heldensage 192) paraphrases 'aber da eine ganzes Heer seine Spur in Cethern zurückgelassen habe'.

Unless we include the sentence added in C, the word *ar* should be omitted before *atbéla*.

3289 *Is and tucaib dorn dó* *Tucaib* possibly for *tocaib, tócaib* (the *ó* is short in the earlier language), but one would not expect *ó* > *u*: I have no other instance of *do-fócaib* with *dorn*. Perhaps a scribal misreading of *tuc buille dá durnn dó* or *tocaib a láim* ⁊ *tuc dorn dó*? Actually *dorn* is not the word to be expected here. Better *lúa* as in Recension II: *Agus dobretha trénlúa tarpech dá choiss úad riss* Táin 3766. *Lúa* is needed here to explain the place-name *Úachtar Lúa*.

3289–90 *co ndreised in carpat huile* The verb *dreisid* is given in Contributions as of doubtful meaning. I connect with *dresacht*, and adj. *dresachtach*, commonly used referring to the noisy creaking of a chariot.

3293 As sometimes happens in this MS. the word *beós* is misplaced. (It is also misplaced in C). Cf. *Gorop de atá Úachtar Lúa i Crich Ruiss ó sein anall gosindiu* Táin 3768–9; *Conadh de ata Uachtar Lua i cCrich Rois beos* Stowe 3689.

3294–5 *oldás for legi* The Y sentence is quoted by Thurneysen (Gramm. 232) as an exceptional use of *ol* without a verb. I have taken the C reading and assume that the reading *ol* in Y is a mere scribal error.

3299–3301 Here the recensions differ. In Recension II it is Cú Chulainn who kills the cattle. Here in Y the passage is ambiguous, perhaps intentionally so if the scribe thought that the gravely wounded Cú Chulainn could not be expected to kill the cattle.

3300 *smirchomairt* Synonymous with *smirammair*. See Táin n. 3777.

3308 *frisnid* (< *frisndid*), *fri* + copula. Cf. *condid* (*conid*), *óndid, diandid* (*dianid*) etc. Mistaken for negative by the C scribe.

3310 *carpat Finde Becce* She is called *Finda ingen Echach* in LL, Táin 3788, *Inda ingen Eachach Salbuidhi* Stowe 3725. The name is *Findbec* in Talland Étair (LL 13428) and in Fled Bricrend (LU 8408). The C compiler, drawing on both Y and Stowe, has in one passage *carpat Findbéice* (2411) and in another *Inda ingen Echach Salbuidi* (2427).

3315 *marb* is written in the margin in Y. I have adopted the reading of C which puts *marb* after *in liaig*. We might perhaps read instead ... *ro bai marb itir collaib na legi*. Cf. *Dorala-saide marb de múaid móir eter chollaib na llega aile* Táin 3790. For *marb* in the sense 'unconscious' see CF² n.1338.

3322 *Is iarom conmelt foroib* I take the verb to be *meilid* with *con-*, relative prefix. In the older language a relative would not be required here. Or possibly the verb is *con-meil*.

I have no other instance of the idiom *meilid for*, 'he attacks', but *meilid* seems to be used like *imm-beir*. Cf. *arna meala .i. arna himri* O'Davoren 63, and *nicon méla in fer sa a baraind for Ultu ni bus móo* infra 4065.

laithe co n-aidche One would expect 'three days and three nights'. Cf. supra 3287, where he is promised *nert trí lá ⁊ trí n-aidchi* to attack his enemies. In Recension II the three days and nights are the time spent by Cethern in the marrow-mash. Some confusion here.

Mane Specifically *Maine Andóe* in Recension II.

3328 *Fiacalgleó Findtain* No explanation of the name is given here, and for it we must turn to Recension II: *Is amlaid ra geibthe in fer de muntir Fintain meic Néill ⁊ in fer d'feraib Hérend ⁊ beóil ⁊ sróna cáich dib i ndétaib ⁊ i fiaclaib a chéile* Táin 3831–2, to which Stowe adds *ar dtaircsin a n-arm*, to explain why Fintan's men were reduced to fighting with their teeth.

3332–3 *fón amdabaid sciath* (Read *fó?*) That the words are misplaced here is shown by the LL reading: *Ro hainced-saide fo amdabaig sciath la hAilill ⁊ la Meidb* Táin 3821.

3336 *Rúadrucca Mind* Again the name is explained in Recension II: *And sain ra ráidsetar fir Hérend: Is rúad in rucce se, bar íat-sum, do Mend . . . a munter do marbad ⁊ do mudugud ⁊ a guin féin corop rusti rúadderg fair* Táin 3843–5.

3337 *tricha fer n-imrind dó* In Recension II *Dá fer déc ba sed a línsaide* Táin 3838, a better reading, for it was the total destruction of his force while he himself was merely wounded which caused Mend's 'blush of shame'.

3342–3 'There was no crime to be laid to their charge'. Alternatively one might read *ni boi cin 'no* (= *'na*) *mbeith dóib*, 'There was no reason (lit. fault) for them [Mend's people] to be at enmity with them [the men of Ireland] or 'for them to attack them'. Cf. *ni nach cin aile no taid dom* Wb. 19ᵃ26, 'it is not any other fault that makes you vexed with me'. The C reading would seem to support this meaning.

3346 *Bángleó Rochada* Thurneysen takes as *bangleó*, 'Weibskampf'. It is of course a fight fought because of Finnabair. But *bangleó* should mean 'a fight fought by a woman'. Cf. *bangal* supra 3204 which O'Clery glosses *gail nó gaisgeadh mná*. Meyer, Contribb., gives *bángleó*, 'a bloodless fight'.

Again in LL here the title is explained: *Is and sain ra ráidsetar fir Hérend: Is bán in gleó sa, bar íat-som, do Reochaid . . . ocht cét láech lánchalma do thuttim trina ág ⁊ trina accais ⁊ a dul féin cen fuligud gen fordergad fair* Táin 3890–2.

3352–3 *Focres a phupall do suidiu a Findabair* I take *Findabair* here to be the place-name. Cf. infra 3365 *Is de atá Findabair Slébe*. (For the place-name *Findabair*, 'white water', which is of frequent occurrence in Ireland see Hermathena 1933 210–12). But Thurneysen seems to have taken as *ó Findabair*, for he renders it 'Sie schlägt ein Zelt für ihn auf und schläft bei ihm (Heldensage 195).

3358-9 *Bátar oc forairi ón tslóg* Hardly to be taken as a scribal mis-reading of *oc f. an tslúaig* The preposition *ó* here denotes that they had been sent to watch on behalf of the army. Cf. the equivalent passage in Recension II: *oc foraire dar éis in tslúaig* Táin 3879.

3365 *Atbail ar féili and sin* In RIA Dict. s.v. *féile* the reading *ar* [*a*] *féile sin*, 'from the shame of that' is suggested. Emendation unnecessary if we take C- reading.

3366 I have taken the first element in *Mellgleó* as *mell*, 'pleasant' ('playful'?) Cf. Mellbretha. I base this on *contibset in fear tarnocht* 3376 and the final sentence of the passage 3386. The compiler of Recension II on the other hand has taken *mell* to mean 'a round mass, a round missile'. His closing sentence is *Is aire atberar Mellgleó nIliach ris dáig de chlochaib ⁊ chorthib ⁊ táthleccaib móra fogní-seom a gleó* Táin 3929-30.

3375 *clapar* Meaning doubtful. See Contributions.

3387 *Airecor nArad* For *airecor* meaning 'a hail of missiles' see Stowe TBC n.3898. In Stowe alone an explanation of the name is given: *As de at-berar aireagar n-aradh uair is do clochaib ⁊ do corthib ⁊ do tháthlecaibh in talman ro cuirsit ár bfer nErenn* (3897-9). Airecor nArad is a doublet of Aided na Macraide in the earlier part of the tale.

3399-3400 *co ndechaid a áltaib dó* I have attempted to justify my translation of this passage in Stowe TBC n.3986. If the meaning were, as has been suggested by previous translators, that his joints had been dislocated (reading *altaib* pl. of *alt*), one might have expected not an impersonal use of *téit* but something like *co ndechaid cach alt dó asa inad.* Cf. *ro laad cech alt asa choir damm* Ml. 44ᵃ2, 'My every joint has been put from its proper place'. In the description of the wounded Cú Chulainn in the episode Sírrabad Súaltaim the emphasis is wholly on bleeding and loss of blood.

3408-9 *a mac Conall Cernach* No reference to Conall Cernach here in Recension II. The sentence reads like a scribal addition.

3413 *fri dá mac déc Gaile Dána ⁊ mac a sethar* The remarkable point here is that there is no reference to the fight with Fer Diad. LL reads *ri Calatín Dána cona secht maccaib fichet ⁊ ra húa* Táin 3984. Stowe TBC alone adds *⁊ re Fer Diad ier sin.* See Táin Introd. xxiii-xxiv.

There is a confusion here in Y with the fight against Ferchú Loingsech and his twelve followers. Recension III shows a somewhat similar confusion of the two episodes when a passage describing the fight with Gaile Dána and his sons occurs in Recension III in the fight with Ferchú Loingsech and his twelve men (RC xv 207 §§225-6).

3421-3 Note that there is no reference to Cú Chulainn's having been healed by the rivers of Conaille Murthemne. But that passage occurs in the later interpolated Comrac Fir Diad.

3415-6 *In nem maides* ... A common motif. The speaker first asks if any of two or three cataclysms is taking place and finally asks the question to which the answer is affirmative. Cf. an almost exactly similar passage in Talland Étair where Cú Chulainn hears the groan of his fosterling Mess Dead: *Is nem maides nó is muir thráges nó talam conscara no búriud mo daltai-se oc imbirt ecomluind fair* LL 13411–2 (with statements, not questions). Compare also a passage in TBDD. At the sound of Dond Désa's sons' landing, Conaire says that it is an earthquake or a cataclysm caused by the leviathan which surrounds the globe striking the earth with its tail or—finally—the boat of Dond Désa's sons coming to land (BDD² 591–4).

3427 *for Duma na nGiall* Called *Lecc na nGiall* in Recension II, which explains *forsind liaic* 3446, *liaic* as. of *lia*. See Bergin's note on *lia* Ériu xii 217. *Lecc* and *lia* were sometimes confused.

3428–9 *Ba airmert di Ultaib* ... *Acht* has twice been added later in Y. Here the compiler has confused *re n-, ria n-* with *fri* (*ri*). The original reading must have been something like *ní labrad nech díb ria Conchobar; ní labrad Conchobar riasna druidib*. This is the reading in Recension II and in MU. Cf. *Geiss d'Ultaib labrad rena ríg, geis don ríg labrad rena druidib* Táin 4017. Again MU² 234–5.

3430 *Cista brata* ... This is a repetition (or doublet) of an earlier passage in the section called *córugud aile* (1211–8). There it is Cú Chulainn who takes the account of the foray to Conchobar.

I have expanded *cisda ben* where the editors of TBC² take it as *cisdabeir*. In the earlier passage in LU the question asked is *ciche brata, ciche áig, ciche goin* (1215).

3434–5 *Túaga* ... The use of these hoops is explained more fully in Stowe TBC when Cú Chulainn complains of his grave wounds to Súaltaim: *Atá do met mo chnedh ⁊ mo chrecht conach fuilngim mo earradh no mo ededh do buain re mo cneas conadh tuagha urchuill congbas mo brat os mo chionn* (3965–7). In AS these hoops are called *lúbáin findchuill*, 'bent twigs of white hazel': *corub lubá[i]n findchuill ro boí ac imfhulung a n-étaig tarsu ina cossairleapaid chró* AS 5201–2.

3442 *a n-aithesc* n., but m. in C.

3444–5 One of the passages where the compiler of Y or of Y's exemplar has condensed the narrative and so distorted the meaning. I would take *isa tech* to be a misreading and misplacement of *in t-ech*, and read *Dobeir in t-ech i nEmain aitherroch a chend forsin sciath*. (Although often in Y *ind emain* is the spelling for *ind Némain*, we can hardly read *Dobeir ind Némain* etc. here).

In Recension II Súaltaim goes on his mission to the Ulstermen mounted on the Liath Macha: *Tánic Súaltaim reime forin Liath Macha d'óeneoch* Táin 4009. Then when Súaltaim receives an unsatisfactory answer *driuchtrais* [*lingis* Stowe] *in Liath Macha ba Súaltaim ⁊ tánic reime fa urdreich na hEmna. Is and sain imsuí a sciath féin bar Súaltaim co tópacht bil a scéith féin a chend de Súaltaim Luid in t-ech féin bar cúlu aris i nEmain ⁊ a sciath barsinn eoch ⁊ in cend barsin sciath* Táin 4035–9. It is this last sentence which is distorted in Y. I am not convinced that the Y reading *isa tech* is the original one. If it were, we should have to assume that the LL- compiler, like the present editor, read *Dobeir in t-ech* etc., and then added all the details about Súaltaim's arriving on horseback, the sudden shying of the Liath Macha and Súaltaim's consequent fall. One remembers too that messengers were frequently sent on hoseback. Hence *echlach, marcach* = 'messenger'.

3445 ⁊ *asbeir an cend an focol cétna* The common motif of a severed head speaking. See Táin 4039 n.

3446 *is inna chotlud ro boi-som* In the earlier passage of which Sírrabad Súaltaim is a doublet, Cú Chulainn takes the warning to Conchobor and the passage is introduced with the words *.r. Cú Chulaind dixit* (1213), that is, the whole passage, Cú Chulainn's message, Conchobar's question, Cú Chulainn's answer all form a *rosc*. Such a *rosc* was commonly spoken in a mystic trance. The only possible explanation of Súaltaim's falling asleep here is that the scribe took his message *Fir gontair, mná brattar, bai agthar* as a *rosc*, or the beginning of one.

3448 ff. *Muir ara cendaib* . . . That the sentence has the force of a vow is shown by the equivalent passage in Recension II (Táin 4042–7). Cf. infra 4043–4.

3451 *Forrumai* . . . *láim fora mac* The same meaning as in *lám do gabáil ar x*. Cf. *Ra gab láim ara araid ara ṅgabad a eochu* Táin 2800–1, 'He ordered his charioteer to harness his horses'.

3454–97 For this catalogue see Táin n. 4054–4100 and Stowe TBC n. 4011–24. Of the twenty leaders described later in the section Toichim na mBuiden fourteen are mentioned here. Noteworthy in the catalogue is the inclusion of Illann mac Fergusa who was with his father in Connacht and had attacked Cethern mac Fintain. Though Cethern's death has been recorded already, he too is included here.

3502 *comérge do Chonchobar* The same meaning here as in *mo diuchtrad-sa asin ches a raba*, as Conchobar himself calls it (3510–1) = Recension II *mo chomérgi-sea assin león ⁊ assin chess i rraba* (Táin 4115). It refers to Conchobar's recovery from the debility rather than his rising up in arms.

3508 *a ndá trichaid cét sin* That is, the Ulster division which had gone to fetch Erc and Erc's own division.

3512–6 This episode is told in very obscure fashion in Y and C. Thanks to Recension II we can discern the meaning. Some such sentence as that in LL (*& baralsat* [= *doralsat*] *dóib and ocht fichti fer mór do šainmuntir Ailella ⁊ Medba* Táin 4118–9) might be inserted after *tríb cóictib cairptech*, and the sentences *cu tubartadar* . . . *Féne* put after *din brait*.
There is inconsistency here. If Conchobar and Celtchair kill 160 of the enemy at this point, Ailill's doubt as to whether the Ulstermen are on the march (3549ff.) is inexplicable. Probably this passage, like the later one in LL where Conchobar fights in person against Medb and her forces (Táin 4228–78), is from another version. Thurneysen (Heldensage 105) suggests that for Sírrabad Súaltaim and this paragraph there stood in the old version a brief account of the Ulstermen arising from their debility and marching against the enemy army.

3515 *dofaídi* For *do-s-faídi*, 'sends them'.

3540 *huair Aililla* MS. Corrupt. Not in C. I have suggested that it is a scribal misreading of *Buadris A*. Cf. in Recension II *Buadris Celtchair and so innossa*, prefixed to a *rosc*, *Taible lethderg* etc., spoken by Celtchair Táin 4127.

3562 *Atchondarc ... in gaith móir* Cf. *co n-acasa in gaith n-úair ...
bec nád ruc ar folt díar cennaib* LU 9240–1 (Siaburcharpat C.C.). Again in Togail Troí: *Is í esnad gaithi adúari ... atchonnacais* LL 32221–2. For this interchange of a verb descriptive of a sense we might compare W. *clywed*, 'hearing', which is also used of 'smelling', 'tasting.'

3574 *in tormgal* (*tromgal* MS.) In the corresponding passage of Táin the collocation *toirm ⁊ torann* occurs three times 4179, 4191, 4312. Dr. Dillon has remarked on the fact that many of the *-gal* compounds refer to noise (Celtica viii 197 n.5). Here *-gal* intensifies *torm*. The C- compiler must have found the spelling *tromgal* in his exemplar. He changes it to *tromnélgal* which does not refer to noise but means 'cloud-rack'. Cf. CCath. 470.

3590 *Ar* is at the line-end: *Is ar | trichaid cét inti*. The reading in LL is: *Dóig ri farcsin ⁊ ri fégad tricha cét indi* Táin 4298.

3605–6 *Eó óir húasa dóit* Again *Eó óir fora dóit* 3636. *Dóit* (earlier *doé*) means 'upper arm, shoulder' and is frequently given as the position of brooch or pin. Cf. *Milech óir ecair ina brutt uasa gelgualand* LL 39463 (MU). (I note that in a passage in Táin Bó Fraích 236 Dr. Meid misunderstood *dóit* and translated *milech* as 'bracelet', TBFr² 19n). In the present text we have *Trí delgi óir húasa ndóitib* 3774, and in Recension II *Delgi órda airegda | iar ndóitib dendglana* Táin 4563–4).

3611–2 *a nglúine fri talmain ⁊ imbel a scíath fria smecha* That is, each man is ready and eager to attack, one knee to the ground, and shield held in defensive position. Recension II makes this clearer by adding *ara fat leó go léctar chucaind* Táin 4326–7, 'in their eagerness to be let at us.' Cf. *Ro bátar didu ara chind ⁊ immbél a scíath fria smechu* Trip.² 468, expressing the hostile attitude of Láegaire's people to Patrick.

3618 *Scíath erradach* The meaning of the adj. is doubtful. O'Clery gives *sgiath erreadhach .i. eangach:* and *engach* is used of a shield Stowe TBC 4543, and in many other texts = 'variegated'.

3630 *slúag argara Ulad* *Argara* here for gen. of *airgaire* vn. of *ar-gair*. Cf. *am teist ergaire cluichi* Fél. 150, 'I am a proof of the prohibition of sport', with v.l. in 15c. Franciscan MS. *argairthi*. The reading of Recension II is *slúag acallma Ulad* Táin 4364.

3635 *foga forgabalach ina farrad* Phrase omitted LL, *fogae fogablaighi* (= *fogablaigthi*) Stowe TBC 4325–6. Cf. supra 2096.

3635–6 *iarna c[h]inddruim* Some part of body. I assume that the meaning is as in *iarna imdae, iarna formna*.

3680 *Ergal án riam* See Celtica x 147–8 where I suggest that this was originally a marginal note here misplaced. Again 3721, 3820. I have not translated the sentence which means some such wish as 'Good luck to him in his fight!'

3681 *comendaisc* Meaning obscure.

3681 *Cromrosc Crundrosc* Táin 4401, *cronnrosg* Stowe TBC 4356 'a round eye'. In the same passage Táin has *Crundscíath derg* (4402) corresponding to *dercscíath* here. O'Clery gives *crom-rosc .i. gormrosg .i. súile gorma nó glasa*. We might take the first element of *cromrosg* to be a confusion with *cromscíath* which is not uncommon. Cf. infra 3736 and supra 2233. The better reading is that of Recension II.

292   TÁIN BÓ CÚAILNGE

3687   *laimnid* The meaning 'one who dares' is suggested in Contributions.

3694-5   *Cuinsiu chain c[h]orcarda chumdachtach* Perhaps better omitted in this passage. Already *gnúis* and *aged* have been described. But I note that in the description of Cormac Cond Longas in TBDD we get first *Aiged fochâel forlethan* followed by other details and finally *Coínso chóir chain chorcorda lais* (LU 7081).

3701   *Is leth gliad* Again *is leth catha* 3740 In Táin I have translated 'He is half a battle (in himself)'—perhaps too literal a rendering. 'Fitting opponent in battle' is the meaning given in Contributions.

3716   *Baithi* The *-th-* has been taken over from the present *táthai*, 'he has'. One would expect some such word as *lór* to follow, *Baithi lór do gail* etc.

3723   *cúicroth óir fair* Caechruth (read *cúicroth*) *óir fair .i. a sciath* Táin 4452. Cf. also *sciath co cóicroth óir fair* LU 7080 (TBDD) In the Second Battle of Moytura Stokes translates *Coicroith oir uara muin* as 'Five circlets of gold on his neck' (RC x 60 §16). It refers to his shield on his back. The sentence comes between the description of spears and of sword.

3752-3   *Méit a béil beólu eich* The accusative *beólu* because the sentence is taken as the equivalent of *Métithir a béil beólu eich*. Cf. *Samla beolo fidchuaich indara súil dó* LL 12636, where *samla* too is the equivalent of an equative.

3753   For my rendering of *lethglóir* see Stowe TBC Glossary s.vv. *lethgabar, lethgleóir*. O'Clery was mistaken when he glossed *lethglebie* as *leathshúil ghlóire*, which actually means 'a wall-eye'. Plunkett gives, under glaucoma, *glóireacht a súil eich, súil ghlóire*.

3755   *húasa dóit* MS has *dot* with mark over *o*, probably due to an attempt to insert *i*. Editors of TBC² read ... *huasa . dondbocoit* ...

3771-80   The three sons of Fiachna are not described here in LL though they are named among those summoned by Findchad. Stowe TBC includes them here, no doubt drawing on Recension I.

3785   Here Recension II has merely *Gae gorm tanaide úasa* Táin 4509-10 We might take the Y- reading to be for *co n-ag anmas* (*oag am amainse* MS.) or *co n-agaib amainse*. For the plural of *ag* cf. the description of Mac Cécht's spear: *Cethri traigid tromthomsidi eter a dá n-ag* LU 7284-5, 'between its two points'.

3788-9   *Is é in lamnid leatarthach* Possibly the same word as supra 3687. But *luibne*, 'a casting spear', fig. 'a warrior', is the term used here in Recension II: *in lumne léitmenach* Táin 4513, *an lubne létmech* Stowe TBC 4423.

3791   *Comla*, 'a door-valve', fig. 'a (protecting) hero'. *Comla catha* is common, so also *comla ergaili*. Or we might read here *comla chothaigthe*, as in Fianaigecht 86.9.

3825   *Contúaissi* here, like *ar-túaisi*, must mean 'falls silent.' Contrast *contúasiset fris uli* LU 1450, 'they all listened to him'. If the meaning were 'he listens to him' we should expect the addition of *fris*.

NOTES TO TEXT 293

3828–9 *Ní 'mmuscarat tairrid.* Corrupt? Perhaps originally a marginal note; the text reads smoothly without it. The sentence has been taken over and still further corrupted in both LL and Stowe.

3833 *oc teasarcain luig a crídi Lóeg*, 'calf' = 'favourite, beloved, darling'. LL reads *oc tessarcain laíg a mbó* Táin 4559; Stowe has *ic teasarcain a n-úa* 4590.

3834 *Dos-icfe Dosuicfe* MS. with deleting mark above *u*.

3839 ff. From this point on the narrative in Y is disconnected, jerky and obviously inaccurate or corrupt here and there. Recension II on the other hand has a smooth-flowing narrative with events recorded in logical sequence.

3842 *Ní thánic didiu Conall Cernach cona mórbuidin* Conall Cernach and his men are described, however, in Stowe TBC 4551–67. So also are the three sons of Conchobar ib. 4539–50. For remarks on this point see Stowe TBC Introduction pp. xii–xiii.

3847–58 The description of chariot, horses, warrior and charioteer is quite superfluous here. The unequal combat referred to (*iarna chréchtnugud i nn-écomlund*) is Cú Chulainn's fight with Gaile Dána and his sons.

3848 *fossenga* An attempt has been made to delete the first *s*. Read *fosenga*. See BDD² Glossary s.v. *foseng*, 'leanflanked'.

3850 *Pupull úainidi huaithne* Here *huaithne* is perhaps a scribal change of reading for the first adjective. Faraday begins a new phrase *Uaithne intnaise*, 'the pillars carved'. But *uaithne* as part of a chariot does not occur elsewhere.

intnaise If not a by-form of *esnaisse*, part. of *in-snaid*, 'inlaid', we might take as meant for *intlaise*.

3852 *Cethochruss nó ceatharfochrus* A scribal correction of the first word? *Cetharfochrus* may = *cethirdiabail*. But the form *cathfochrus* occurs (supra 93) *Fer i cathfochrus bruit deirg*. *Fochrus, fo + cris*.

3853 Text corrupt, but again there is an echo of the early verses so it is possible to correct. Cf. *Cethri claidbíni, cles n-án | fil i cechtar a dá lám* (supra 87–8). *Dóit* here used = 'hand'.

3854 Again text corrupt. Cf. *secht cneslénti fichet* (supra 2216) in the description of Cú Chulainn's attire.

3856 *ina ladair* I have translated 'between his fingers', but as he is engaged in playing chess it may mean 'between his toes'.

3857–8 *Búanbach . . . ardai* The exact relevance of these sentences here is obscure.

3860 *a sidaib* It was Lug mac Ethlend, not Súaltaim, who was Cú Chulainn's father *a sidaib*.

3870 *Fer muinter . . .* I can make no sense of this. Should we read something like *Ferda muinter*? Or is it a scribe's guess at an illegible line in his exemplar, e.g. *Formna fer nUlad adchonnarcais ém*? About one third of the line is blank after the words *or Fergus*. Something was written in the blank space and overflowed into the margin. Unfortunately it has been erased so completely that nothing of it can now be read.

3872–3 ⁊ *basisestar A*.... ⁊ *basisestar C.* = *fo-sisestar*. In a note on the conjunction *agus* Celtica ix 131–2 I have given instances of interchange of preverb in a non-relative verb after *ocus*. The interchange *ba-* | *fo-* is common.

3874–6 I have given the MS. reading in the text. The translation would be: 'Then Conchobar's tents were pitched. There was scarcely a bare patch of earth between them [i.e. between the tents], and the Ulstermen came before sunset.' I think the emended reading gives better sense. We have already been told *Luid Conchobar trá cona slógaib co ngab dúnad hi comochraib dia chélib*. *Pupaill Conchobair* would be a repetition, so I have suggested *pupaill fer nÉrend*. Further I suggest *eturru* ⁊ *dúnad nUlad*, taking *eturru* to refer to *fir Érend*. Only with a copyist as careless as the scribe of Y would one suggest such drastic emendations.

3877 *itir in dá dúnad* LL reads *oc indloch* ⁊ *oc etarchossait eter na dá dúnad chechtarda* Táin 4601. The two encampments referred to are that of Conchobar (*Luid Conchobar . . . co ngab dúnad* supra 3871) and that of the men of Ireland (reading *focertar pupaill fer nÉrend* supra 3874 as I have suggested).

3881–2 *mairc Iarnaib . . . cén mair Iarnaib* 'Woe to the Érainn . . . Hail to the Érainn'. According to T. F. O'Rahilly this was a simple scribal blunder; the scribe took the word to be *iarn*, 'iron' (Ériu xiv 8 n. 8). LL reads *Bó mair Érno* Táin 4606–7.

3882–3 *Is ed dobreth hi cluasaib Iairn* Read *hi cluasaib Érann*. *Dobreth* with active meaning, probably intended for *asbert*. Cf. LL- reading.

3884–6 *Dobreth biad dó* . . . Not in Recension II here, but twice in Comrac Fir Diad of that recension we get the sentences: *Raptar biattaig Brega dano do Choin Culaind. Tictis dá acaldaim fri dé .i. cach n-aidche* Táin 3133–4, 3176–7. This passage in Y would seem to be an echo of the LL-passages. It is not really relevant here. In the LL- Comrac Fir Diad it follows a sentence which tells us that the men of Ireland supplied Fer Diad with food.

3894 *Bá bág dóib-som . . . Bág* in sense of 'obligation, bond'. In LL- TBC *Ba bág ám dait-siu ga dobertha do greimm catha . . . lind* Táin 4704–5 = *Ba coir duit-si . . . do grem catha do tabairt . . . linde* Stowe TBC 4812–3.

3903–4 *Nó is hé Conchobar* . . . This uncertainty as to the attribution of the various *roscada* is peculiar to Y. Again infra 3928. Cf. also supra 3523, 3538 where the *rosc* beginning *Taibli lethderga* etc. is attributed first to Celtchair, and then in an afterthought, 'possibly it was chanted by Cúscraid Mend Macha.' No uncertainty at any point in Recension II.

3905 *Comérgid, ríg Macha* Again infra 3911–2, 3930 and *Afraigid, ríg Macha* 3918. For nominative used as vocative see supra n. 54.

3927 *oc terorcain* MS. LL has *ac tulargain na mbuden rempu* Táin 4667. The verbal noun must have been indistinct in the exemplars of both Y and LL.

3939 More clearly explained in Recension II with the words *ara fat leis tiachtain timchell* Táin 4644, 'deeming it too long to go around (to the opening of the tent)'.

3940   *Is degchobair éigne*   The editors of TBC² read . . . *ēigme*, adding
"The *m* is doubtful' in a footnote. I read *eigne* plainly, but there is a later
prolongation of the final bar of the *n*. *Is degóir éigmi* Táin 4648–9, which
Windisch took to be for *degúair éimgi* and translated 'eine gute Stunde
geeigneter Zeit'. Marstrander suggested the reading *degfhóir éigme*, 'goodly
help in answer to a cry of distress.' One of the late Recension II^b MSS.
actually reads *deaghfhóir eimhghe* (Stowe TBC p. 152 n.5).

3941   *Imthúsa Ulad* . . .   This is a turn of phrase found both in Comrac
Fir Diad and in the continuation of TBC Recension I, in YBL. It does not
occur in the LU portion of TBC. The phrase is used when one topic has been
dealt with and a different character now appears. Here it seems to denote a
breaking off in the narrative to introduce an interpolation *Tochustul Fer*
nÉrend. When the interpolation finishes the narrative returns to Cú Chulaind
with the words *Imthúsa Con Culaind immorro is ed indister sund coléic.* (3984).

3945   *Tochostul Fear nÉrend*   This catalogue of warriors summoned
to Ailill was evidently intended by the compiler of *Y* to be a counterblast
to the earlier list of warriors summoned to Conchobar, *Tochestul Ulad* supra.
As I have noted (Stowe TBC p. 196) there is one big difference between the
two lists: in *Tochustul Fer nÉrend* none of the men named appear earlier or
subsequently in the fighting nor are there any well-known figures among them.
The list would seem to have been one memorized by scribes. It has been
drawn on in the 15th-century tale Cath Finntrága to provide the names of
the Túatha Dé Danann chiefs who came to the aid of the Fianna. Again in
Tóruigecht Diarmada ⁊ Gráinne a more garbled version of the CF list occurs
(ITS xlviii 50–52).

In LL only thirty-three triads are named against the hundred and one
of *Y*. There are echoes of names found elsewhere in Irish tales, in particular
some triads which occur in Fled Bricrend and Togail Bruidne Da Derga.
See Stowe TBC p. 196.

3982   *Ferchuidred Fer nÉrend*   See Stowe TBC n.4795. A member of
the *ferchuitred* was *ferchuitredach*. In LL the list of names is preceded by
And sain dariachtatar chucu-som 'na ferchuitredaig fer ṅHérend Táin 4689.

3985–9   This passage comes earlier in Recension II before the catalogue
of warriors. The phrase *ni regad crua ná fonnad trít* is made clearer in LL by
the addition *ara dlús ⁊ ara deimne ⁊ ara daiṅgne coṅgbaither a n-airm i llámaib*
na mmíled itráthsa Táin 4676–7, 'so densely, so firmly and so strongly are their
weapons held in the hands of the soldiers now'.

3997   I have suggested the reading *ferchuitred ind athślógaid*, 'the
triads of the second mustering'. The editors of TBC² have *ina ferchuidreda*
('the *a* has been added later beneath') *ind áth slógaid* which Faraday translates
'the men of the body guard [came] to the ford of the hosting'. I take *athślógad*
to refer to *Tochustul Fer nÉrend*; the first *slógad* was *Tochustul Ulad*.

3997–8   *I n-inam trá hi tuladar fianna íarom* . . .   For the last two words
I suggest that the exemplar of the *Y* compiler was partly illegible. The obvious
reading would be *fir Érend*.

4001   *Nistailcc Medb* . . .   The scribe often misplaces words. Here I
suggest that he has displaced a whole sentence which should rightly come
after *ferchuitred ind athślógaid* supra 3997. As it stands here in *Y* it is the

296 TÁIN BÓ CÚAILNGE

warriors from Irúath who act as bodyguard for Medb and Ailill. In Recension II it is the *ferchuitredaig*. Before the list of warriors in LL, *ferchuitredaig fer ṅHérend*, we get the sentence *ba hed a ṅgnim uile 'sin chath ar bíth gona Conchobair diambad fair bad róen ⁊ ar bíth aṅcthe Ailella ⁊ Medba dámbad forro conmebsad* Táin 4689–91. Cf. *Maidid for Meidb iar sin . . . ⁊ nos berat na ferchutredaig ass hi iar sin amal ba bés dóib* LL 34125–6 (Tochm, Ferbae), where they certainly act as Medb's bodyguard.

4004 *nárbo chol dó* 'that it would not be wrong for him', with the overtone of the guilt attached to one attacking his own kinsmen.

4015 *doruchtfaid* Some corruption here? One would expect a transitive verb with object *na haeru*. There is a word *drocht* (2 *drocht* Contribb.) meaning 'dark, obscure'. Might one read *drochtfaid na haeru*, 'will darken the air'? The meaning given in Contribb. for *ruchtaid* 'emits a *rucht* or sound of some kind' will hardly fit here.

4020 *isin letir i crích nUlad* In LL *barin lettir i Crúachnaib Ai* Táin 4715. See my note on this discrepancy Táin Introd. l-li.

4027 *Fo chen* etc. This is spoken by Fergus in answer to Ailill's *rosc*. This is made clear in Recension II: *Acus firis Fergus fálte risin claideb. 'Mo chen Caladbolg, claideb Leite', bar ésium* etc. Táin 4719f.

4032 *do thoitim i roi remur* Remur does not seem to give sense. I have met no other instance of it used figuratively = 'crowded'. Should we read *remum* ,'before me', Mid. Ir. for *rium*.

4033–5 Not in Recension II. The passage, which is a repetition of earlier ones, seems out of place here.

4047 *fair, thairrse* Sciath fluctuates in gender (especially for pronominal prepositions) even in the same sentence, as here. Cf. BDD² 977, 978 where *dó* refers to *sciath* in one line and *tarse* in the next.

4049 *Cia . . . argab in sciath?* One would expect the addition *frim*. Táin reads *Cia concoṅgbathar sciath rum-sa* (4748). *Argab* here used with same meaning as *do-furgaib*, 'raises'. Cf. *tócbaid in sciath fris* supra 4045–6.

4056 *Ainbchellach* [*nád*] *ainbchellach* O'Clery has *ainbhcheallach .i. ainmín nó garb*. For the idiom cf. *Mét mo boithe—bec nád bec* EIL 8.10a, and *Atconnarcatar úadib mod nad mod .i. in fat rosiacht índ radairc a roisc* LU 10056–7.

4066–73 Not in Recension II. The passage is a repetition of Fergus's encounter with Cormac. There is actually no definite implication here that Conall Cernach is with the Ulstermen. Note that Fergus asks him the same question as he asks Cormac who is with the Connacht forces.

4074 *nó for sciath Conchobair fodeisin* The alternative here is the Recension II version.

4088 *Rethaid* (= *rethait*) *immorro anaill ille as* 'They sprang out of him hither and thither'. The scribe, probably re-reading the sentence, misunderstood and took it to be for *immar anáil i lés* 'like air in a bladder', a stereotyped simile. Hence he made a marginal note *am̄* (= *amail*), intended as a correction of *.im̄.* (= *immorro*).

Gabaid (= *gabait*) *a fuile ergraim de* = *Ra gabsat a fuli ilgremma de* Táin 4791–2. Lit. 'His wounds took hold of him, prevailed over him.'

4089 *cend ceachtair de in dá inailte* In Recension II it is two female satirists (*dá banchánti*) who come from the Connacht encampment to feign to lament over Cú Chulainn and to bring him news of defeat. They are first mentioned after Toichim na mBuiden (Táin 4596–9) where their names are given as *Fethan* and *Collach*, and they are mentioned again in this passage, as in Y, where they are called *Fethan* and *Colla* (Táin 4793–6). Their killing is described there as the first exploit performed by Cú Chulainn after rising from his sickbed.

4092 *ar adroas . . .* I assume that the scribe forgot to put marks of deletion under -*ag*-. Cf. *at-rós a thairmesc*, 'he could not be prevented' Fingal Ronáin 14; *at-roas techt ar in orggain* ib. 397.

4093 *secht cneslénti fichit* Similarly 27 in the BMMM episode supra 2216, but 24 in the description given by Mac Roth 3854.

4099 *notninus . . .* The verb *nigid*, 'washes', comes to mean 'washes vigorously, drubs'. See note s.v. *nigid* Stowe TBC Glossary.

4102 *Cia do feraib Hérend . . .* One would expect *Cia di Ultaib . . .* as supra 4049 or merely *Cia* as in Recension II.

4106 *Dó duit* (*do thuit* MS.) The scribe's *t* and *d* are hard to distinguish sometimes, but here he definitely has *thuit*. I take it that the scribe of his exemplar had the same confusion of *t* and *d*. For *dó duit*, 'begone', cf. O'Clery's *dó .i. chuige, dó dhuit .i. chuige duit*. In the Etarcomal episode where Recension I reads *Airgg úaim* (supra 1348) Recension II has *Dó duit* (Táin 1649). Cf. also Táin n. 8o.

4107 With the scribe's correction of *asat* to *basat* cf. *Cia bátar do gnima in tan ropsa* (v. ll. *ropsat, basat*) *gilla?* Tec. Corm. §82. The scribe altered because of the past *romimgabais-siu*. We might omit that verb, however, and read *Maith, or Fergus, in tan asat tretholl-sa*, 'I agree, said Fergus, since you are pierced with wounds'. But emendation is pointless here for obviously the compiler had quite forgotten the details of the earlier episode, Comrac Fergusa fri Coin Culainn. In that incident Medb asks Fergus to fight with Cú Chulainn. After much persuasion he goes, but Cú Chulainn retreats from him on condition that at a later date, on the occasion of the great battle, Fergus will in return retreat before Cú Chulainn, and in doing so will induce the men of Ireland to follow his example. There is no reference to Cú Chulainn's being wounded.

The passage where Fergus makes his promise is not told in any great detail in Recension I: *Teilg traigid dam, a Chú Chulaind, or Fergus. Teilgfe-so dano dam-sa arísi, ar Cú Chulaind . . . Is and sin dolléci Cú Chulaind traigid for cúlu re Fergus . . . ara telced Fergus dó-som traigid i lló in chatha* (supra 2510–4). In Recension II it is described in more detail (Táin 2494–9).

In the present passage, as it is given in Recension II, only Cú Chulainn speaks. He reminds Fergus of his earlier promise: *Ro gellaisiu teiched remum-so inbaid bad chréchtach crólinnech tretholl mé for cath na Tána dáig ro thechiusa romat-sa ar do chomlond féin for Tánaid* (Táin 4809–11). The Stowe compiler adds *an tan nach raibi do cloidemh agat-sa* (4935).

4109 *fácbaid* We may take as active 'they, i.e. the Gaileóin and the Muimnig, leave (behind)', or as used intransitively with passive sense 'they i.e. the forces of Medb and Ailill, are left'. See RIA Dict. s.v. *fo-ácaib* II (a).

298 TÁIN BÓ CÚAILNGE

4118 *tairis* Perhaps for *do-airis* Mid. Ir. = O.Ir. *tarrasair* pret. of *do-airissedar*. But to whom does the singular verb refer? To Cú Chulainn? I suggest reading ⁊ *tairis*, 'and across (the ford)'. The phrase used in Recension II is *dar Áth Mór siar* Táin 4837, 4841–2.

4118–9 *Beanaid trí bémend . . . forsin licc* A plural noun might be better. Recension II reads ⁊ *rabert béim dona trí Máelánaib Átha Lúain i n-agid na trí Máela Mide goro ben a trí cindu díb* Táin 4843–5. This was a counterblast to the three blows struck by Fergus on the *Máela Mide* (supra 4072).

4122 *Correcad lochta* ⁊ *fulachta* Meaning obscure. Obviously some proverbial saying with a play on words.

4129 The reference to the quarrel between Fergus and Bricriu (Echtra Nerai RC x 212) is much more detailed in Recension II, and so is the account of Bricriu's death. I have translated *tor*, 'sorrow, pain', rather freely as the context demanded. Original reading probably *i n-othor*?

4134 *conidgres Fergus* In Recension II it is Cormac Cond Longes (Táin 4886–8).

4138 *co mebaid a fergaire* The context suggests that it was the Donn Cúailnge's leg which was broken as he drew it away from the Finnbennach's horn. However the Stowe compiler, using a copy of Recension I, takes over this sentence (which is not in LL) and definitely states that it was Donn Cúailnge who broke Finnbennach's leg: *coro bhris a gerrgara do buille* (5050).

4141 *Bertius riam iarom* The meaning is 'he carried her' or 'he carried them'. Neither meaning will suit here unless we assume that the Y- scribe has omitted a sentence, found in Recension II, which describes the Donn Cúailnge coming from Crúachu with the body of Finnbennach a mangled mass (*ina ascarnaig*) on his horns (Táin 4894–6). (Plunkett gives *ascarnach* s.v. stupa, the coarse part of flax, tow hards, hence a tangled mass. Here *ascarnach* describes the mangled remains of Finnbennach). Assuming that the Y-scribe had overlooked some such passage *bertius* could refer to *ascarnach* f.

It would perhaps be too bold an emendation to read *berthi as*, 'He (D.C.) carries him (F.) off.' Alternatively *beirthi as* could be taken to mean 'he betakes himself, he goes'. Cf. *beirthi i n-imirghi a Cleitech*, 'he made a flitting to C.' Tochm. Étaíne, Ériu xii 146 §8, lit, 'betakes himself'. But if we took this to be the meaning here, it does not explain how he emerged from the lake with the shattered body of his opponent impaled on his horns.

A final suggestion to explain *bertius*: in Mid. Ir. the infixed pronoun -*s*- has spread beyond its bounds and is frequently used for 3 s.m. May *bertius* be an instance of -*us*, the suffixed pronoun, used = 'him'? An instance occurs in Serglíge Con Culainn; *Tofobairt iar sin Senach Siabortha . . .* ⁊ *marbthus Cú Chulaind* LU 3790 (H).

I note that Thurneysen, influenced no doubt by the reading of Recension II, gives the gist of this sentence as 'Der Donn Cuailnge trägt nun den Finnbennach einen Tag und eine Nacht auf den Hörnern' (Heldensage 217).

uide lá co n-aidche One would expect *lai*, but here *lá co n-aidche* is taken as an indeclinable phrase.

4142 *co tulaid dó ass* = 'and he came away out of it (the lake)'. In Contributions s.v. *do-tét* (g) this sentence is taken as an impersonal construction with *dó* of the person. I take *dó* to be used adverbially here, like English 'off' or 'away'. There are several instances of this use of *dó* in LL- TBC, e.g. *Lotar . . . na echlacha dó co tech Dáre* Táin 88, *Lotar na echlacha ar cúl dó samlaid* ib. 141. In LU alone in Aided Cúir, we get the sentence *Luid dó iarom* (1711 H), 'He went off then'.

4155 *Druim Tairb* One would expect an explanation of this place-name as of all the others. LL-TBC has *Tuc a druim risin tilaig* Táin 4916, but does not give the place-name.

4156–9 This last paragraph in which the death of Finnabair is ignored is purely a scribal addendum. We might compare the ending of the tale called Fled Bricrend ⁊ Longes Mac nDuil Dermait in the same MS. written by the same scribe (YBL 114ᵇ–117ᵇ): *Is iarsin didiu dogensad cairdes ⁊ Eocho Rond, ⁊ anaid Findchoem la Coin Culaind. Dodeachaid iar suidiu [siudiu MS.] do Emain Macha co morcoscor. Is de sin ata Fled Bricrenn ar in sceol sa. Ainm aili do didiu Loinges mac Duil Diarmait. Finit* (IT II 185. 296–300). The resemblance in wording is too striking to be mere coincidence.

INDEX TO MAIN NOTES

alailiu, arailiu (adverbial), 'or else' 1170-4
Allechtu 955.
amal, 'where' 1498
anaill ille 4088
anam (a m'anom) 2609
anarma 1924
apraind 2173
arco 2178
argara 3630
aspiration of relative 2341

bág, 'obligation, bond' 3894
biruich 2288
braine 3254
buadris 211, 3540

cadessin 947-8
cáem 1754 (see also 655-6)
cairíni 2246
cess Ulad (noínden) 51
cia arránic 2166
clangdírech 2285-6
cliabach 2949
co matain 457-8
co topachtur 1758-9
coinne 1923
contúaisi 3825
corob (fut.) 2613, 2750; (pres. ind.) 2887
cros 3231
crosach 2599
cúicroth, cóicroth 3207-8, 3723
cuitbiud 864

dagéini .i. tic 947
dáig ar bith 2100
degchobair éigne 3940
denn céttamun 3164
Dia do bethu 489
dó (in adverbial use) 4106, 4142
doíagat 532
do-inchoisc sén 618
dóit 3605-6
do-selba 1775
do-soí (for) 29
dotria (búaid ⁊ bennachtain) 2615
dreisid 3289-90
ergal án riam 3680

ferda sin 2106
fichid (trans.) 2025
fochlacht 1171-4
fóitech 198
fótmar 2290
frisnid 3308
fuil, 'wounds' 3230

Galióin 148
gilla = ara 1662, 2332

Iarnaib = Érnaib 3881-2
imathcosán, athchomsán, 'attack' 3252
imthúsa 3941
infixed pronoun *-s-* 89, 869-70,
i n-íam 2043

la (agent with impersonal verb) 804
lamnid 3788-9
leth (brandaigechta) 2703-4
lethgleóir 3753
líath léna 2728-9

mad mani, mad dia 1697, 2139
marginal *.r.* (before catalogue) 114;
(before syllabic verse) 190
má thecra 1315
meilid (for) 3322
mellgleó 3366
mod (is ed mod) 3165

ind Némain 210
noínden = tinól 3224-5
nominative for vocative 54, 3905

oldás 3294-5

passive form for active 1974, 2242,
2297, 2577

saiget 2231

tormgal 3574
túaga 3434-5
tuillem écraite (fri) 727-8

INDEX OF PERSONS

trí **Aeda Aidne** 3958.

Ailill 2, 4, 149, Ailill mac Mátae 1217, 3539; g. Ailella 145, 870, 890.

Ailill [Ardágach mac Mágach] 4.

trí **hAilill hUaiti** 3966.

deich **nAilella** 1916.

Aimirgin *See* Amairgin.

Aindiaraid 3465.

dá **Áinle** 1969.

trí **hAirig Cluichiur** 3975.

trí **hAirig Insi Úan** 3977.

trí **hAirt Arda Ladrann** 3962; trí hAirt Arda (repetition) 3967–8.

Alamiach 3478.

Allechtu 955. *The Fury Allecto.*

Amairgin cosin rígfilid co hA. 3462–3; Amargin 3403, 3406, g. Aimirgin 3393, 3394, a. Amargine 3401, 3402; Amorgene mac Ecetsalaig Goband 3728; Amargind mac Eicit (*sic*) 3928–9.

Amargin co hAimirgin co hEas Rúaid 3481.

trí **hAmalgaid Aí** 3953.

Ambuach 3471.

Ánlúan mac **Mágach** 4.

trí **Ánraid Turbi** 3964.

dá **Ardáin**, dá mac Licce 1942.

trí **hAthchuirp Tulcha** 3972.

Badb 210ᵃ, 3942, 4033.

trí **Bailcbroindi Móenmaige** 3978.

Bairech 3476 (*n. loc.* ?).

trí **Bairrchais Eille** 3962.

Barrene 3471 (*n. loc.* ?).

Bascall mac **Mágach** 5.

Bé Néit 3942, 4033.

Blae Brugaid 3488.

Blae Fichit 3488.

Bláirige 3493.

Bodb 1525, trí **Boidb Búaidnige** 3950.

Bogaine 1526.

Boirche 3043. (*Possibly a common noun* = '*strong man, warrior.*' *See Contribb. s.v.*).

Bó Mailce 2060.

trí **Bratruaid Locha Rí** 3952.

Brecc 3483.

Breic 3476.

trí **Bresail Bodgna** 3953.

Bricir 3476.

Bricirne 3476.

Bricriu Nemthenga mac **Carbada** 1990, 4129, g. Bricriu 485, Bricrinn (*sic for* Bricrenn) 4132.

Bróen mac **Ríg Caille** 3235.

trí **Brónaig Bethra** 3969.

Bruachur 3478; trí Bru[a]chair Glais Febrat 3955.

Búadgalach 3470.

trí **Búaideltaig Berba** 3950.

Búan g. Búain 1849.

Búan 3476.

Buide mac **Báin** 1491, 1502.

trí **Buidir Búaisi** 3949.

Bun 3228.

Cairbre Nia Manand 2667.

ceithre **Caiss** 2322.

trí **Cais Cuile** 3979.

dá **Chalad** 2032, 2321.

Cathbad Druí 603, 610, 612, 613, 3459.

trí **Caurith** 2321.

cúic **Caurith** 2323.

Celtchar mac **Guthidir** 56, C. mac Uthidir 365, Celtchar mac Cuithechair 3472, g. Celtchair meic Uthidir 1532; n. Celtchair (Y) 3512, 3517, Celtchair mac Cuitheochair 3741–2.

trí **Celtchair Umuill** 3961.

secht **Celtri** 1916.

cúic **Cermain** 2323.

Cet mac **Mágach** 5.

Cethern mac **Fintain** 3169, 3175, 3461, g. Cethirn 3161, 3190.

dá **Chíar** 2321.

Cimb 3474.

Cimling 3474.

Cimmene 3474.

dá **Chír** 2321.

cúic **Cobthaig** 2323.

Cóemdele 1011.

trí **Coinchind Shile** 3960.

trí **Coirbri** 3459–60.

302 TÁIN BÓ CÚAILNGE

trí Coirp Cláiri 3967.
trí Coirpre Cliach 3956.
trí Coirpri Luingi 3974.
ocht Coirpri 2325.
Coirpre mac Fedelmtheo 2400.
Col 2064.
trí Combirgi 2322.
secht Conaill 1915.
trí Conaill Collamrach 3955-6.
trí Conairi Sléibe Mis 3948.
Conall Cernach 143, 542, 666, 3479,
   4067, g. Conaill Chernaig 681, 3988,
   voc. a Chonaill 672.
Conchobar mac Nessa 51, 402, 436 et
   passim, g. Conchobair meic Nessa
   610, 476, 589, voc. a popa
   Chonchobair 440, 648.
trí Conchobair Collsen 3976.
trí Congbaidi Cliach 3963.
Conla Sáeb 3485.
Connad mac Morna 3479–80, 3688.
Cormac Colomon ind Ríg 3266.
Cormac Cond Longas mac Conchobair
   (C. Con Longes Y) 6, 9, 16, 1705.
Cormac Maíle Ogath 3266-7.
trí Cormaic Cúanach 3973-4.
trí Cormaic Uiscrenn 3971.
Corp Gliath (*read* Clíach) 3466. Cf.
   TBDart. 149 ff.
trí Coscraig Clothra 3961.
Cremath 3488.
Cronn 1011.
dá Chrúaid 2032, 2320.
trí Cruim 2321.
Cruthen 1524.
Cú Chulaind mac Súaltaim 102, 217,
   220 et *passim*, g. Con Culaind 262,
   1169, voc. a Chú Chulaind 494,
   1930, a. Coin Culaind 255, 318, d.
   Coin Chulaind 1657, 1742; dimin.
   voc. a Chúcán 2176, a Chúcacán
   2702.
Cuilén 3490.
Cuillius ara Conchobair 1039, 1042,
   1045.
Culand Cerd (Cauland) 545, 546, 567.
Cú Rí mac Amargin 3482.
Cú Roí mac Dáire 1396, 1617, 1620, g.
   Con Roí 1398, 1609.
Cúr mac Da Láth (Cáur) 1695, 1720,
   1727, g. Cáuir 1694.

Curethar 3490.
Cúscraid Mend Macha mac Conchobair
   484, 521, 3487, 3523, 3624.
sé Dáich 2323.
náe nDaigith 2326.
dá Daigri 1969.
Dáir rí Rómán 2194.
Dáire mac Fiachna 3780.
sé Dáiri 2324.
náe nDáiri 2326.
trí Dáiri Tiprat Find 3962.
Daithen 1943. (Cf. BDD² 1155).
Dam Derg 3465.
Dam Dremed 3464-5.
náe nDámaig 2326.
trí Damaig Dergderce 3952.
Damán athair Fir Diad 2525.
trí Dauig Leamna 3961.
Dechtere g. 444.
Dedad 3455.
trí Deirg Sruthra 1691.
trí Deiscertaig Droma [Fornochta]
   3957.
trí Deiscirt Úaga 3960.
deich nDelbaíth 1916.
Delt 1943. (Cf. BDD² 1155).
Derg Induruc 3457
Dernu 2064.
Derothor 2032.
Diarmait mac Conchobair 2465-6.
   2467, 2470. Cf. CA §255.
Díliu mac Gárach 909.
Dócha mac Mágach 5, 2457, 3377, g,
   Dóche 2462.
trí Doíl Eirrig 3951-2.
trí Dornmair Maigi Uisce 3980.
Dornu 2064.
Drenda 3474 (*n. loc.* ?).
Drendas 3474 (*n. loc.* ?).
Drúcht 1943. (Cf. BDD² 1155).
trí Dúadaid Áine 3959
Dubthach Dóel Ulad 189, 2371, 2426,
   3527, mac Lugdach meic Caorubai
   2402, g. Dubthaige (v.) 191,
   Dubthaig 211ᵇ, 3530.
trí Duib Drúad 3975.
trí Duib Imlig 1691.
trí Duirn 3978.
sé Dúngail Irruis 860.
ceithre Dúngais Imlig 1969.
dá Ecell 2321.

co hEchdaich (*read* Eochaid) Lathach 3467–8.

co hEchtaich (*read* Eochaid) Sainmech 3467.

trí Échtaig Áne 3951.

trí Échtaig Findabrach 3970.

Eirr mac Iraird 256, 333.

Eirrge Echbél (Airigi) 3471–2, 3758–9.

Eithbenne 3491 (*n. loc.* ?).

trí Eitirscél Temrach 3964.

trí Elair Deiuais 3976.

Emer Foltchaín 2811.

Én mac Mágach 5.

Eo mac Oircne 3484.

Eógan mac Durthacht 367, 482, 3489, 3640, g. Eógain meic Derthacht 481.

Eraise 2065.

Erc mac Cairpre Niad Fer ⁊ Fedelme Nóichridi 3828, g. Eirc 3507.

Etarcomol mac Eda ⁊ Leithrinne 1290, 1296, 1321, g. Etarcomail 1287.

trí Eterscéle Etarbáne 3958.

Fachtna mac Senchath 3475.

Fáeladán 3458.

Fallach 3456.

Fandall mac Nechta Scéne 703, 741.

deich Fedelmid 2327.

seser Fedelmthe 1559.

acht Féic 1916.

deich Féic 2326.

trí Féic Findabrach 3956.

Feidelm Banfáith 49, 54, 304, Fedelm banfili 41, voc. a Feidelm B. 48.

Feidelm Nóichride g. Fedelmae Nóichridi 223, 3507–8.

Feidlimid Cilair Cétaig 3457–8, 3678.

trí Feidmnig Rotail 3965.

ceithre Feochair 2322.

Férach 811b, 812c.

trí Ferad Find 3971–2.

Feradach Find Fechtnach 3750.

trí Feradaig Foltchais 3965.

Fer Báeth 1746, 1750, 1757, g. Fir Baíth 1788, 1829, voc. 1778, 1791.

Ferchú Loingsech 2520.

Fer Diad mac Damáin 2577, 2581, 2592, g. Fir Diad 2577, 2781, 2818, voc. a Fir Diad 2590.

Fergna mac Findchoíme 3471, 3803.

Fergus mac Leite 3477, 3718.

Fergus mac Róich (Roeich) meic Echdaich 57, 141, 1217 *et passim*, Fergus mac Rossa Róich (*rosc*) 1088, g. Fergusa 264, 1044, 3546, voc. a Fergus 351, 1555, 1669, a Fergais 231, 1893, 2775, a popa Fergus 489, 1312, 1364, a popa Fergais 4097, a mo popa a Fergais 2726, a popa a Fergais 4059.

deich Fergusa 1559.

Fernél 3491.

Fer Tedil 936.

Fer Toíthle 2061–2.

Fer Ulli mac Lugdach 703a.

Fiacha mac Conchobair 3768, g. Fiachaig 2398.

Fiacha mac Fir Febe 143, 822, 1428, 1725, 1771.

Fiacha Fialdána Dimraith 2456, 2458–9, d. Fiachaig Fialdána mac Fir Febe 1635.

deich Fiachaig 2326.

trí Fiach Fernna nImbais 3978.

Fiachna 3464.

Fiachna mac Conchobair 3768.

Fiachna Fuilech mac Fir Febe 1634. (= Fiacha mac Fir Febe *supra*). g. Fiachrach meic Fir Febe 1647.

sé Fiachraig 1560.

trí Fiachraig Feda Némain 3953–4.

trí Fiadail Duinergin 3976.

Fiatach Fer Doirre mac Dubthaig 3496.

trí Fidaig Saigthi 3973.

Find Bec g. Finde Becce 3310. Wife of Cethern mac Findtain.

Findabair ingen Ailella ⁊ Medba 145, 1570, 3349, 4158, g. Findabrach 1604, 1751.

Findchad Fer Benn 3451–2, 3498, voc. a Fiṅdchaid 3455.

Findchad Sléibe Betha 3491.

Findmór ben Celtchair 1532.

Findtan 3329, g. Findtain 3328.

Fíngin Fáithliaig 3189, 3196, 3201, co Fíngin 3487.

trí Fintain Femin 3957.

Flidais 145e.

Fochlam mac Iraird 257, 333.

Fodail rechtaire Ailella ⁊ Medba 3256.

Foich mac Iraird 256, 333.

Fóill mac Nechta Scéne 703, 734.

Senchaid 3475.

Senlobair 3469.

Senoll Úathach 3144–5, 3460–1.

Sétanta mac Súaltaim ⁊ Dechtere 444 (= Cú Chulainn).

Simón Druí 2193.

trí Sochaidi Sinna 3968.

Srubgaile mac Eóbith 1735.

trí Sruthmair Maige Ochtair 3979.

Súaltaim 217, 3414, 3431, g. id. 255, 261, 3410.

trí Suibne Siúire 3951.

Tamun Drúth 2484, g. Tamuin Drúith 2483.

deich Tasaig 1917.

Tascur 1944.

Taur 1944.

Téa 1943.

trí Tigernmais Túath Ambrais 3970.

trí Tigirn Taince Tipraiti Talindi 3981

Toillchenn 3484.

Torathar (Aurothor U) 3462.

Traig 2064

Traigthrén techtaire Medba 1926, voc. a Thraigthréin 3948.

Triscod trénfer tigi Conchobair 2529.

trí Triúin Maige Éle 3979.

Túachell mac Nechta Scéne 703. 748.

Túalang 1944.

trí Túathail Tanni 3972.

Úalu 1003, g. Úaland 1002, 1006.

Úalu mac Gárach 909.

secht nÚargusa 1915.

Uathadach Fodoblaid 3463 (read Uathach Bodbda as in LL?).

trí hUidir Buaile 3971.

trí hUidir Conchobair 3974.

trí hUilleith Arda Airthir 3967.

Uma mac Remarbisi 3468. Cf. MU² 99. 620.

INDEX OF PLACES, PEOPLES, RIVERS

Aelai co hA. 3460.

Aidne g. (= Mag nAidne) 3958.

Aigle g. (= Cruach Aigle) 3955. *Now Croaghpatrick in Connacht.*

Áine co hÁ. 3471, g. Áine 3951, 3959.

Airgdech (Airgthech) ocond Airgdig 400.

Airther Fúata g. Airthir F. 3779.

Aisse for Assi 124.

Alba a hAlbain 43. *N. Britain.*

Ánmag for Á. 129.

Ard g. Arda 3968.

Ardachad for A. 124.

Ard Aignech (= Focheird) 1938.

Ard Airthir g. Arda A. 3967.

Ard in Dírma 2482.

Ard Ladrann g. Arda Ladlarn (*sic*) 3962.

Ard Róich 1620.

Asal g. Asail 3542.

Áth Airthir Mide 3513.

Áth mBuide 1506.

Áth Carpat 951–2.

Áth Céit Chúile 2068, 2071.

Áth Craíbe g. Átha Croíbe 3977.

Áth Cruinn 1147.

Áth Cuillne 1231.

Áth Da Ferta 2491, 2496, 4151.

Áth Duirn 1227.

Áth Feidle 3368.

Áth Féne 3513.

Áth Fir Diad 2548, 3868, 3886. *Now Ardee, Co. Louth.*

Áth Fraích 853.

Áth Fúait 837.

Áth nGabla (= Áth nGrencha) 335.

Áth nGrencha 330–1, 1872, 1917. *N. of Knowth, Co. Meath.*

Áth Lethan (for Níth) 950.

Áth Lúain 4118, 4119, 4147, 4148, g. 4119. *Athlone.*

Áth Medba 1535.

Áth Taiten (*read* Taíden?) 859.

Áth Tamuin 2486, 2487.

Áth Tarteisc (Darteisc) 1873, 1981.

Áth Tíre Móir 2065.

Áth Tolam Sét 1520.

Áth Traiged 2029–30.

Báil Scena for B.S. 128. (Ball Scena LL.)

Baile for B. 127, g. Baili 3790.

Baile in Bile 2923.

Banba g. id. 3242. *Ireland.*

Bedc 3148. *A river in Conaille Muirthemne.*

Belach nÁne 832.

Belach Caille Móire 335[b]. *N. of Knowth.*

Belach Eóin 2464, g. Belaig Eóin (Eúin) 2455, 2463, 2464, 2480.

Bélat Alióin 1021.

Berba g. id. 3950.

Bernas co B. 3492, g. Bernais 3790.

Bernas Bó Cúailnge 1010, 1015.

Bernas Bó nUlad 1035, 1038.

Berramain g. Berramnach 3973.

Bile Medba 1534–5.

Bir 3148. *A river in Conaille Muirthemne.*

Bithślán 3147. *A river in Conaille Muirthemne.*

Bóann for Bóaind 3343. *R. Boyne.*

Bodgna (Badgna) g. id. 3953.

Bolga for Bolga 117.

Botha 1016.

Brega g. Breg, d. Bregaib 764. *Plain S. and S.W. of Dundalk.*

Brenaide 3148.

Breslech Mór 2074, 2328–9.

Brí Eirrgi 3759.

Bríg Dumae 3703.

Broinfeirste 2921.

Búaidnech g. Búaidnigi 3950. *A Leinster river.*

Búaile g. id. 3971.

Búan 3147.

Búas ó Búais 3728. *River Bush.*

Búas g. Buaisi 3949. (*Must be a different river*).

Caínbile g. 942.

Cairthenn Clúana Da Dam 2812.

Callann co Callaind (Felunt Y C, *corrupt*) 3480, ó Challaind 3688.

Canainn Gall co Canaind nGall 3469.

Carn for Carnd 119. Cf. *Mag Cairn, Co. Roscommon.*

co **Carlaig** 3461.

Ceithe 2065.

Cellenn 3148. *A river in Conaille Muirthemne.*

Cenannas 309ª, 700. *Now Kells, Co. Meath.*

Cenn Coriss g. 2058.

Cenn Ferna 127.

Cingit Ferchon 2522.

Clann Dedad d. clannaib Dedad meic Šin 110, clannaib Dedad 1690.

Clár g. Cláiri 3967.

Clithar Bó nUlad 2075.

Clíu g. Cliach 3956, 3963.

Clothra g. id. 3961.

Clúain Carpat 1020.

Cluichiur g. id. 3975.

Cluichre (-th-) d. 1042.

Cnogba 335ᵇ. *Knowth, on N. side of Boyne.*

Cóicer Éngoirt 2034.

Cóicsius Focherda 2033.

Coirenna (Coranna) hi Correndaib 3343, co Coirenda 3482, ó Chorannaib 3792.

Colomna hErcoil 3583. *The Pillars of Hercules, Calpe and Abyla.*

Colptha for Colbtha 130, do Cholptu 1018, g. Colbta 1021, Colpthai 3791.

for **Coltain** 117. Cf. Áth Coltna.

for **Comur** 122.

Conaille (Muirthemne) la Conailliu 947, 1223, co Conaille 1029, g. Conailli 3146. *Level part of present Co. Louth from Cúailnge to the Boyne.*

Connachta 2, 3545, d. Connachtaib 41, g. Connacht 1403, 1405, 2619. *Connacht, the men of Connacht.*

Coronn 3804.

Cotail hi C. 1618.

Cremath co C. 3488.

Crích Rois 2519, 3293, 3301, 3319.

Cróen Chorann 1794.

Cróinech (Cróenech) 1796, hi Crónig 1561, isin Chrónig 1949, g. fir Chrónige 1948-9.

Cronn (Crann) 130, 198, 1160. *A river in Cúailnge.*

Crossa Caíl (= Iraird Cuillenn) 219ᵈ, 256ª.

Crúachu, Crúachain g. Crúachan 3211, 3880, 4142, d. Crúachnaib Aí 8, 22, Crúachnaib 136, a Crúachain 2596, ar Crúachain 2657. *Rathcroghan, Co. Roscommon.*

Cruithne g. 1490. *The Pictish district of Down and Antrim.*

Cúailnge 130, 966, 968, g. 956, 961, 978 *Cooley, Co. Louth.*

Cuib 1488, 1524, 1534, 4153, g. Coba 3778. Cf. Mag Coba, *part of barony of Iveagh.*

Cúil Airthir 1210, 1228, 1232.

Cúil Sibrinne (Sibrilli) 121, 309. *Old name of Kells.*

Cúil Silinne 116, 137. *Now Kilcooley, Co. Roscommon.*

Cuillenn Cinn Dúin 2071.

Cuinche 969, 976.

Cumang 3148. *A river in Conaille Muirthemne.*

for **Dáil Scena** 128.

Dál Riata g. Dáil Riatai 1533-4. *N. Co. Antrim.*

for **Deilt** 120. (for Deilt 129. Cf. Delt).

for **Deinn** 129. (Cf. 3149).

Delga 1246, 1248, 1299, 2036. D. Muirthemne 2058. *Dundalk, Co. Louth.*

for **Delinn** 120.

Delt 3149. *A river in Conaille Muirthemne.*

Den 3149. *A river in Conaille Muirthemne.*

Dergderc g. Dergderce (= Loch Dergderce) 3952. *L. Derg. near Killaloe.*

co **Diabal Arda** (Débul A.) 3461.

Dichu 3148. *A river in Conaille Muirthemne.*

Dindgna Medba 1535.

Dísert Lóchait 871.

Domnannaig d. Domnandchaib 2524. *A tribe in Connacht.*

Druim Baiscne 863.

Druim Cáemtechta 126-7.

Druim Caín 125.

Druim Féne 1026, 1233. *In Conaille Muirthemne.*

Druim Fornochta g. Droma [F.] 3957.

Gort Sláne 123.

Gránaired Tethba Túaiscirt 214 (= Gránard).

Gránard 214ᶜ. *Granard, Co. Longford.*

Granasc g. Granaisc 3966.

Greciae 3582. *Greece.*

Grellach Dolluid 2514, 2515. *Now Girley S. of Kells.* (See RC xii 8).

Gúala Mulcha 953.

co hIalla Ingraimme 3493.

co hImchláriu (*recte* co hImchláir) 3457.

Immail (= Ráith Immail) co hImpail 3486, ó Impuil 3654.

Imorach Smiromrach 3150.

for Imscúaip 127

Indeóin for Indiúin 119.

Inis Úan g. Insi Úan 3977.

Inse Faíche d. Insib Faíche 530.

Inse Gaid 3583.

Inse Orc 3582-3.

Iraird Cuillenn (= Crossa Caíl) 219, 256, 869, 3504, 4148. *Six miles due W. of Kells, Co. Meath.*

Irgáirech See Gáirech. E. Gáirech.

Irrus g. Irruis 3968. I. Domnann 2571-2. *Erris barony, N. W. Co. Mayo.*

Irúath g. na hIrúaithi 3248, 3999. *Norway. Here probably some mythical northern land.* (*See Windisch TBC* 625 *n.* 8 *and Contribb. s.v. Irúait*).

Laigin d. Laignib 1225. *Leinster, Leinstermen.*

Latharna co Latharnu 3468. *Larne Co. Antrim.*

Lecc Derg g. Leici Dergi 3951.

Léire co Léiri 3481.

Lemain co Leamain 3456.

Lemain g. Leamna 3961.

Lerga 2112, i lLercaib 2076, 2155.

Lethbera d. 2061.

Lethglais (= Dún Lethglaise) 3472. *Now Downpatrick, Co. Down.*

Lía Fiachrach (meic Fir Febe) 1647.

Lía Mór oc Líac Mór 945.

Lía Toll 3319 (i crích Rois).

Lía Tuill 1646.

Lía Úalann 1006.

co Liana 3490.

Líasa Líac 1022.

Líne g. id. 3470, 3718. *Cf. Mag Line, Moylinny.*

Loch Carrcín 137ᵇ

Loch Echtra g. Locha E. 677.

Loch Érne g. Lacha Érni 3953. *L. Erne, Co. Fermanagh.*

Lochmach for Lochmach 129.

Loch Reóin 928.

Loch Rí (Ríb) g. Lacha Rí 3952. *L. Ree on the Shannon.*

Lúachair g. Lúachra 3949.

Lugmod 2491. *Louth.*

Macha g. id. 3525, 3905, 3912.

Machaire (Conaille) 1027.

Máelana Átha Lúain 4119.

Maethail g. Maethla 3967.

Mag nAí 1141, d. Maig Aíi 1240, g. 1876, 2596, 3969-70. *A plain in Roscommon.*

Mag nAidne g. Aidne 3958. *A plain in Co. Galway.*

Mag mBreg 699, g. 954. *Plain between Liffey and Boyne.*

Mag Clochair 1615-6.

Mag nDobla g. 3494.

Mag nDula g. 3492.

Mag nÉle g. 3979.

Mag Femin g. 3963.

Mag nInis (Manes MS.) 3487.

Mag Lethan g. Maigⁱ Letha in 3980.

Mag Mannachta 2546.

Mag Mucceda 827.

Mag Muiresce g. 3954. *Now Murrisk in Connacht.*

Mag Muirthemne 251, 1527, g. 1239, 1876. *Plain S. of Dundalk.*

Mag nÓchtair g. 3979.

Mag in Scáil g. 2792.

Mag Trega 117, 188. *Moytra, Co. Longford.*

Mag Túag 4087. *In Connacht.*

Mag nUisce g. 3980.

Marga g. id. 3950.

Méithe hi Méthiu 921, oc Méthiu 2065.

Méithe Tog[maill] 126, 924.

Méithe nEóin 126, 925.

Mide 119.

Midlúachair 3479, g. Midlúachra 3778.

Miliucc 3149. *A river in Conaille Muirthemne.*

Mitain g. Mitaine 3959.

Tíarthechta 118.

Tipra Finn g. Tibrat Find 3962.

Tír Marccéni 966.

Tír Mór 2030. T. M. Tarteisc (Darteisc) 1981.

Tír Tairngire g. 2243.

Toíthle d. Toíthlib 2062.

Tor Breogain 3583. *In Spain.*

Tráig Thuirbe g. Turbi 3964. *Turvey, N. Co. Dublin.*

Troma 122, 4150, d. Tromuib 4149.

Túaim Móna 116.

Túath Ambrais g. 3970.

Túath Bressi g. 3543.

Tulach g. Tulcha 3972.

Úachtar Lúa (Óchtar Lúi) 3293.

Uarba 3485.

Uata 121.

Uí Echach 4154–5. *Present baronies of Upper and Lower Iveagh, Co. Down.*

Uiscre g. Uiscrend 3971.

Uisnech g. Uisnich 3919. *Now Usnagh Hill, Co. Westmeath.*

Ulaid 476, 479, 525, g. Ulad 409, 509, a. Ultu 246, 374, d. Ultaib 228, 422, 668. *Ulster, men of Ulster.*

Umall g. Umuill 3961. *Now the Owles, Co. Mayo.*

Umarrith 1522. (Umansruth LL).

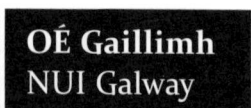

Leabharlann James Hardiman

Chun seiceáil cathain atá an leabhar seo le tabhairt ar ais agat, nó chun an leabhar a athnuachan, féach ar do chuntas leabharlainne.

To check when this book is due back or to renew it please check your Library Account.

http://tinyurl.com/NUIGLibraryAccount

Gearrann an leabharlann fíneálacha as leabhair a thugtar ar ais go mall.

A fine will be charged for books returned after their due date.